Ontario Geological Survey
Miscellaneous Paper 110

The Geology of Gold in Ontario

**edited by
A.C. Colvine**

1983

Ministry of
Natural
Resources

Ontario

Hon. Alan W. Pope
Minister

W. T. Foster
Deputy Minister

D1227664

©1983 Government of Ontario
Printed in Ontario, Canada
Reprinted 1983

ISSN 0704-2752
ISBN 0-7743-8113-2

Publications of the Ontario Ministry of Natural Resources are available from the following sources. Orders for publications should be accompanied by cheque or money order payable to the *Treasurer of Ontario*.

Reports, maps, and price lists (personal shopping or mail order):
Public Service Centre, Ministry of Natural Resources
Room 1640, Whitney Block, Queen's Park
Toronto, Ontario M7A 1W3

Reports and accompanying maps (personal shopping):
Ontario Government Bookstore
Main Floor, 880 Bay Street
Toronto, Ontario

Reports and accompanying maps (mail order or telephone orders):
Publications Services Section, Ministry of Government Services
5th Floor, 880 Bay Street
Toronto, Ontario M7A 1N8
Telephone (local calls), 965-6015
Toll-free long distance, 1-800-268-7540
Toll-free from area code 807, 0-ZENITH-67200

Every possible effort is made to ensure the accuracy of the information contained in this report, but the Ministry of Natural Resources does not assume any liability for errors that may occur. Source references are included in the report and users may wish to verify critical information.

Parts of this publication may be quoted if credit is given. It is recommended that reference to this report be made in the following form for each individual author:

Marmont, Soussan
1983: The Role of Felsic Intrusions in Gold Mineralization; p.38-47, *in* The Geology of Gold in Ontario, edited by A.C. Colvine, Ontario Geological Survey, Miscellaneous Paper 110, 278p.

3000-83-Maracle
1500-83-Tri Graphic

FOREWORD

Increases in the price of gold have resulted in renewed exploration activity over the past few years, following a long period in which both exploration and research related to gold were at a very low level. Recently, new studies have proliferated, but these are often being carried out in isolation. The purpose of the gold program of the Mineral Deposits Section is twofold: to conduct new field based studies of gold mineralization, and to work in close co-operation with industry and other researchers in order to ensure relevance, avoid duplication and maximise the benefits of the work.

This volume, which includes submissions from workers outside of the Ontario Geological Survey, constitutes a coordinated report of much of the work on the geology of gold mineralization which is presently in progress. It is therefore a preliminary report and will be superceded by separate publications and also by a more comprehensive and rigorous volume within two years.

E.G. Pye
Director
Ontario Geological Survey

CONTENTS

The Geology of Gold
in Ontario

Introduction to the Geology of Gold in Ontario

A.C. Colvine
Chief, Mineral Deposits Section, Ontario Geological Survey, Toronto

INTRODUCTION

This volume constitutes a coordinated compilation of papers written by authors presently active in studying aspects of the geology of gold mineralization in Ontario. Papers are largely descriptive and are intended to add to the available data base on this topic. It is not intended to be a volume on the genesis of gold deposits but inevitably interpretations can be drawn from thorough studies; where interpretations are made by individual authors the distinctions between descriptive and interpretive data are clearly identified.

These papers are the product of work carried out by geologists at the Ontario Geological Survey and other agencies. Most are field based, applied research projects, as a thorough field component is considered to be not merely a useful, but an essential component of meaningful new work. Unfortunately our work is restricted to the Early Precambrian rocks of Ontario, but we consider that these provide a reasonable representation of gold deposit characteristics in the Superior Province of Canada.

Individual papers constitute progress reports on work which is continuing and will proceed to separate publication. This volume must also be considered preliminary in regard to its rapid assembly and release; we have considered it more valuable to make what we have available as quickly as possible, rather than to delay for a more formal and rigorous publication.

STATE OF KNOWLEDGE

Until the recent upturn in the real price of gold there had been a 25-year hiatus during which there was a dearth of both practical and theoretical new studies relating to gold mineralization. While many theories have been expounded in recent years, they have not successfully provided systematic criteria whereby we have advanced significantly beyond the adage "gold is where you find it".

Much of the thorough descriptive work on gold deposits was written prior to 1960. The Structural Geology of Canadian Ore Deposits (CIMM 1948) is one of the most valuable reference volumes. There is a tendency to largely disregard previous work as being outdated; this is considered unwarranted as many of these studies were

conducted in a more systematic and thorough fashion than is prevalent today, and they commonly contain comprehensive mineralogical descriptions. As well many of these areas are no longer accessible for studies applying our supposedly more advanced techniques.

Recent regional geological and metallogenetic studies have emphasised volcanic stratigraphy and its association with base metal massive sulphide mineralization. The location and geological association of gold within these sequences has generally been given scant coverage, and has rarely been addressed systematically.

Similarly in the theoretical and experimental field, only marginal advances have been made. For example, the source of the gold is still unknown. Boyle (1979) gives considerable data on gold abundance in various lithologies, and while certain lithologies have a relatively higher gold content, no clear source rock has been defined. There is not even general agreement as to the necessity for an enriched protore unit in the vicinity of gold deposits.

The means of transport of gold is also a subject of conjecture. Several mechanisms have been evoked including chloride, thio, carbonate and carbonyl complexing but few experiments in complex solution chemistry systems have been carried out; the work of Seward (1973) is the most extensive. Fluid inclusion studies have not been undertaken on a comprehensive basis and the limited oxygen or sulphur isotope data, alone, do not provide conclusive evidence.

Inevitably, therefore, there is little direct evidence as to the cause of deposition and concentration of gold. It is clearly a function of both structural site preparation and chemical reactivity of the host rocks, but the relative importance of these and their systematics have not been defined adequately to allow target definition.

We are left, therefore, with very poorly defined criteria which may be useful in definition of exploration target areas for gold:

1. common occurrence in quartz ± carbonate (ankerite) vein systems and almost ubiquitous association with pyrite;

2. occurrence with mafic volcanic rocks, usually of greenschist or lower amphibolite grade;

3. common spatial association with
- alteration zones (predominantly carbonatization and silicification)

This report is published with the permission of E.G. Pye, Director, Ontario Geological Survey.

- chemical sedimentary rocks
- felsic intrusions
- regional transitions between volcanic and clastic sedimentary sequences
- komatiites;
4. common association with tellurides, arsenopyrite, tourmaline, scheelite and molybdenite; and
5. local structural control on the final siting of gold concentrations and apparent concentration of deposits along major deformational zones.

In order to successfully apply the above criteria in delineating areas for exploration and specific target selection it is necessary to systematically define the role and relative importance of each in the gold forming environment. Most gold deposits have been located by surface prospecting and to sucessfully discover others, particularly in overburden covered areas, a more comprehensive geological understanding is essential. This is particularly important as there is presently no widely applicable geophysical technique comparable to the electromagnetic systems used sucessfully in base metal massive sulphide exploration in the past 20 years and similarly there are limitations on presently developed geochemical techniques. Geology must therefore play a key role both directly and also in aiding development of geophysical and geochemical techniques.

PRESENT WORK

The numerous and varied projects initiated in recent years have commonly been launched rapidly without a firm foundation of field work; as such the results of these projects are difficult to interpret and apply. The gold program of the Ontario Geological Survey has therefore been designed to first examine and establish the complete geological setting of individual occurrences of gold mineralization before attempting to undertake more comprehensive research upon them which might lead to a better overall understanding of gold mineralization; it is the first phase of the program which is being reported upon in this volume. In order to maximise the descriptive content of the volume, papers were requested and received from workers, conducting similar studies, in other units of the Ministry of Natural Resources, universities and the exploration and mining industries (Figure 1).

In order to ensure that the results of previous work were not omitted, the initial phase of the program included a comprehensive literature review; a by-product of this was the publication of a bibliography of selected references on gold (Cherry *et al.* 1982). A review of available literature is also included in each of the major topic papers in this volume.

1. GEOLOGICAL ASSOCIATIONS

In addition to the general review it was considered that there was much pertinent information to be gleaned on the geological associations of specific deposits. Gross generalizations have been made as to the most important geological (particularly lithological) associations of gold

mineralization, but these theories have not been substantiated with hard data. In an attempt to address this problem, Hodgson (this volume) undertook a systematic compilation of all known gold occurrences in the Abitibi Belt of Ontario; this work followed his study of the geological characteristics of 33 major gold producers in the Shield of Canada (Hodgson and MacGeehan, in press). The study included data on 725 deposits in the Abitibi Belt; all available geological information was recorded in computer processable form. The most prevalent lithologic association of gold is with mafic volcanic rocks; more than half of the gold occurrences have a spatial association with felsic intrusions. Most other lithologic types are present in less than 20 percent of deposits. In addition, minerals such as tourmaline and scheelite appear to be present most commonly in the larger known deposits. A report covering this compilation should be released in summer 1983 and a user accessible computer file made available later this year.

These associations between gold and felsic intrusions, iron formation, alteration and structures are commonly cited in the literature as important but are poorly defined. Projects were established by the Mineral Deposits Section to directly investigate these associations in specific areas. Other papers which relate directly to each topic are included in the relevant sections.

2. FELSIC INTRUSIONS

Felsic intrusions host or are closely associated with many gold deposits. Localization of mineralization within them must be synchronous with or postdate the emplacement of the intrusion. The role of the intrusion in localization of mineralization is, however, not clear; if pre-existing gold mineralization were present in the country rocks, the intrusion may have caused its remobilization; conversely the intrusion may have been the source of the mineralizing fluid or acted as a structural and/or chemical trap for a fluid not directly related to the intrusion.

Marmont (this volume) is completing a multi-year study of the associations between felsic intrusions and mineralization in a variety of geological settings in the Shield; deposits chosen for study were outside the main gold belts and initially focused on the copper, gold and molybdenum (porphyry?) associations. These intrusions have certainly had an effect in reconcentration of pre-existing mineralization through assimilation of wall rock material and also the "heat engine" effect of hydrothermal re-concentration; in the deposits examined gold concentration by this mechanism appears to be limited. Molybdenum has been concentrated by a late hydrous phase of specific intrusions; the role of the magma as a source of gold is, as yet, not well understood. Lastly there is a clear structural control on siting of gold deposits around the margins of intrusions, and there is evidence of both syn-intrusion fracturing and later fracturing due to competency differences with wall rocks during deformation. Most intrusions appear to be composite dynamic systems resulting in interaction of several mineralizing processes. A full report covering this topic will be released in the summer of 1983.

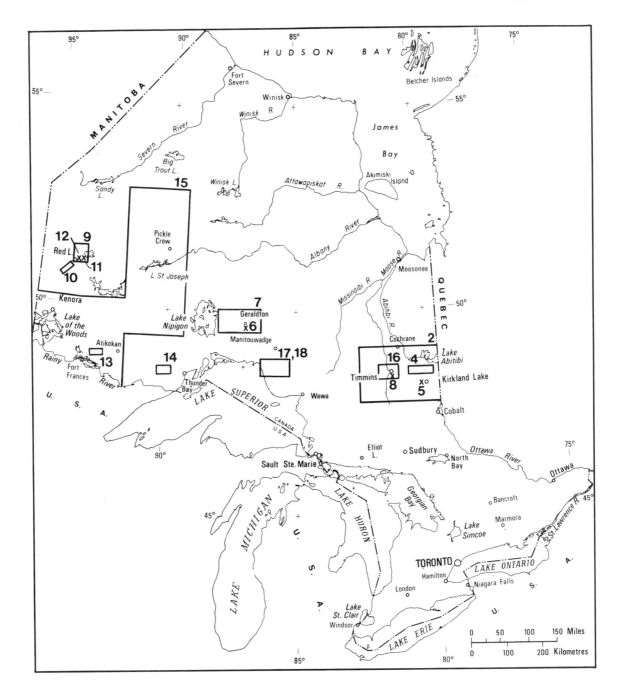

Figure 1. Locations of Projects

2. Hodgson
4. Cherry
5. Watson and Kerrich
6. Macdonald
7. Mason and McConnell
8. Fyon, Crocket and Schwarcz
9. Andrews and Wallace
10. Durocher

11. Lavigne and Crocket
12. Rigg and Scherkus
13. Poulsen
14. Stott and Schnieders
15. Blackburn and Janes
16. Hodgson
17. Patterson
18. Muir

Province-wide Projects
3. Marmont
19. Springer
20. Fortescue
21. Riddle

Cherry (this volume) addresses directly the association between felsic intrusions and gold in the main mining camps. He describes two detailed studies of this association in the Abitibi Belt. Gold mineralization closely associated with a specific fracture set occurs in quartz veins and alteration halos to the fractures; greatest ore concentrations are located in rocks with highest fraction density along a zone of shearing in the intrusion.

Cross-cutting relationships demonstrate an unequivocal relative order of events. The intrusion postdated major regional deformation and the gold mineralized fracture set transected all other intrusive units and fracture sets; the present siting of gold is one of the last events in the geological development of these areas. The apparent localization of these intrusions along major structural zones is also discussed.

Watson and Kerrich (this volume) provide a detailed description of the intrusion-hosted Macassa deposit in the Kirkland Lake area. Siting of gold concentration within the intrusion is structurally controlled. They use oxygen isotope data in a discussion of the source of mineralizing fluids. This work was largely carried out as a thesis research topic by Watson at the University of Western Ontario with assistance from Long Lac Minerals Limited.

3. IRON FORMATION

The spatial relationship between gold and iron formation has resulted in considerable interest; iron formations are an attractive exploration target as units can be readily traced by magnetic techniques, a process which also aids in definition of stratigraphy. Although the spatial association is emphasised, there are no data available to date to demonstrate syngenetic gold ore concentration as a chemical sediment, or even relative enrichment of gold in iron formation as a protore.

Macdonald (this volume) discusses briefly the worldwide iron formation gold association and then describes in detail the geological features of the MacLeod-Cockshutt deposit near Geraldton. The first significant observation, reported clearly by Horwood and Pye (1955), is that the majority of the gold is not within or immediately adjacent to iron formation, but along a porphyry clastic sedimentary rock contact; ore is concentrated along the hinge of a major Z-fold. In the open pit area, mapped by Macdonald, gold is within and adjacent to iron formation, again in a shallowly plunging Z-fold structure. The gold bearing veins transect foliation developed in a first phase of regional deformation and are apparently related to a second phase of deformation. Gold-bearing veins cut the three lithologies present, iron formation, porphyry and clastic sedimentary rock, and their siting is clearly the result of competency differences between these lithologies; where veins cut iron formation a pyritic and auriferous alteration halo is developed around them, particularly along iron-rich beds; this is clearly not a primary sulphide facies of iron formation. Carbonatization is pervasive in all

lithologies near the deposit, but apparently absent within a few hundred metres from it. Systematic analyses to determine background gold distribution in the iron formation have not, as yet, been carried out. Macdonald also discusses the apparent zonation of vein mineralization around the adjacent granitic batholith.

Mason and McConnell (this volume) briefly describe the geological setting of the main gold deposits of the Beardmore-Geraldton Camp. The majority of gold deposits are distributed along the broad interface between the Wabigoon and Quetico Subprovinces; the western extension of this zone is discussed later (Poulsen, this volume).

Fyon, Crocket and Schwarcz (this volume) provide a description of iron formation associated gold at the Carshaw deposit near Timmins. The paper includes a detailed, band-by-band, description of the iron formation. Again, gold is hosted by late veins and pyritic alteration halos to veins, best developed where these transect iron formation. The relative order of events and possible sources of gold are thoroughly discussed; the iron formation cannot be excluded as a possible protore source, but work to date has not identified adequate concentration within it to have provided the observed magnitude of vein concentration. This work was carried out as part of a thesis research project by Fyon at MacMaster University. The iron formation association in the Dickenson Mine, near Red Lake, is also discussed later (Lavigne and Crocket, this volume).

4. ALTERATION

The possibility that gold deposits are associated with an alteration halo thereby providing a larger and possibly more recognizable target for exploration is a topic of considerable interest. Base metal massive sulphide alteration zones have long been recognized, but usually have been defined after deposit discovery; in recent years alteration linked to detailed studies of volcanic stratigraphy have proven successful in location of new mineralization.

In gold deposits, carbonatization is clearly a spatially related alteration effect in many areas (Fyon and Crocket 1981); silicification is also associated with many deposits and in some instances potassic enrichment (biotite and sericite) has also been recognized. As yet, definitive alteration criteria to apply in gold exploration are lacking. A project was, therefore, initiated to study alteration associated with gold deposits, with initial work directed to the Red Lake district following documentation of a large altered zone around many of the deposits (Pirie 1981); other papers related to gold mineralization in the Red Lake area are also included in this section.

Andrews and Wallace (this volume) describe the geological setting of the gold deposits of the Cochenour-Balmerton area. In this first year of the study, emphasis has been placed on determining the regional patterns of alteration and metamorphism before examining these features adjacent to gold mineralization. As part of this study, a possible interpretation of the structural development of the area to explain the complex structural and stratigraphic trends has been presented for discussion. Within the highly altered zone outlined by Pirie (1981) detailed mapping in specific locations has defined a complex history of deformation and alteration in which localization of quartz veins appears to postdate a major event of ankeritic carbonate introduction; again final siting of gold is very late in the development of these areas.

Durocher (this volume) provides a detailed description of the geology of the Madsen – Starratt Olsen portion of the Red Lake camp. Gold mineralization hosted by the complex Austin Tuff unit is associated with a broader alteration halo in the upper part of a tholeiitic-komatiitic volcanic sequence. Alteration characterized by biotite was originally recognized megascopically and has been better defined by subsequent petrographic and geochemical studies. This preliminary work has documented element enrichment and depletion in halos around the main mineralized zone and further work may provide more systematic criteria for its application. In this area also the gold zone is roughly conformable with a zone of structural deformation.

Lavigne and Crocket (this volume) have conducted detailed studies of the East South C ore zone at the Dickenson Mine. This work has addressed specifically the association between the mineralization and the adjacent sulphidic iron formation. Detailed mapping has demonstrated that the mineralization is restricted to a planar zone of schistose rocks which transects the complexly folded volcanic rocks and chemical sedimentary rocks. Sulphides in the ore zone are distinct, both mineralogically and chemically from those in the sulphidic iron formation. The gold mineralizing event is a relatively late event and no evidence has been found to substantiate the derivation of gold from the adjacent chemical sediments. This work was carried out as part of a thesis research project at MacMaster Univeristy.

The work of Rigg and Helmstaedt (1981) in the Campbell Mine has demonstrated the immediate structural controls on gold mineralization and its relatively late localization in the deformation and alteration history. Rigg and Scherkus (this volume) describe the geology of the Wilmar East zone, documenting the complex geological development of this area and again the relatively late and apparently structurally controlled localization of gold ores. This work was carried out by Wilanour Resources Limited.

5. STRUCTURE

Localization of many gold deposits is structurally controlled; it is not clear, however, whether this merely indicates remobilization of pre-existing gold into late dilatent structures or that the structures themselves are a component of a major structural system which plays an active role in the formation of gold deposits. Poulsen (this volume) has undertaken a multi-year study of the geology and mineralization of the Fort Frances – Mine Centre

area; a report covering this area will be released in the summer of 1983. Detailed structural studies of the gold deposits of the Mine Centre area show them to be localized in ductile shear zones developed in more competent, predominantly felsic intrusive, units. Gold mineralization occurs in three sets representing the primary, secondary and tertiary elements of ductile shear. No spatial association with a potential protore source unit is present. On a regional scale the shear elements are related to a dextral strike-slip mega shear system which constitutes the boundary between the Wabigoon and Quetico Subprovinces. Poulsen discusses the characteristic features of major structural zones and presents a preliminary interpretation of the structural framework of the Wabigoon Subprovince thereby delineating possible target zones.

Stott and Schnieders (this volume) similarly describe the structural setting of the Shebandowan Belt, demonstrating that gold veins are localized close to structural domain boundaries and hosted by structures related to the second major phase of deformation recorded in the rocks of this area. A tabulation of the major gold deposits of this area is also included.

Blackburn and Janes (this volume) describe the geological associations of gold deposits in northwestern Ontario, excluding those of the Red Lake district. Again they present evidence for the relatively late siting of gold in the geological development of each area and also the common association with felsic intrusions.

As part of his compilation of the gold deposits of the Abitibi Belt, Hodgson (this volume) re-examined the structural and stratigraphic interpretations which have been published for the Porcupine gold camp. Inevitably in such a geologically complex area, problems exist in any comprehensive interpretation. The paper presented in this volume is included to stimulate further discussion of this topic. As presented, felsic intrusions were emplaced relatively late, but prior to the final regional deformation, along major structural zones; highly carbonatized zones are shown to be locally conformable but regionally disconformable with the defined stratigraphy and are localized along major structures. Gold mineralization is interpreted to be syn-or post-intrusion of the felsic rocks.

6. THE HEMLO AREA

The recent discoveries in the Hemlo area have aroused considerable interest and new hope that there are many substantial new deposits still to be found even in areas which have a long history of prospecting and exploration. A striking characteristic of the Hemlo discovery is that it is so readily accessible; an outcrop of the ore zone was exposed in a road cut during construction of the Trans-Canada Highway more than 20 years ago; there are obviously many less well explored or accessible "greenstone" sequences within the Shield.

Although exploration for gold in the area dates back more than 100 years and significant discoveries were made, the much higher potential of the area was not recognized until recently, probably because gold occurs in an innocuous looking unit with little veining, minor pyrite and fine molybdenite. Patterson (this volume) describes the exploration history of the area.

Muir (1982) mapped the Hemlo-Heron Bay belt in 1978 and 1979. In his initial report (Muir 1980) he presented assay data from a previously unreported occurrence and recommended the Hemlo area for further gold exploration. Muir (this volume) describes the general geology of the belt based on his previous work. In addition he describes from his work and available published information the geology around the Hemlo deposits. Most importantly he points out that this is a geologically complex area and needs a more thorough field study before all of the geological features can be determined. Much attention in recent articles has been given to the planar and locally conformable stratabound nature of the mineralized zone in the immediate deposit area; more work will be necessary to show if this association holds on a regional scale.

7. INVISIBLE GOLD

The Hemlo area has highlighted the fact that visible gold, particularly in quartz veins, has been the principal prospecting target. While there is visible gold at Hemlo, examination of some surface material from the deposit leaves the question in the mind of the observer, "How often have I seen this type of rock and not even thought to sample it for assay?". There is still a large field in which we have very little information, that is the actual state in which gold occurs, its form and its association with other minerals.

This is a field that has not been neglected over the years, all be it that the work may not have been directed towards gold. A considerable amount of work has been carried out in mineralogy, ore dressing and metallurgy which, if synthesised, can provide considerable insight into the occurrence of gold. Springer (this volume) has undertaken a research project in this area which is already providing interesting and useful results. She has demonstrated that certain sulphide minerals are capable of containing in solid solution large quantities of gold, which if recognized and treated correctly would be recoverable; arsenian pyrite, which apparently tarnishes more than normal pyrite, is one such mineral. Gold also occurs in a sub-microscopic colloidal form in layer-lattice minerals such as muscovite; sericite schists are rarely considered for assay. The role of carbonaceous material in the adsorption of gold is also under study; carbonaceous units are present in many gold deposits. Not only is this important in understanding processes of gold concentration, but also in gold milling where addition of hydrocarbons such as kerosene in the milling process can suppress the adsorption effect of carbonaceous material and substantially improve gold recovery.

8. GEOCHEMISTRY

Lastly, two review papers are presented covering as-

pects of geochemistry. Fortescue (this volume) reviews the application of geochemical exploration techniques for gold emphasizing surficial geochemistry. The paper includes a discussion of the most promising techniques for exploration in glaciated Shield terrain.

Riddle (this volume) reviews the available analytical techniques for gold determination and discusses the interpretation of gold analytical data. He also discusses briefly sampling techniques and preliminary work on a field staining technique for gold detection which shows considerable promise.

DISCUSSION

Clearly there is a substantial and rapidly increasing amount of information available on the geology of gold deposits. Much of the work from the past was carried out thoroughly and should be used and expanded upon. Modern technological and scientific advances have provided us with powerful new tools to aid our studies, but these can only be successfully applied in conjunction with reliable field data.

There is a pattern emerging of consistent similarities and some differences in the geological characteristics of each of the areas studied. There are, as yet, no clearcut answers but there are certainly many questions which this work has highlighted; some of the questions arising are presented below, along with a discussion of the work which we consider necessary to answer them.

1. Is there any lithological type which clearly contains a primary gold ore or protore concentration?

Many units have been proposed as syngenetic gold hosts, primarily chemical sediments or units interpreted as chemical sediments. Certainly many gold deposits are associated with units which could be interpreted as such, but only if the definition is broadened to such an extent that it ceases to provide guidelines for specific target area selection. Iron formation hosts many gold deposits but is absent from many more; iron formation units occur too commonly to present specific targets.

2. What is "remobilization"?

This is a term commonly used to explain the present structural control on siting of mineralization. Certainly gold appears to have been an extremely mobile element. However, if it is to be successfully used as a criterion in exploration the sources of the gold, the process of transportation and the cause of deposition must be better defined. Unless these processes are addressed, the term "remobilization" should not be used as it merely disguises potentially valuable geological characteristics.

3. What is the role of structure?

Certainly local structural control on gold concentration is an important characteristic. On a very detailed or mine scale it is probably one of the most important avenues of study.

On a regional scale it may also provide specific guidelines for exploration target area selection. If a major deep seated structural zone is necessary to provide a conduit for mineralizing fluid, a hypothesis not adequately substantiated at present, then we can apply it with advanced field expertise and remote sensing technology to better define the structural framework of the Shield. In this, single faults would not be the targets but large scale deep seated zones of long term crustal weakness.

4. Can the syngenetic and structural models be rationalized?

The answer to this is, for the most part, yes. The important point to note here is that the targets will not change as theories change, but a better overall understanding should aid target selection.

Many of the geological characteristics of gold deposits can be readily explained by both models:

– the occurrence of gold deposit concentrations in major linear belts as a result of their representing hinge zone-growth fault facies changes or conversely major structural zones;

– their occurrence with highly deformed schistose rocks as a result of exhalite and tuffs being more susceptible to deformation or conversely the result of focused deformation zones;

– their occurrence with conglomerate units as a result of growth faults or conversely subsequent graben style faulting;

– their occurrence with felsic intrusions, focused along zones of weakness; in one model, causing remobilization of pre-existing mineralization; in the other, following structures which were also conduits for hydrothermal transport or even the possibility that the intrusions themselves were the source of a magmatically derived hydothermal fluid;

– their association with alteration as a result of extensive hydrothermal activity, either syndepositional or subsequently superimposed;

– their occurrence with iron formation either as a result of syngenetic concentration or as a result of the structural and chemical characteristics of the iron formation allowing deposits in and around it.

5. Can alteration be used as a guide to ore?

The answer to this is not yet, but it does show considerable promise. Before it can be applied, more detailed studies of alteration and metamorphic history must be carried out and more test cases examined.

It may be also that the preliminary sulphur isotope data at the Dickenson Mine given by Lavigne and Crocket, which shows ^{34}S enrichment in gold vein pyrites, may become an applicable geochemical exploration tool.

6. What is the absolute age of mineralization?

This is unknown beyond the obvious fact that the final localization of most gold is, relatively, one of the latest events. The dating of felsic intrusions and their age relative to volcanic stratigraphy would allow us to determine if these are part of the volcanic continuum or a distinct later superimposed event. This work will be started shortly. Similarly direct dating of ore vein minerals is a research technique which may be possible to develop, and beyond that possible dating of structural and metamorphic episodes.

7. What is the source of gold?

This question is not as esoteric as it might appear. Inevitably, in refining exploration target selection, a distinction between syngenetic and epigenetic concentration processes is important. If gold is concentrated syngenetically then lithology is of paramount importance. If gold is derived from a deep seated source, for example granulite facies metamorphism or through magma generation, then structure is paramount.

8. What is the difference between a gold and a base metal hydrothermal system?
It is generally accepted that base metal deposits are formed by synvolcanic exhalative hydrothermal activity. Gold deposits have relatively low base metal contents; therefore, their hydrothermal system must have been substantially different. This indicates that different processes were in operation in the formation of each deposit type.

SUMMARY

Historically we have progressed from a stage where structure and epigenetic emplacement of mineralization was considered to be the principal mechanism for ore concentration. In more recent years the very important role of syngenetic concentration has been recognized in both volcanic and sedimentary environments, a major advance in the field of mineral deposits geology. Unfortunately this has led to epigenetic processes and the role of structure being largely discredited and considered passé. It may be that the pendulum has swung too far and we are now trying to fit everything in a syngenetic mould as was once done with the epigenetic theories.

If we are to make a significant contribution not only to science but also to exploration, it is essential that the theories do not become of overriding importance. We must conduct comprehensive and thorough work in an unbiased fashion, based on field studies, identifying and assessing all of the geological features of each area of study.

This has been and will continue to be the goal of work carried out by the Ontario Geological Survey.

ACKNOWLEDGEMENTS

The confidence of individuals at the Ministry of Natural Resources, particularly Ed Pye and George Jewett allowed us to follow through on this work which was started under the leadership of Jim Robertson. I would like to thank those contributors outside of the Mineral Deposits

Section who often gave of their own time to prepare submissions, which have made this a more comprehensive volume. The cooperation of the various companies whose properties are reported upon is also gratefully acknowledged.

In preparation of this publication the assistance of Mike Cherry, Soussan Marmont and Janet Springer in editing was greatly appreciated by myself. Kerry Gould, Geri Atkinson and Chester Kasprzak rapidly and systematically worked their way through the mounds of drafting. Iva Sherrett dealt calmly with impatient prima donnas and unrealistic deadlines to type the majority of this material.

Lastly the cooperative team effort to which all members of the Mineral Deposits Section contributed made the product of this work much greater than the sum of individual studies carried out in isolation.

REFERENCES

Boyle, R.W.
1979: The Geochemistry of Gold and Its Deposits; Geological Survey of Canada, Bulletin 280, 584p.

Cherry, M.E., van Soeren, F.M., Andrews, A.J. and Springer, J.S.
1982: Gold - Selected References; Ontario Geological Survey, Open File Report 5382, 69p.

CIMM
1948: Structural Geology of Canadian Ore Deposits, A Symposium of the Geology Division, Canadian Institute of Mining and Metallurgy; Mercury Press, Montreal, 948p.

Fyon, J.A. and Crocket, J.H.
1981: Volcanic Environment of Carbonate Alteration and Stratiform Gold Mineralization, Timmins Area; p.47-58 in Genesis of Archean, Volcanic-Hosted Gold Deposits, Symposium Held at the University of Waterloo, March 7, 1980, Ontario Geological Survey, Miscellaneous Paper 97, 175p.

Hodgson, C.J. and MacGeehan, P.J.
In Press: Geological Characteristics of Gold Deposits in the Superior Province of the Canadian Shield.

Horwood, H.C. and Pye, E.G.
1955: Geology of Ashmore Township; Ontario Department of Mines, Annual Report, Volume 60, Pt. 5, 105p.

Muir, T.L.
1980: Geology of the Hemlo Area, District of Thunder Bay; Ontario Geological Survey, Open File Report 5280, 78p.
1982: Geology of the Hemlo Area, District of Thunder Bay; Ontario Geological Survey, Report 217, 65p. Accompanied by Map 2452 (coloured). Scale 1:31,680 or 1 inch to 1/2 mile.

Pirie, J.
1981: Regional Geological Setting of Gold Deposits in the Red Lake Area, Northwestern Ontario; p.71-93 in Genesis of Archean, Volcanic-Hosted Gold Deposits, Symposium Held at the University of Waterloo, March 7, 1980, Ontario Geological Survey, Miscellaneous Paper 97, 175p.

Rigg, D.M. and Helmstaedt, H.
1981: Relations Between Structures and Gold Mineralization in Campbell Red Lake and Dickenson Mines, Red Lake Area, Ontario; p.111-127 in Genesis of Archean, Volcanic-Hosted Gold Deposits, Symposium Held at the University of Waterloo, March 7, 1980, Ontario Geological Survey, Miscellaneous Paper 97, 175p.

Seward, T.M.
1973: Thio Complexes of Gold in Hydrothermal Ore Solutions; Geochimica et Cosmochimica Acta, Volume 37, p.379-400.

Preliminary Report on a Computer File of Gold Deposits of the Abitibi Belt, Ontario

C.J. Hodgson

Department of Geological Sciences, Queen's University, Kingston

ABSTRACT

A computer-processable file has been constructed of the economic and geological characteristics, discovery date, discovery method, and extent of exploration of the 725 known gold deposits in the Timmins-Kirkland Lake area. The data show that almost all of the major producing and past-producing deposits from which most of the gold ore in the area was obtained were found by surface prospecting in the first 10 years of major exploration (1905-1914).

The lithological environment of the deposits is characterized by an unusual abundance of dikes and stocks of felsic porphyry. Quartz-bearing porphyries, scheelite, tourmaline, arsenopyrite, galena, molybdenite and telluride, are all more common, although to differing degrees, in the economically better than in the economically poorer deposits. Iron formation, on the other hand, occurs preferentially in the poorer deposits. These features may be used, therefore, to help determine a priority rating for poorly exposed deposits in terms of their ultimate economic potential.

Although half of the gold zones in the area are oriented parallel to stratigraphy, and in almost 20 percent the dominant form of mineralization is disseminated, the weight of the geological evidence indicates that the ores are epigenetic.

Preliminary studies indicate the distribution of the minerals which correlate positively with the economic rank of deposits, and spatial variations. The studies also indicate that the ratio of economically better to economically poorer deposits in an area shows a systematic spatial relationship to the highly productive centres of gold mining (i.e. the gold camps). These parameters can be used, therefore, to determine a priority rating for larger exploration areas, i.e., at the regional scale of area selection.

INTRODUCTION

Prospecting for gold deposits is both technically difficult and expensive. Therefore, it is worth spending considerable time and effort trying to identify the best possible exploration areas, using existing geological knowledge. As a contribution towards this end, the writer undertook a comprehensive review of the geological and economic characteristics, and extent of exploration of all of the 725 gold deposits located in the area covered by Ontario Geological Survey Compilation Map 2205, Timmins-Kirkland Lake area (Pyke *et al.* 1973). The data were compiled in computer processable form. Some of the preliminary results of the project were described by Hodgson (1982). This paper describes in more detail the manner in which the data were compiled, and additional results of the study. As noted by Hodgson (1982, p.192), the objective of the compilation was to attempt to answer such questions as:

What are the geological differences, if any, between economically better and economically poorer deposits? Is it possible to define anomalously mineralized areas (mining camps), independently of 'exploration intensity' or 'percent exposure', using parameters such as the ratio of economically better to economically poorer deposits, the incidence of certain assemblages of rocks or ore-associated minerals, or the incidence of alteration types in the gold prospects? How common (and thus important in geochemical exploration) is the association of gold with minerals like tourmaline, scheelite and arsenopyrite? Are there any as yet unrecognized spatial relationships between gold mineralization and particular rock types? How common, and thus significant in exploration, is the association of gold deposits with rock types like iron formation?

The original concept of the project was proposed to the Mineral Deposits Section of the Ontario Geological Survey by the writer while he was associated with the Mineral Exploration Research Institute, McGill and Ecole Polytechnique Universities, Montreal. The study was carried out as a research contract awarded to that Institute. All of the data were obtained from the published literature and, to a much lesser extent, the assessment file records of the Ontario Ministry of Natural Resources. The coding was done by the writer and one assistant, Gordon McRoberts; the areas coded by each are outlined on Figure 1. Bruce Everenden worked for several months on the project, mainly verifying and manipulating the computerized data.

INPUT DOCUMENT

The input document used in constructing the file is shown on Figure 2, and the coding system is outlined in Appendix 1. A number of recommendations concerning changes in the type of data which should be recorded are noted with the appropriate file items in Appendix 1. These recommendations will be discussed, along with

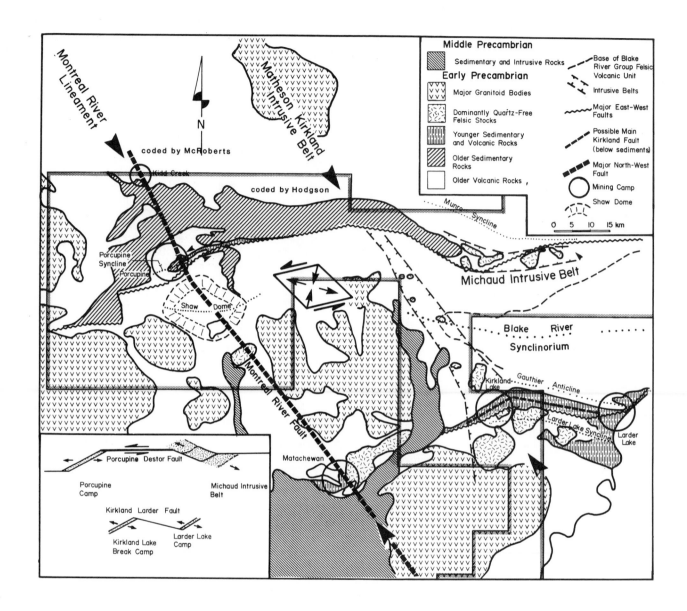

Figure 1. *Generalized geological map of the area covered by the Gold Deposits File, showing the division of coding responsibility (modified after Hodgson 1982).*

GOLD DEPOSIT CODING SHEET 1

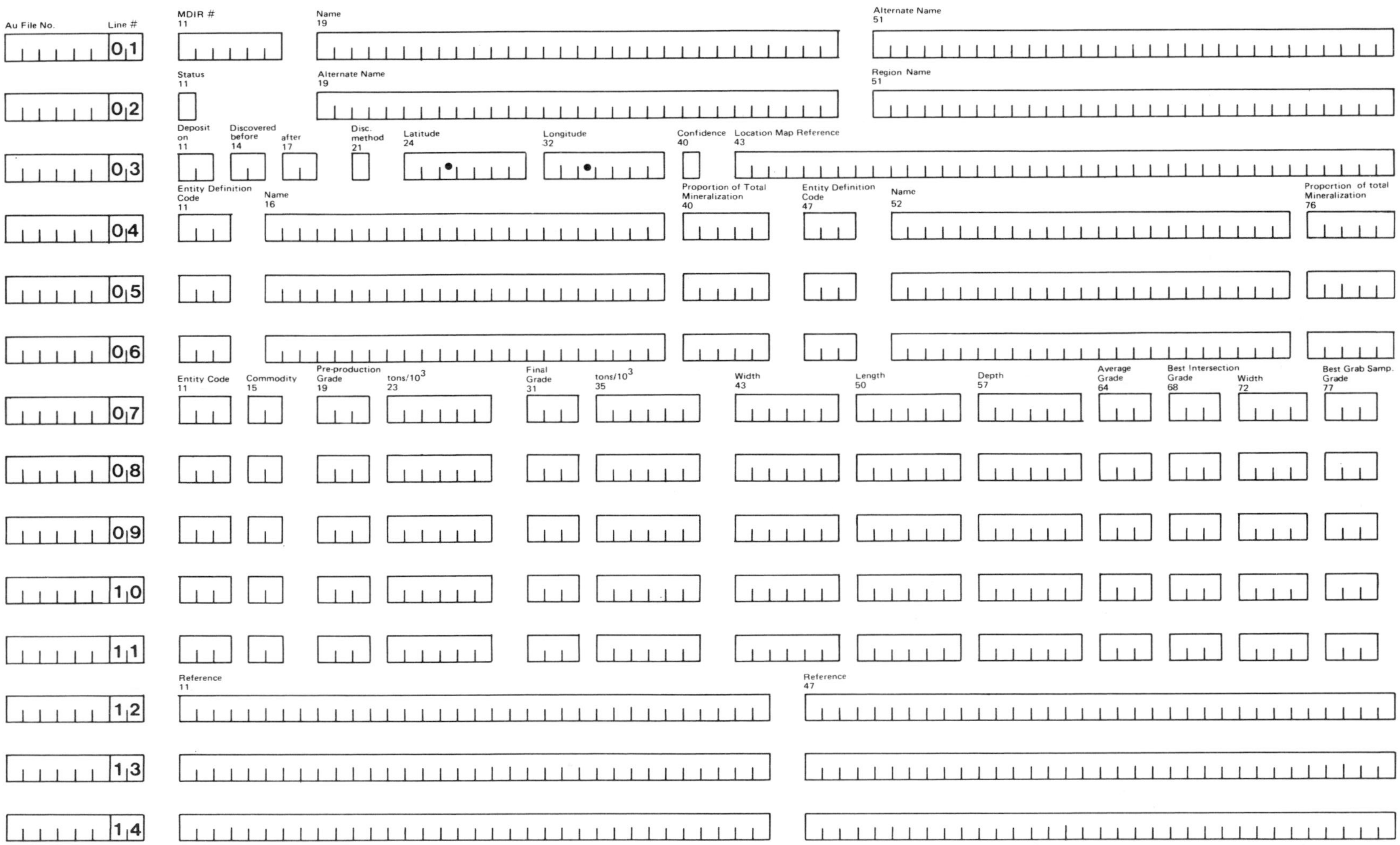

Figure 2. Input document for gold deposit file (continued next page). See Appendix 1 for coding guide.

GOLD DEPOSIT CODING SHEET 2

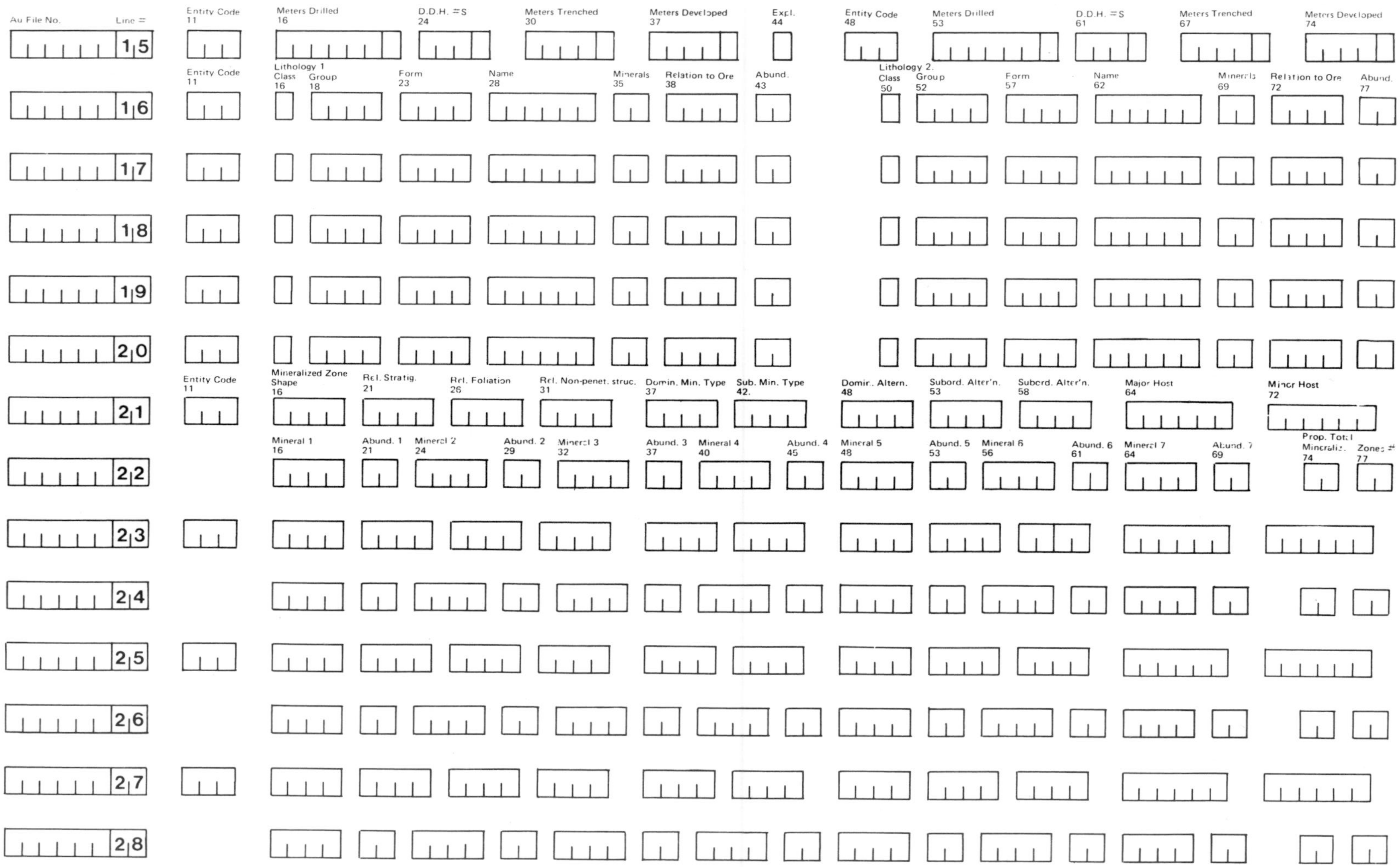

Figure 2. Continued.

14

Table 1. *Gold file listing.*

1. DEPOSIT#	156. WIDTH	190. ROCK-CODE
2. MDIR#	157. LENGTH	191. LITH-CLASS
3. DEPOSIT NAME	158. DEPTH	192. LITH-GROUP
4. STATUS	159. AVR-GRADE	193. LITH-FORM
5. REGION	160. INT-GRADE	194. LITH-NAME
6. DISCOVERED	161. INT-WIDTH	195. LITH-MINER
7. DISCOVERED-BEF	162. GRAB-GRADE	196. RELATION-TO-ORE
8. DISCOVERED-AFT	164*. TOTAL OZ AU	197. LITH-ABUND
9. DISCOVERY-METHOD	165*. OZ AU PER VERT METRE	20. MINERALIZED ZONE (RECORD)
10. LATITUDE	166*. METRE 0.1 OZ AU EQUIV	200. PETR-CODE
11. LONGITUDE	163*. ECON QUALITY	201. MINER-SHAPE
12. CONFIDENCE	17. REFERENCES (RECORD)	202. STRATIGR-REL
13. LOCATION MAP REFERENCE	170. REFERENCE	203. FOLIATION-REL
30. ALTERNATE NAMES (RECORD)	18. EXPLORATION (RECORD)	204. STRUCT-REL
301. ALTERNATE NAME	180. ENTITY-CODE	205. DOMIN-TYPE
14. ZONES (RECORD)	181. METRES DRILLED	206. SUBOR-TYPE
140. ZONE-CODE	182. DRILLED +	207. DOMIN-ALT
141. ZONE-NAME	183. DDHS NUMBERS	208. SUBOR-ALT1
142. PROPORTION OF MINERALIZATION IN ZONE	184. DDHS +	209. SUBOR-ALT2
15. COMMODITIES (RECORD)	185. METRES TRENCHED	210. MAJOR-HOST
150. COMM-CODE	186*. EXPLOR INTENSITY	211. MINOR-HOST
151. COMMODITY	187. METRES DEVELOPMENT	212. PROP-TOT
152. PRE-PROD-GRADE	188. DEVELOPED +	213. ZONES#
153. PRE-PROD-TONS	189. EXPLORATION POTENTIAL	22. MINERALS (RECORD)
154. FINAL-GRADE	19. LITHOLOGY (RECORD)	220. MINERAL
155. FINAL-TONS		221. MINR-ABUND

*Not directly recorded.

Table 2. *Economic class ranking scheme.*

Econ. Rank	Total	No. Deposits Sub Groups	Percent Deposits	Definition 3 Dimensional Data	2 Dimensional Data	1 Dimensional Data
6	18		2.5	Prod. + Res. >10^6 ounces		
5	25		3.4	Prod. + Res. <10^6 ounces		
4	37	33	– 4.6)) 5.1	Prod. + Res. <10^5 and >10^4 ounces		
		4	0.5)		> 100 oz vert. metre	
3	33	17	2.3)) 4.6	Prod. + Res. <10^4 and >10^3 ounces		
		16	2.2)		< 100 and > 10 oz vert. metre	
2	54	5	0.7)	Prod. + Res. <10^3 ounces		
		10	1.4) 7.4		<10 and >1 vert. metre	
		39	5.4)			>1.0 m of 0.1 oz/t equivalent and "best inters." >0.2 oz./t.
1	353	1	0.1)		< 1 oz/vert. metre	
		107	14.8) 48.7			<1.0 m and >0.1 m of 0.1 oz/t equivalent and "best inters". >0.2 oz/t
		245	33.8)			grab grade >0.5 oz/t or "high" or "visible gold".
0	205		28.3			<0.1m of 0.1 oz/t equivalent or "best inters." <0.05 oz/t. Grab grade <0.5 oz/t or "low".

Table 3. *Exploration intensity ranking scheme.*

Rank	Deposit Rank No.	Percent	Total Metres Drilled	No.	Percent	No. of Drill Holes	No.	Percent	Total Metres Development	No.	Percent
4	169	23.3	> 1800	111	15.3	>20	72	9.9	> 2,000	62	8.6
3	135	18.6	> 700, <1800	109	15.0	>8, <20	110	15.2	> 300, <2,000	61	8.4
2	119	16.4	> 200, < 700	108	14.9	>3, < 8	100	13.8	> 25, < 300	62	8.6
1	96	13.2	> 0, < 200	104	14.3	>0, < 3	134	18.5	> 1, < 15	42	5.8
0	206	28.4	0	293	40.5	0	309	42.6	0	498	68.7

the specific techniques of file construction and the program used for data manipulation, in a more comprehensive report now in preparation.

FILE LISTING

The data items recorded and the way they are organized in the file are listed on Table 1. Five items not directly recorded have been derived by manipulating the recorded data:

C164. Total ounces Au. This is calculated as the total gold content of the entity (See Note 4, Appendix 1). Where the entity is 'deposit', it includes all recorded past production and existing reserves.

C165. Ounces Au per vertical metre. This is calculated where the best available economic data for an entity are width and length dimensions, and a corresponding average grade.

C166. Metres 0.1 ounces Au equivalent. This is calculated where the best available economic data for an entity is a 'best intersection', and is the product of the intersection width, in metres, and the grade of the intersection, in ounces per ton, multiplied by 10.

C163. Economic quality. The economic class or rank of the deposit is defined as outlined on Table 2. Although individual entities within a deposit may have separate C164-166 records, there is only one C163 record for each deposit.

C186. Exploration intensity. The extent of exploration, by diamond drilling and/or underground development work on the property, is defined as outlined on Table 3.

DEPOSIT CHARACTERISTICS

The characteristics of the deposit population are described in the following sections. Each section describes data in particular file records, and the section heading refers to that file record and its number as listed on Table 1.

WHAT IS A DEPOSIT?

In order to speak meaningfully of deposit characteristics, it is necessary to define the term "deposit". The definition used in this study is shown on Figure 3, and includes an area around a single or group of mineralized bodies which is somewhat larger than their maximum probable extent. All rocks, structures, and mineralization types known to occur within this area are considered to be part of the deposit, and are entered in the file under the name and number of that deposit.

Where the "natural geological entity", termed here a "deposit", is split in its ownership, as is the case of the Kerr Addison Mine and the Chesterville Mine shown on Figure 3, then two "deposit" records, one for each mine, occur in the file. However, only the geological features within the subjectively defined, natural deposit boundaries which occur on the Chesterville property are coded in the Chesterville record, and the same for the Kerr Addison record. No attempt has been made to be more quantitative in the definition of deposit than this, since there are so many different variables which affect the data coded (and thus the recorded characteristics of the deposit), including extent of exploration, outcrop exposure, size of mineral deposit, the "theoretical bias" of the geologist who originally described the deposit, and extent of geological study. In some cases, these factors may have significantly affected the patterns described below, and every attempt has been made to identify these situations and qualify the conclusions accordingly. The fact that all the coding was done by only two individuals and in one continuous time period (December 1981 - June 1982) tends to minimize the subjective factors.

DEPOSIT STATUS (C4)

The system of categorizing deposit status is that used in the present Mineral Deposits Inventory Record (MDIR) file of the Ontario Geological Survey. Where a deposit had been previously coded in this file, the status recorded there was entered in the present Gold File. The correspondence between grade and dimensional data recorded in the file, and the MDIR status assignments, has not been checked.

It should be emphasised that there is much more data available on many of the deposits than is recorded in publicly accessible records, and that a great deal could be done to improve the quality and quantity of the economic data in the file. This would involve a more careful search of assessment file records and other available data sources than we have been able to do. Nevertheless, the great majority of deposits which belong to the "prospect" class probably do so because exploration failed to disclose continuous zones of economic (or even subeconomic) mineralization.

DISCOVERY DATE AND METHOD (C6-C9)

The discovery of gold in the Abitibi Belt area of Ontario was closely related to the building of a railway, which brought prospectors north from Cobalt, in the first decade of the century. By the beginning of the 1914-1918 war, both of the major camps, Timmins and Kirkland Lake, had been discovered, and the mines which have

dominated the production from the area were either in production or under active development. Thus, while the data on discovery dates are incomplete (exact dates are available for 400 of the 725 deposits), the discovery date of the great majority of the significant producers is known (discovery date is known for deposits accounting for 94 percent of total tons produced), and indicates that the 112 deposits known to have been discovered before 1915 (15.4 percent of the total of 725, or 26.9 percent of the 400 deposits with known discovery dates plus the 16 deposits known to have been discovered "before" 1915) eventually accounted for 86 percent of the total of 255 x

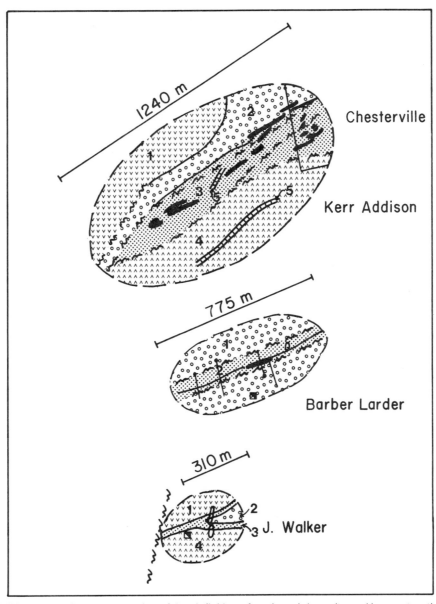

Figure 3. *Diagrammatic representation of the definition of a mineral deposit used in constructing the file.*

10^6 tons of gold ore produced from the area (Figure 4, Table 4).

The historical change in the rate of discovery, as shown on Figure 4, can be related almost entirely to two factors: opening up of the area to exploration, and the price of gold. A minor contributing factor was the change in exploration technology, from dominantly surface prospecting and underground development in the early part of the century, to the extensive use of diamond drilling starting in the 1930s, to, in very recent times, the widespread use of overburden drilling, combined with soil, till and rock geochemistry, and geophysical methods.

The first, and most productive (in terms of economic benefit) phase of exploration activity covered the period 1905-1929, with the peak discovery rate occurring in the period 1910-1914. Discovery rate then declined gradually, presumably due both to declining opportunity (most of the obvious deposits had been found) and declining gold price, in real dollar terms, up until the beginning of the depression in 1930. It is notable that if economic value is measured in terms of tons or ounces of gold eventually produced, then the average economic value of deposits discovered in this period decreased continuously and exponentially during the period. During this first phase of exploration, 41 percent of the deposits which eventually accounted for 92.5 percent of the total gold ore tonnage produced from the area had been discovered.

The second phase of exploration occurred in the period 1930-1960, with the peak of discovery rate occurring in the five year period 1935-1939, just preceding World War II. This gold rush was initiated by the rise in the real price of gold in 1930 and, like the first, declined both due to the decline in the real dollar gold price, and due to declining opportunities. During the war years, 1940-1944, there was a very obvious decline in discovery rate, and a minor peak in discovery rate immediately followed the war. This probably reflects the disruption of the normal trend of business by the war. As in the first exploration phase, virtually all the deposits which eventually produced were discovered in the first part of the exploration cycle but in total, only 19 million tons of ore (eventual production from new mines) was discovered, which accounted for less than 10 percent of the total gold produced from the area.

The final, third phase of exploration is the current one. Discovery rate has been increasing steadily, although slowly, up to the present. No new production has come from this effort, although at least two new deposits, Owl Creek and Hoyle Pond of Kidd Creek Mines Limited, appear likely to become producers. The causes of the

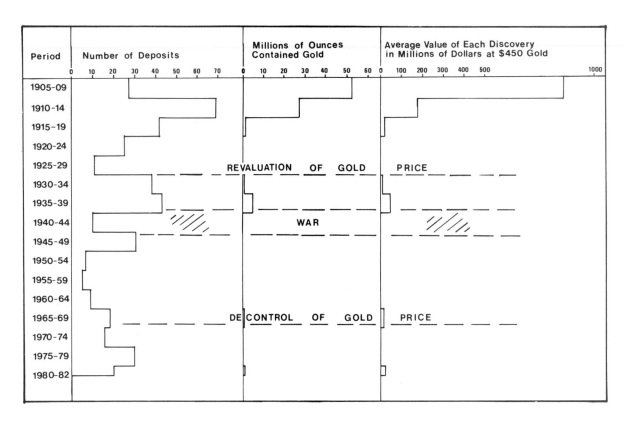

Figure 4. History of gold exploration in the Timmins-Kirkland Lake area

Table 4. *Relationship between discovery date and economic significance of deposits as measured by tonnage gold ore produced.**

Period	Number of Discoveries**	Production: tons/10^3	Avge. tons per deposit discovered	Gross value *** of each discovery
1905-09	27	126,948	4,701,778	$470,177,800
1910-14	69	83,285	1,207,029	120,702,900
1915-19	42	10,581	251,929	25,192,900
1920-29	25	0	0	0
1930-34	36	4,092	113,667	11,366,700
1935-39	38	14,712	387,158	38,715,800
1940-44	10	16	2,420	242,000
1945-present	153	none	0	0

* Note that while virtually all the production from the area is known, discovery dates for only 55% of the deposits are known. Assuming that these discoveries of unknown discovery date were made at a rate equal to those with known discovery date, then the amounts in each of the last three columns of the table would be approximately halved.

** Only deposits for which discovery date is known.

*** Assuming 100% recovery, average grade of 0.25 oz/ton, and $400/per ounce gold price.

third exploration cycle are mainly an increase in the real price of gold. However the upturn in discovery rate preceded the gold price increase. This was probably due to the increased general level of exploration in the area brought about by high base metal prices and the widespread use of airborne geophysics for sulphide deposit exploration in the 1960s. This activity led to the reassessment of many of the old gold properties, and the discovery of new gold deposits as an "accidental spin-off" of exploration for base metal deposits.

Almost all of the deposits were found by traditional prospecting methods and drilling of geological targets, mainly on the extensions of deposits discovered by surface prospecting (Table 5). Sixty-three deposits appear to have been discovered by drilling or trenching of geophysical targets, and only two are attributed to drilling of a geochemical target. Part of the increase in discovery rate associated with the second period of exploration activity (1930-1960) is probably attributable to the increased use of diamond drilling in exploration in the 1930s. In the last ten years, much effort has gone into developing geochemical and geophysical methods for gold exploration. However, the record shows that none of these "new" techniques has led to the type of dramatic increase in discovery rate which occurred, in the case of volcanogenic massive sulphide deposits, in the late 1950s to the early 1970s as a result of the introduction of airborne geophysical methods, and improvements in ground methods. It would appear, therefore, that there is

very considerable potential for the discovery of many more, economically significant gold deposits in the area, especially considering the amount of overburden-covered ground, the lack of a clear geophysical signature for most of the gold deposit types present, the difficulty in assessing the economic merits of gold deposits by surface drilling, and the relatively primitive state of geochemical exploration technology used for gold exploration in glaciated Archean terrains (Fortescue, this volume).

ECONOMIC CHARACTERISTICS (C150-C166)

The assessment work regulations do not specifically require the recording, in the public domain, of the eco-

Table 5. *Discovery method.*

SURFACE PROSPECTING	74.7
DRILLING/TRENCHING GEOLOGICAL TARGET	13.7
DRILLING/TRENCHING GEOPHYSICAL TARGET	8.6
DRILLING/TRENCHING GEOCHEMICAL TARGET	0.3
UNKNOWN	2.7

nomic characteristics of deposits. Therefore the data in these records for non-producing deposits are of very uneven quality and it is not possible to assign a high level of confidence to the economic rating of any one deposit. Nevertheless it appears likely that the economic characteristics of the population can be reasonably accurately described from the available data. It is very important to attempt to economically rank the deposits, since it is the relationship between geological and economic characteristics, i.e., the geological difference between the "better" and the "poorer" deposits, which is the primary concern of exploration geologists. Tentatively, the economic ranking scheme outlined in Table 2 has been used. The largest deposits in the area, ranked in the top group on Table 2, have production and reserves of 84.2 x 10⁶ ounces of gold, or 88.6 percent of the gold in the production and reserves category in the area (Table 6). These deposits represent only 2.5 percent of the total deposit population, or 18.4 percent of the deposits for which sufficient dimension and grade data are available to allow the calculation of total ounces contained gold. A similar, very high proportion of the gold produced from deposits with more than 100,000 tons production in the Superior Province as a whole was found by Hodgson and MacGeehan (1982) to have come from those deposits with greater than 1 x 10⁶ ounces production — in this case 84 percent of the production from 25 percent of the deposits. The amount of gold in the smaller deposits, of Economic Rank 2-5, decreases very rapidly with rank, as shown on Table 6.

The distribution of deposits in the population among the different economic classes is shown graphically in Figure 5. The relationship between economic class and geological features of deposits is considered with the specific geological features below.

The spatial distribution of deposits in relationship to their economic rank is a subject which merits much more study than the time constraints of this project have allowed. Without attempting to consider the problem quantitatively, although this can and will be done with the data recorded in the file, it is obvious that the higher rank deposits are spatially associated, and occur in areas of anomalous concentration of deposits of all ranks. This clustering of deposits is undoubtedly partly a function of the positive feedback relationship among the variables: total deposits discovered per unit time, total number of these which are of any particular rank (including each of the higher ranks), and the total amount of exploration

done per unit time in any specific area. A good discovery leads to further exploration, which leads to more discoveries, and so on. However, this effect appears to be only a minor one, since most of the best deposits were discovered very early in the history of exploration of the area, before exploration intensity was nearly as high as it is today in even the least explored parts of the area. The increase in the intensity of exploration in the years following the first discoveries did not result in the discovery of a significant amount of new gold ore, and the ratio of high rank to low rank deposits appears to have fallen continuously since the first five-year period when the area was opened up, with the exception of a slight reversal in the last half of the decade of the 1930s. This reversal was perhaps due to the increased use of diamond drilling to prospect covered areas at this time (Table 4, Figure 4).

A factor which plays a major role in determining prospect distribution is the effectiveness of exploration, which in turn is related to the amount of bedrock exposure, given the present state of development of gold exploration technology. This effect may be very significant. The influence of cover can probably be deduced by comparing areas of similar outcrop exposure but different economic significance in terms of gold production. It appears likely that in such a comparison, the economically more significant area will have both more deposits *and* a higher ratio of high to low rank deposits than the economically less significant area. If this proves to be the case, then the ratio of high to low rank deposits may be a parameter which can be used to rate the exploration potential of an area independently of the extent of cover. Similarly it is possible that the incidence of certain lithological and mineralogical features (those which in general correlate with economic rank; see below) in the deposits of an area may be used to rate the potential of the area.

EXPLORATION INTENSITY (C181-C186)

In general, data on exploration intensity are probably of better quality than the data on the economic characteristics of deposits. However, in about 20 percent of the cases for each of the three data items recorded in this record (total metres drilled, total number of drill holes, and total metres development), only minimum values could be determined (see "Lines 15-19", Appendix 1). An additional problem in comparing exploration intensity among deposits is the change in the style of physical exploration over the past 75 years. In the first part of the

Table 6. *Distribution of production and reserves among deposits of different economic class.*

Economic Class	% Deposit Total (725)	Population Deposits with P & R (98)	Production + Ounces x 10⁶	Reserves %
6 (>10⁶ oz)	2.5	18.4	84.2	88.6
5	3.4	25.5	9.5	10.0
4	4.6	33.7	1.2	1.3
3	2.3	17.3	0.1	0.1
2 (<10³ oz)	0.7	5.1	0	0

century, the ratio of development to diamond drilling was much greater than is presently normal practice. It might be possible, by statistically manipulating the data and comparing exploration intensity parameters with economic characteristics, to develop a refined method for equating the three measures of exploration intensity. However, the time limitation of the study, and the inability of the computer program for which the file was designed to make any but the simplest mathematical manipulations, preclude this for the present. The rating scheme tentatively adopted is based on dividing the data sets for each of the records into four approximately equal subpopulations, and equating these as outlined on Table 3. A fifth subpopulation is defined by the absence of any drilling or development work. An "intensity of exploration"

rank was then assigned to each deposit on the basis of the highest rank assigned to any one of the individual data items for that deposit. For example if a deposit record showed 150 m drilling, five drill holes and no development, then the rank of these data items would be 1, 2, and 0, respectively. The rank of the deposit would be the highest value of the three, that for the number of drill holes, which is 2. The number of deposits in each of the ranks determined in this way is shown in the first column on Table 3.

The main reason for recording exploration intensity was to look for relationships between economic rank and exploration intensity rank which might (1) lead to a more reliable scheme for rating the economic merits of deposits (since economic data are commonly unavailable,

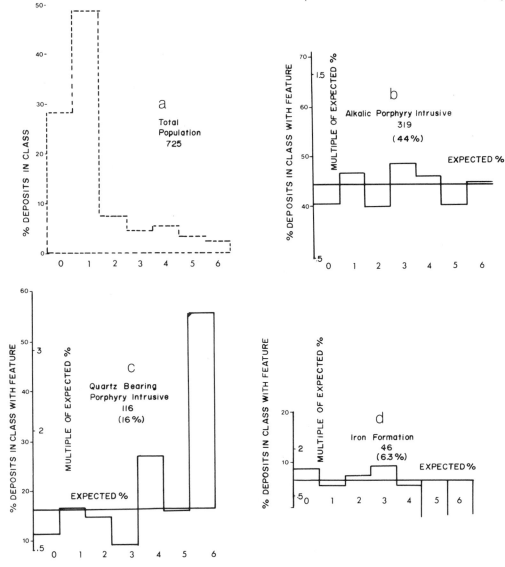

Figure 5. *Distribution of gold deposits according to economic class (see Table 3). (b-d) Relationship between economic class and incidence of selected rock associations in gold deposits (see text for discussion).*

Table 7. Incidence of rock groups, and their relationship to gold mineralization in the deposit population.

Lithology Class	Group or Form	No.	% Deposit Population	MJHR or ISOR	MNHR or ISOR	Host Rock
A	CSTC	6	0.8	33.3	33.3	66.6
	VOLC	70	9.6	45.7	14.3	60.0
	INDT-SHST	67	9.2	35.8	23.9	59.7
M	SHST	5	0.6	60.0	0	60.0
I	VOLC-VLCI	561	77.4	49.2	16.4	65.6
	VLCC-VLCF-VLCU	226	31.2	35.0	24.3	59.3
	DIKE(-DIABAS)	304	41.9	24.3	22.7	47.0
	SILL	66	9.1	31.8	12.1	43.9
	STCK(-DIABAS)	188	25.9	53.2	11.7	64.9
	BTHL	26	3.6	46.2	7.6	53.8
S	CSTC	246	33.9	27.6	21.5	49.1
	CHEM	77	10.6	51.9	16.9	68.8
				41.2±10.8	17.1±8.4	58.2±7.8

* See Appendix 1 for key to abbreviations

whereas the assessment work requirements result in the disclosure of a large proportion of the physical exploration), and (2) lead to the development of a method for defining the exploration potential of a deposit (high economic rank associated with low exploration intensity = high exploration potential).

A second objective was to look at spatial patterns in the ratio of economic rank to exploration intensity rank, to see if this parameter is related to proximity to major mining centers. Neither of these objectives have been realized yet, but are planned for the future.

LITHOLOGY (C190-C197)

The incidence of rock groups, defined on the basis of their lithology and/or form, and their relationship to gold mineralization is summarized on Table 7. A number of significant, although not suprising, features are shown by this compilation, as follows.

1. Despite the very large differences in the incidence of rock units in the population of deposits (0.8 - 77.4 percent: almost a factor of 10), there is relatively little variation in the proportion of cases where the rock is a host rock (43.9 percent - 68.8 percent: less than a factor of 0.6). In other words, all of the rock groups listed on Table 7 are almost equally likely to be host rocks if they occur within a deposit, even though there are very great differences in the likelihood of the units occurring in a deposit. This strongly indicates that gold ores are dominantly epigenetic (that is introduced into these lithologies, rather than being selectively concentrated in specific lithologies at their time of formation).

2. Most highly altered rocks appear to be derived from a volcanic protolith, where the protolith can be identified. Relatively rarely is a sedimentary protolith identified. However, in about half the cases the protolith cannot be identified. This reflects the well known tendency for alteration (which is most commonly carbonatization, see below) intensity to be strongly controlled by the Ca, Mg and Fe content of the host, and the higher levels of these elements in most volcanic rocks, relative to most sedimentary rocks, in gold deposit environments.

3. Highly altered rocks are more common in gold mineralized areas than in "greenstone" belts in general, occurring in 10-15 percent of deposits. However, it should be

kept in mind that at least 85 percent of deposits do not contain units which are so highly altered that they merit names like "carbonate-chlorite schist". It is possible however, that such highly altered rocks are more common in economically good than in economically poor deposits. This possibility has not been checked yet. Very rarely do deposits occur in or near rocks which are so highly metamorphosed that their original protolith is uncertain, i.e. in high amphibolite facies rocks.

4. The most common lithology of gold deposits is volcanic flow rocks, which occur in over 75 percent of the deposits. This is not unexpected, since these rocks are by far the most common lithology of Archean greenstone belts. Volcaniclastic rocks occur in almost one-third of the deposits, which again may be roughly normal for the Superior Province, since small amounts of volcaniclastic rock are extremely common in the dominantly flow sequences.

5. Anomalously common in the vicinity of gold deposits, relative to unmineralized greenstone belt environments, are dikes and stocks, which occur in 41.9 percent and 25.9 percent, respectively, of deposits. Diabase intrusions are not included in these percentages, but are also common (see below) and if counted, the incidence of dikes would be increased.

6. The rock groups can be divided into two groups on the basis of how commonly they are major host rocks when they are present in deposits: a group which is a major host in the range of one-quarter to somewhat over one-third of the cases, and a group which is a major host in the order of half the cases. In the less commonly mineralized group are dikes, sills, clastic and volcaniclastic rocks, and highly altered rocks of indeterminate origin. In the more commonly mineralized group are stocks, chemical sedimentary rocks, volcanic flows, batholiths and highly altered rocks of volcanic protolith.

On Table 8, the incidence of some specific rock types and assemblages of rock types in the population of deposits is shown, along with their relationship to gold mineralization. The following are notable features of this summary.

1. In the group of coarse grained rocks, syenite is the most common, followed by mafic, intermediate and felsic lithologies, which are about equally common, followed by ultramafic lithologies, which are much less common. Of these rocks, syenite and the felsic and intermediate rocks are ore hosts in about half the deposits in which they occur, and major ore hosts in about 40 percent. The mafic rocks are ore hosts in only one-third of the deposits in which they occur, and in only one-quarter are they major ore hosts.

2. The porphyritic and finer grained intrusive rocks are dominantly felsic, and again, alkalic lithologies are more common than subalkalic lithologies of equivalent colour index. "Lamprophyres" occur in 10.9 percent of the deposits. Many of these occurrences are probably true lamprophyres, i.e. alkalic mafic igneous rocks, but an unknown proportion are probably normal basaltic or andesitic dikes which have been given the field name "lamprophyre". Except for coarser grained syenite porphyry, most of the porphyritic and fine grained lithologies are less commonly major ore hosts, but more commonly minor ore hosts than their coarser grained equivalents.

3. There is a very strong association of gold deposits in the Abitibi Belt with felsic igneous intrusive rocks, and in particular, with alkalic, felsic igneous rocks: 40 percent of deposits contain one or more of the lithologies syenite, syenite porphyry or felsic feldspar porphyry, and 14 percent (almost all of which do not contain alkalic felsic igneous rocks) contain quartz or quartz-feldspar porphyry intrusions. As noted above, the coarser grained, and in general larger bodies of such rocks are much more commonly major host rocks, and less commonly minor host rocks than the finer grained and smaller bodies.

4. A somewhat surprising common lithological association of gold deposits is diabase dikes. These occur in 27.4 percent of the deposits, and are particularly common in the small showings which occur away from the main centers of gold mineralization. However, in all but two deposits, the dikes are not host rocks and in most deposits they clearly post-date the mineralization. From these facts, it is concluded that the dikes occur in the same structures which played a major role in localizing gold mineralization before dike emplacement, as in the case, for example, of the correlation between volcanogenic massive sulphide deposits and diabase dikes in the Noranda area of Quebec (Price 1948).

5. Volcanic rocks are much more common than intrusive rocks in gold deposits. Furthermore, the mafic volcanic lithologies are almost twice as common as the felsic, and three times as common as the intermediate, in contrast to intrusive rocks, which are dominantly felsic. The ratio of the incidence of mafic to that of ultramafic volcanic rocks in deposits is high, and similar to the same ratio for coarse-grained intrusive rocks. Again, in contrast to the intrusive suite, the mafic volcanic rocks are more commonly major hosts (46.8 percent of the cases) than the felsic (25.9 percent of the cases), although because the felsic rocks are more commonly minor ore hosts than the mafic, the incidence of each as an ore host is not greatly different (mafic, 59.1 percent and felsic, 48.5 percent).

6. Clastic sedimentary rocks occur in 33.9 percent of deposits, and in half the cases, are ore hosts. However, as in the case of most of the finer grained and porphyritic felsic rocks, the ratio of deposits where clastic rocks are major hosts to those where they are minor hosts is relatively low, near 1:1. Of the clastic sedimentary lithologies, conglomerate is conspicuous by its common occurrence, being present in 14.3 percent of the deposits in the population, although it is no more commonly a host rock than any of the other clastic sedimentary rocks.

7. Chemical sedimentary rocks are anomalously common in gold deposits, relative to unmineralized areas, but still, they are absent from 90 percent of the deposits. Where they occur, chemical sedimentary rocks are ore hosts in two-thirds of the cases and major host rocks in half the cases. In other words, there is no lithology more likely to be a major host rock in a deposit than a chemical sedi-

Table 8. *Incidence of rock types in mineralized zone and deposit populations, and their relationship to gold mineralization.*

Lithology Class,Group,Form,Name	No.	% Deposit Population	% Deposits with unit where it is a..		
			MJHR or ISOR	MNHR or UNHR	Host rock
INTRUSIVE IGNEOUS					
COARSE GRAINED					
FELSCG	57	7.9	38.6	7.0	45.6
INTRCG	63	8.7	42.8	11.1	53.9
MAFCCG	83	11.4	26.5	7.2	33.7
ULTACG	17	2.3	4.8	11.8	6.6
SYNITE	105	14.5	41.0	13.3	54.3
PORPHYRITIC APHANITIC					
FLSQFP	80	11.0	27.5	23.8	51.3
FELSQP	20	2.8	20.0	25.0	45.0
FLSAPH	20	2.8	25.0	35.0	60.0
SYNITP	116	16.0	36.2	17.2	53.4
FELSFP	97	13.4	20.6	18.6	49.2
LAMPRP	79	10.9	13.9	10.1	24.0
OTHER					
DIABAS	199	27.4	0.5	0.5	1.0
COMBINATIONS					
FELSQP, FLSQFP	100	13.8	27.0	24.0	51.0
SYNITE,SYNITP,FELSFP	289	39.9	35.2	15.9	51.1
SYNITE,SYNITP,FELSFP,LAMPRP	319	43.8			
EXTRUSIVE IGNEOUS					
FLSAPH	274	37.8	25.9	22.6	48.5
MFFLAP	15	2.1	40.0	26.7	66.7
INTAPH	119	16.4	29.4	15.3	44.7
MFCAPH	470	64.8	46.8	12.3	59.1
MAFCCG	21	2.9	4.8	38.1	42.9
ULTAPH	59	8.1	32.2	8.5	40.7
TRCYTE	63	8.7	19.0	28.6	47.6
SEDIMENTARY CLASTIC					
CONGLM	104	14.3	21.1	19.2	40.3
ARKOSE	26	3.4	19.2	11.5	30.7
GRYCKE	139	19.2	24.5	18.0	42.5
SLTSTN	75	10.3	24.0	25.3	49.3
ALL TYPES	246	33.9	27.6	21.5	49.1
SEDIMENTARY CHEMICAL					
FEFORM	50	6.9	52.0	14.0	66.0
CHERT	29	4.0	48.3	20.7	69.0
ALL TYPES	77	10.6	51.9	16.9	68.8

*See Appendix 1 for key to abbreviations

mentary rock, but the chances of such a rock occurring in a gold deposit are relatively low.

The incidence of the various rock units in the deposits, and their occurrence as ore hosts, is shown graphically on Figure 6. The relationship between rock type and economic class has been investigated so far for only three rock groups: (1) the alkalic intrusive suite (syenite, syenite porphyry, felsic feldspar porphyry and lamprophyre), (2) the quartz-bearing intrusive suite (felsic quartz-feldspar porphyry and felsic quartz porphyry) and (3) iron formation (iron formation, sulphide iron formation, oxide iron formation, siliceous iron formation, carbonate iron formation, sulphide-oxide iron formation, sulphide-oxide-silicate-carbonate iron formation and sulphide-carbonate iron formation). The relationships are shown on Figure 5. The plots show the proportion of deposits in each economic class which contain the feature.

If there was no systematic relationship between economic class and the presence of a rock type, then it would be expected that the rock units would be about equally as common, in terms of the percentage of deposits in the economic class which showed the feature, in each of the economic classes, and that this percentage would be equivalent, approximately, to the percentage of the total population which contains the feature. On Figure 6, the expected incidence of the rock type on the classes is shown as a horizontal base line drawn at the percentage incidence of the feature in the deposit population as a whole. Positive deviations from this expected value plot above the base line and negative deviations below it, and can be expressed either in terms of the "percentage of the deposits in the economic class which have the feature", or "multiples of the expected percentage" for the economic class. There is clearly a highly skewed distribution in the case of the quartz-bearing felsic intrusive rocks and the iron formation, but no marked asymmetry in the population of deposits containing alkalic intrusive rocks. Quartz-bearing felsic intrusive rocks are over three times more common than expected in the top economic class of deposits, whereas iron formation, as we have defined these rocks, is completely absent from the population of deposits defined as having > 10^6 ounces contained gold, i.e., the incidence of iron formation is an "infinite number of multiples less than the expected value" in economic classes 5 and 6.

Viewed in terms of the geology of the area, these graphs show in quantitative terms the following relatively well-known geological facts.

1. The part of the area containing the most iron formation is in the Upper Formation of the Lower Supergroup (Pyke 1981) around the Shaw Dome south of Timmins. In this area there is a very large number of almost uniformly poor (economically) gold deposits.

2. The best deposits in the area occur in the Porcupine Camp and, in this camp, there is a very high incidence of quartz-bearing porphyries closely associated with the gold.

3. The great majority of gold deposits outside the Porcupine Camp and the Shaw Dome area occur (1) along the Destor-Porcupine fault zone, extending east from about the centre of Map 2205 to the Quebec border; (2) along the Matheson-Kirkland Lake Intrusive Belt; and (3) along the Kirkland Lake-Larder Lake Break and its extension to Matachewan (see Hodgson 1982). In all of these areas, there is very little quartz-bearing porphyry, but a very common occurrence of alkalic porphyry intrusive rocks with both the economically good, and the economically poor gold deposits.

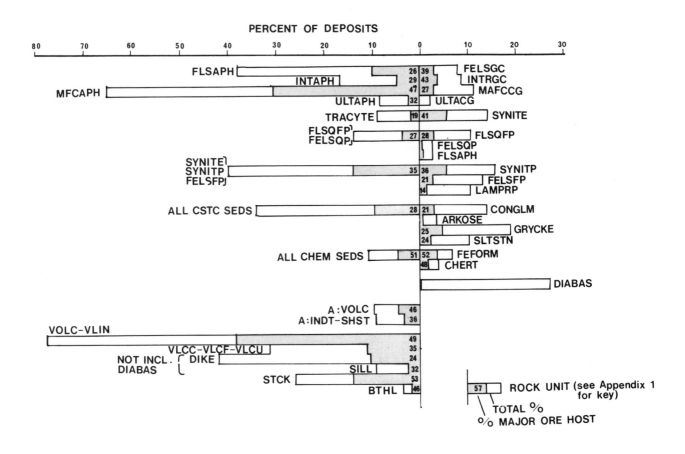

Figure 6. *Incidence of various lithological and geometrical types of rock bodies, and their occurrence as major host rocks of mineralization in gold deposits (see Tables 7 and 8).*

25

SHAPE AND RELATIONSHIP TO STRATIGRAPHY AND STRUCTURE OF MINERALIZED ZONES (C200-204)

In describing the mineralization, a distinction is made on the basis of scale between features of mineralized zones and features of the mineralization which occurs within the zones. The term mineralized zone refers to the larger scale entity which, in the case of economic deposits, would be the body which is mined as a unit. A mineralized zone can be described in terms of its overall shape, its relationship to stratigraphic contacts and structures (which are defined in a similar mineral deposit scale), and its composition in terms of the types of mineralization which it comprises. Mineralization types, on the other hand, are the textural-mineralogical units which can be defined on the outcrop to hand specimen scale. Mineralization may, for example, consist of stockwork veinlets which cross-cut bedding, yet the larger body (mineralized zone) of stockwork mineralization (mineralization type) may be concordant with stratigraphy, i.e. may be localized within a single unit in the stratigraphic sequence. Alteration types are like mineralization types, so that a single mineralized zone may consist of, and/or have associated with it, a number of mineralization and alteration types. In fact the distinction between mineralization and alteration is often artificial, in the sense that the altered (i.e. metasomatized) rock may be auriferous.

Relatively poor data are available on the gross geometrical features of the gold-bearing mineralized zones in most deposits. The main patterns are summarized on Table 9. About half of the gold zones for which shape data were available (470) are described as tabular or sheet-like and about one-fifth are described as irregular. Only 1.1 percent are cylindrical. Data are available on the relationship to stratigraphy of 349 zones. About half are concordant or nearly so, about 1 percent are both concordant and discordant, and half are clearly discordant. Thus, on the basis of this one criterion, of the 809 gold ore zones described in the file, almost one-quarter (22.6 percent) could be stratiform chemical sedimentary ores. However, the weight of the evidence very strongly indicates that none of the gold ore zones in the area are chemical sedimentary ores, as discussed below. No good data could be obtained on the relationship of gold ore zones to the regional foliation.

The type of structural control was indicated in 449 of the zones described. Of these, 343 or 76.4 percent were described as being controlled by or occurring within shear zones, fractures and faults, and 104 or 23.2 percent as occurring on, and being controlled by rock unit contacts, very commonly, dike or other intrusive rock body contacts.

No attempt has been made yet to look for interrelationships among these variables, but the general impression gained from coding the data is that no clear or significant relationships are present.

MINERALIZATION (C205-C221)

Four types of data define the mineralization in the file: the textures of the mineralization; the type(s) of wall rock alteration; the host rock(s); and the mineralogy.

The term "texture" refers here to the geometrical features of mineralization on the hand specimen to outcrop scale. A mineralized zone which is tabular or vein-like in shape might consist of a number of different "textural types" of mineralization, for example, disseminated, thin veinlets or thick "veins". Data on texture were recorded for 93.1 percent of the 809 mineralized zones described in the file. Nine different textural types of mineralization are recorded, but in the great majority of zones, the dominant mineralization type is either vein, veinlet or disseminated mineralization (Table 10). In half of the zone descriptions, a second or subordinate textural type of mineralization is described. The most common subordinate mineralization types are disseminated and veinlet mineralization (Table 10). Although no attempt has been yet made to determine the relationships between the dominant and subordinate mineralization types, it is probable, considering the data in Table 10, that the most com-

Table 9. *Main features of mineralized zones.*

VARIABLE	MAIN VALUES	PERCENT DEPOSITS
SHAPE	TABULAR	50
(n=470)	IRREGULAR	19
	CYLINDRICAL	1
RELATION TO	CONCORDANT	51
STRATIGRAPHY	DISCORDANT	48
(n=349)		
STRUCTURAL	SHEARS, FAULTS, FRACTS.	76
CONTROL	CONTACTS (ESPEC. DIKES)	23
(n=343)		

Table 10. *Textures of mineralization.*

Dominant Mineralization n=753 or 93.1% of zones Type	Percent*		Subordinate Mineralization n=404 or 49.9% of zones Type	Percent*	
VEIN	33.6)			6.9)	
CMVN	8.1)	44.9		1.0)	8.6
BXVN	3.2)			0.7)	
VNLT	22.3)			34.1)	
STWK	8.5)	34.7		3.5)	40.3
SHVN	3.9)			2.7)	
DISS	17.3)			48.5)	
BXMX	2.1)	19.4		1.7)	50.2
BNDS	1.1			0.5	

* Percent of zones in which item recorded
** See Appendix I for Key to abbreviations

mon situations are "vein with disseminated mineralization (in the wall rocks of the vein)", "vein with veinlets (in the wall rocks of the vein)", and "veinlets with disseminated mineralization (in the wall rocks between the veinlets)".

A dominant alteration type is recorded for about half of the mineralized zones described in the file. Of the alteration types noted, carbonatization is the dominant type in over half of the zones, followed by silicification in about a fifth. A subordinate alteration type is recorded for only one-quarter of the mineralized zones with the most common types being sericitization, silicification, pyritization, carbonatization and chloritization (Table 11). The most common alteration pattern, then, would probably be dominantly carbonatization and/or silification associated with any, or some combination of the following minerals: pyrite, sericite, quartz, and chlorite. Although the types of associations recorded will be investigated, it is not expected that an analysis of the data in this record will show anything much beyond the above generalizations, since alteration has been well described in only a very few individual deposits.

The host rocks of gold mineralization have been considered above in the section on lithology. In the original plan of the study, one objective was to look for correlations between features of specific mineralized zones in deposits, and the immediate host rocks of the zone. It was for this reason that "host rock" was noted in the record dealing with individual mineralized zones, as well as in the lithology record, which lists the rocks present on the scale of the deposit. However, as discussed above, it proved very difficult to make a clear distinction between different zones within individual deposits except in a relatively small proportion of the deposit population. Therefore, host rocks at the "mineralized zone" scale and at the "deposit" scale are very similar for the population as a whole, as shown in Table 12.

The mineralogy of the deposits was found to be quite variable. A total of 59 minerals were recorded, but 95 percent of the mineral records are of a group of only 17 minerals (Table 13). Most of the mineralized zones are described as containing quartz and pyrite, and native gold

Table 11. *Alteration types.*

Dominant Alteration n=414 or 51.2% of zones		Subordinate Alteration n=204 or 25.2% of zones	
Type	Percent*	Type	Percent*
CBTZ	52.9		15.2
SILC	21.0		20.1
PYRT	6.5		16.2
SERC	5.8		22.1
CHLO	5.6		11.8
BLCH	3.6		2.0
EPID	1.4		3.9
KFEL	1.0		0.5
HEMT	1.0		2.5
ALBT	0.4		2.0
ARPR	-		0.5
FCST	-		0.5
GRPT	-		2.0
FELD	-		1.0

* Percent of zones in which item is recorded
* See Appendix 1 for key to abbreviations

was noted in about half. Somewhat surprisingly, however, almost as many zones are described as containing chalcopyrite as are described containing carbonate, and galena is reported much more commonly than the well-known indicator minerals arsenopyrite, tourmaline, and scheelite. Molybdenite is also rather common, being present in more zones than any of the above gold indicator minerals.

The distribution, in relation to associated felsic intrusions and to economic class of deposit, of several of the less common but distinctive minerals was investigated, with the results shown in Figures 7 and 8. There is a very strong positive association of galena, molybdenite and tellurides with felsic alkalic porphyry in deposits, and tellurides, molybdenite, tourmaline and scheelite with quartz-bearing felsic porphyries in deposits. Arsenopyrite and sphalerite are less common than expected in each case, and tourmaline less common than expected in deposits with felsic alkalic porphyries. A similar, strong positive association of scheelite and tourmaline with quartz-rich felsic intrusions was noted by Hodgson and MacGeehan (1982).

All of the minerals plotted on Figure 8 show a strong, although variable, tendency to be preferentially associated with the deposits of higher economic rank. The strongest association is with scheelite, which is almost 20 times more common in the best deposits than it is in the population as a whole. Although a part of this correlation is probably due to the correlation between the extent of geological investigation and the economic value of a deposit, it is the writer's impression, from having coded the deposit data, that most of the effect is real. The same conclusion is suggested for tourmaline, arsenopyrite, molybdenite and galena, since these minerals are relatively easily recognized, and in most cases are not particularly rare constituents of the mineralized zones in which they occur.

In the case of tellurides, the significance of the correlation is more doubtful, since tellurides are not abundant (although they are important sources of gold in the deposits of the Kirkland Lake Main Break, Thomson *et al.* 1950), and are difficult to identify in hand specimen.

SUMMARY AND CONCLUSIONS

1. A computer-processable file has been constructed of the economic and geological characteristics, and extent of exploration, of the 725 known gold deposits in the Timmins-Kirkland Lake area.

2. Although there are many uncontrollable and partly subjective causes for variation in the deposit characteristics recorded in the file, the fact that the compilation was done by only two individuals in one continuous time period has hopefully minimized the variations.

3. Most of the economically important deposits were found very early in the exploration history of the area by traditional prospecting methods and drilling of the extensions of surface showings. Considering the extensive overburden cover, this suggests that the potential for

Table 12. Incidence of rock types in mineralized zone and deposit population, and their relationship to mineralization.

	MAJOR HOST % ZONES	OR IS "ORE DEPOSITS" % DEPOSITS	MINOR HOST OR % ZONES	UNKNOWN HOST % DEPOSITS
ALTERED	8.0	7.7.	5.1	3.6
METAMORPHIC	2.6	.4	–	–
INTRUSIVE COARSE GRAINED				
FELSCG	2.3)	3.0)	1.6	.6)
INTRCG	4.4) 9.5	3.7) 9.8	1.0	1.0) 2.4
MAFCCG	2.7)	3.0)	4.1	0.8)
ULTACG	.1)	.1)	.3	0)
SYNITE	4.5	5.9	3.9	1.9
INTRUSIVE FINE GRAINED AND PORPHYRITIC				
APLITE	.1		.3	
FELCEP	.3		.3	
FELSQP	.6) 2.9	.6) 3.8	1.2) 8.2	.7) 3.3
FLSQFP	2.3)	3.0)	7.0)	2.6)
INTERP	.1		1.2	
LAMPRP	.6	1.5)	2.8	1.1)
FELSFP	1.7) 6.8	2.8) 18.6	7.7) 13.8	2.5) 5.2
SYNITP	5.1) +	5.8) +	6.1) +	2.7) +
	synite (4.5)	synite (5.9)	synite (3.9)	synite (1.9)
	"	"	"	"
	11.3	14.5	17.7	7.1
DIABAS	.3	0	–	0
EXTRUSIVE				
FLSAPH	11.4	9.8	11.3	8.5
MFFLAP	1.6	.8	1.9	.6
INTAPH	5.6	4.8	3.2	2.5
MFCAPH	30.0	30.3	16.7	8.0
ULTAPH	2.3	2.6	3.2	.7
TRCYTE	1.7	1.7	2.3	2.5
SEDIMENTARY CLASTIC				
CONGLM	2.0	3.0	3.5	2.7
ARKOSE	0.5	0.7	–	0.4
GRYCKE	4.0	4.7	6.4	3.5
QRTZITE	.4		.6	
SLTSTN	1.4	2.5	4.1	2.6
ALL TYPES	8.3	9.4		9.2
SEDIMENTARY CHEMICAL				
FEFORM	3.7	3.5	1.9	1.0
CHERT	1.6	1.9	1.6	0.8
LIMSTN	.1		–	
GRAPHITE	–		1.9	
ALL TYPES	5.4	5.5		1.8

* See Appendix 1 for Key to Abbreviations

Table 13. Distribution of common minerals in the population of mineralized zones and gold deposits.

	n	% of records*	% Zones	% deposits
Quartz	686	22.3	84.8	
Pyrite	665	21.9	82.2	
Gold	364	12.0	45.0	
Carbonate	294	9.7	36.3	
Chalcopyrite	291	9.6	36.0	
Galena	106	3.5	13.1	13.5
Pyrrhotite	84	2.8	10.4	11.0
Sphalerite	84	2.8	10.4	11.0
Molybdenite	71	2.3	8.8	9.1
Arsenopyrite	49	1.6	6.0	6.3
Tourmaline	42	1.4	5.2	5.4
Hematite	31	1.0	3.8	
Telluride	30	1.0	3.7	4.1
Graphite	27	0.9	3.3	
Fuchsite	21	0.7	2.6	
Magnetite	18	0.6	2.2	
Scheelite	13	0.4	1.6	1.5
		94.6%**	100%**	not determined**
		(n=3036)	(n=809)	(n=725)

*   Records of minerals

** Percent of the units which contain at least one of the indicated minerals;

n= number of units

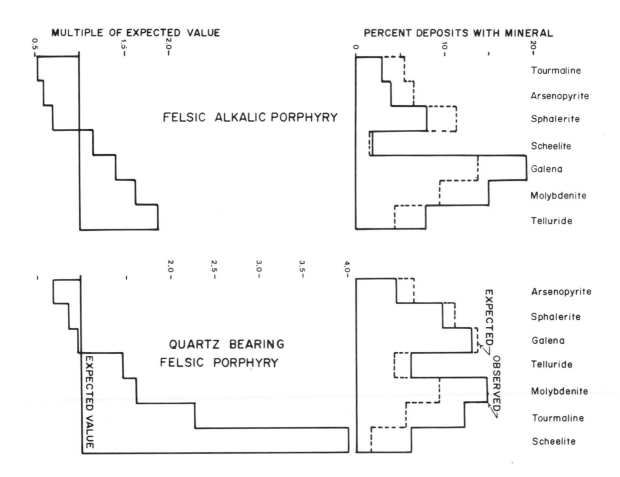

Figure 7. Incidence of selected minerals in deposits with intrusive porphyry.

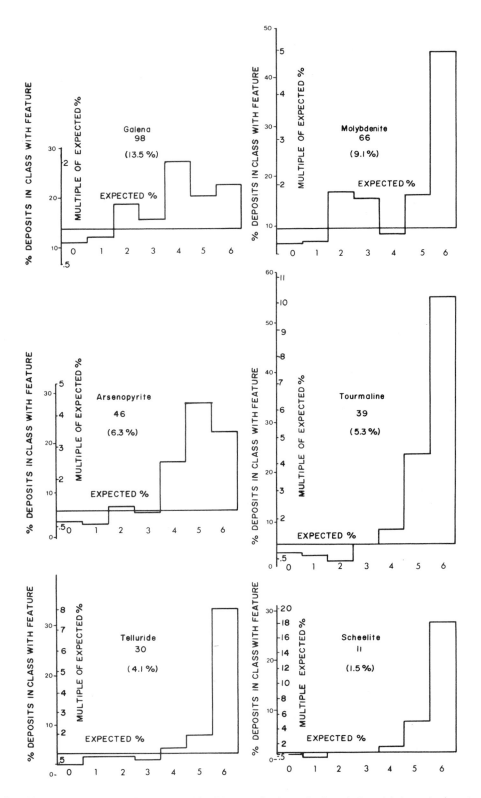

Figure 8. *Relationship between economic class and incidence of selected minerals in gold deposits (see text for discussion).*

finding important new deposits is excellent, if better geological models and methods for exploring beneath glacial cover can be developed.

4. Of major importance in exploration, and a prime objective of this study, is the identification of criteria which can be used to locate the small but highly productive gold-rich areas which constitute the gold mining camps, since virtually all of the gold production has come from the few largest (and many smaller) deposits which are clustered in these areas. One of the indicated results of this study, as yet untested quantitatively, is that camps are characterized by an anomalously high ratio of better to poorer deposits. It also seems likely that the incidence of certain lithological and mineralogical features (those which in general correlate with economic rank) in the deposits of an area may serve as a criterion for regional (mining camp) scale selection of areas for exploration.

5. The lithological environment of gold deposits is characterized by an unusual abundance of dikes and stocks, and either alkalic or quartz-bearing felsic porphyry intrusions. Furthermore, there is a tendency for quartz-bearing porphyry to be much more common in the economically better than in the economically poorer deposits. These facts, along with the relationship between felsic porphyries and gold-associated minerals noted below (8), support the long-held opinion among gold geologists and prospectors that porphyries and gold are genetically related (Knight 1924).

6. Iron formations are more commonly associated with economically poor than with economically good deposits, suggesting they are not a favourable feature of the most gold prospective environments in the area.

7. The following minerals appear to be particularly common in association with gold deposits, and all correlate positively, although to different degrees, with economic rank: galena, molybdenite, arsenopyrite, tourmaline, tellurides and scheelite. Thus within the area, all are a positive sign of the ultimate economic potential of deposit, although their absence cannot be considered a sign of low economic potential, since they are mostly relatively uncommon in the population as a whole.

8. There is a preferential association of galena, molybdenite and tellurides with felsic alkalic porphyry, and tellurides, molybdenite, tourmaline and scheelite with quartz-bearing felsic porphyries.

APPENDIX 1. Timmins-Kirkland Lake Gold Compilation Project — Instructions for Recording Data on Coding Sheets

The following instructions for filling out the coding sheets are those used in the present study. The design of the coding sheets is shown in Figure 2. Added here are 14 notes, each referring to a specific data record, which contain comments and recommendations regarding the items which arise out of our experience in building the file.

LINE 01

Au File#: This is a unique number which will be assigned to each deposit in the area.

MDIR#: In cases where a deposit has already been coded in the Mineral Deposits Inventory Record of the Ontario Geological Survey (MDIR) system, its number is recorded again in the present file.

Name: The existing MDIR name is used where possible, otherwise the name in the source reference is used.

Alternate Name: Use existing MDIR alternate name if one exists.

LINE 02

Status: A single number is entered here. The number system is identical to that used in the MDIR file and is as follows:

Code	Additional Value in Database	Commodity Explanation
1	PRODUCER	Commodity being extracted for sale
2	DEV PROS	Reserves and grades known in 3 dimensions
3	PAST PROD + R	No longer produced, but known reserves or resources
4	PAST PROD	No longer produced, no known reserves or resources
5	RAW PROS	Two dimensional data & grade
6	OCCURRENCE	One dimensional data & grade

Note: A gold operation must have produced more than 100 oz Au in order to be classified as a Past Producer.

Alternate name: A second alternate name: See Line 01

Region name: A unique name which is assigned to "natural" groups of deposits in the area, corresponding to what are normally known as "mining camps".

Region number: Each region will be assigned a unique number.

Note 1: *neither of the last two items were used in the present file, and criteria for objectively defining such areas are still undefined.*

LINE 03

Deposit discovered: Record here the year (e.g.1931 = 31) in which the deposit was discovered, if known, in the column "on". If this date is not known, record the dates "before" and/or "after" the deposit was discovered. Obviously the "before" date must correspond to the date of the first reference to the deposit in the available literature.

Note 2: *It is recommended that this system be amended as follows:*
The "best guess" discovery date be entered in all cases, and an additional data item be defined which specifies the degree of confidence in the discovery date assignment, as follows:
1. ± 1 year
2. ± 3 years
3. ± 5 years
4. ± 10 years
5. ± 20 years

Discovery method: Enter one of the following possibilities:
1. Surface prospecting
2. Drilling and/or trenching of geological target
3. Drilling and/or trenching of geophysical target
4. Drilling and/or trenching of geochemical target
5. Unknown

Latitude: Enter as degrees in decimal form

Longitude: Enter as degrees in decimal form

Confidence: This item refers to the confidence of the compiler that the deposit is accurately located, and depends on a number of factors such as: the scale of the map used to determine the deposit coordinates; the manner in which the deposit was originally located on this map (if this can be determined; do not assume that just because a deposit is located on a large scale published map that its location is known accurately, because it may have originally been placed on this map from a rough claim sketch map); and the number and spatial distribution of "showings" which together are considered, because of their proximity, to constitute the "deposit".
1. Accurate (within 100 m)
2. Approximate (within 1000 m)
3. Inaccurate (within 3000 m)
4. Unknown - probably very inaccurate

Note 3: This item was found to be necessary when the writer was designing the original for the British Columbia Mineral Deposits File (MINDEP FILE), but was not used in the present study.

Location map reference: This refers to the map used to locate the deposit. Data should be entered as in the MDIR file, as follows:
1. Publishing Agency: OGS, GSC, other agency; for OBM, ODM and ODMNA publications use also OGS. For claim maps it is MNR.
2. Year of publication: e.g. 1978 followed by a comma.
3. Map Series: For OGS use either P or MAP followed immediately by the applicable number. For claim maps use CLAIM MAP.
4. Title: Abbreviate where necessary.
5. Accompanying Report: If space permits and if applicable, indicate in which report a MAP occurs, e.g. OGS, MAP2409 UPPER MANITOU LAKE IN REPORT 189.

LINES 04-06

Entity definition: Most gold deposits consist of more than one mineralized zone, and in a very large proportion there is more than one mineralization type (e.g. veins, disseminated mineralization, stockwork mineralization, etc.). Furthermore, in at least some deposits, these different mineralization types have probably formed at different times in the geological evolution of the area, and are "controlled by" (i.e. are spatially and/or genetically related to) different geological features. For these reasons, it is essential that if there is more than one type of mineralization, or more than one spatially distinct mineralized zone in the deposit, that the characteristics of these be recorded separately. This is necessary so that when the data are eventually compared, characteristics of one mineralization type (e.g. fissure veins) are not ascribed to (and counted with) characteristics of another (e.g. interflow sulphide-carbonate iron formations) because in a proportion of the population, both mineralization types occur in the same deposit.

Since the objective is to define as closely as possible the economic and geological attributes of gold ore types, it is more useful to record the characteristics of individual spatially distinct

mineralized zones, rather than to try to generalize for ore types in a deposit. The item "identity definition", therefore, refers to individual zones, and not geological types of mineralization. The data which define such a mineralized zone should be entered as follows:

Code: The first two spaces of this item refer to the mineralization type. Some possible types are as follows:
SV Simple vein.
BV Breccia vein.
CV Complex vein system, consisting of a number of individual parallel to subparallel veins which occur close together, either superimposed on each other (due to reopening of the fissure) or, probably more commonly arranged en echelon in a system.
VL Zone of veinlets + disseminated and massive mineralization of unknown relation to stratigraphy. Mineralized "shear zones" are typically of this type.
VS As VL, but known to be stratiform, or nearly so.
VH As VL, but known to cross cut stratigraphy.
IN Mineralization of disseminated and/or veinlet type coextensive with a dike.
DEP This item refers to the entire deposit, and is used whenever grade-tonnage data are available for the entire deposit, irrespective of whether or not separate mineralized zones have been identified and described in the deposit. For example, the Dome Mine would contain a DEP item since a mine grade and tonnage are recorded in the literature, even though there are several distinctive geological types of mineralization and many mineralized zones of each of these types within the mine.

The last column of code is used for a simple number so that spatially distinct zones of the same mineralization type can be described, e.g. VS1, VS2, etc.

Name: Here is recorded the mine and/or company term for the zone and/or a brief geological description of the zone (e.g. West Zone; Quartz-Tourmaline Vein; Robson Zone; etc.).

Proportion of total mineralization: The objective of recording this item is to give some indication of the relative importance of the different mineralized zones in the deposit. Suggested entries are:
MAJOR
MINOR
UNKWN - unknown
00080 - 80 percent (or some other exact percentage)

Note 4: This entire record (lines 04-06) presented many problems, and a major revision is recommended. Although the rationalization for defining "mineralized entities" is valid, the problem comes in identifying these in the literature, and matching the characteristics described in lines 21-28 of the input document with particular entities. It is suggested that lines 04-06 be given to a short, format-free description of the deposit which focuses on the nature of the mineralized zones and differences (if any) among them. This data can then serve to alert the file user to the possibility of "mixed data sets" (i.e. "the apples and oranges" effect) in lines 21-28. If this change were made, then all references to "entity code" in the entire file could be removed, since the "entity" would be always the "deposit" or the dominant (economically) type of mineralized zone in the deposit.

LINES 07-11

Entity Code: See line 06

Note 5: See Note 4.

Commodity: This refers only to metallic commodities which are abundant enough in the deposit to be of potentially (or actual, in the case of producers) significant economic value. For example "copper" would be a commodity in the Horne Mine, Noranda, the Henderson Mine, Chibougamau, and the McIntyre Mine, Timmins. But "zinc" or "tungsten" would not be a commodity in the Campbell Red Lake Mine, despite the fact that both these elements are quite abundant there. Data on commodities which are geologically, but not economicallly significant, should be recorded in mineralogical terms on Lines 29-42.

Pre-production grade and tonnage: These items would only be entered for deposits of status 1-4. The objective of entering them is two-fold:
(1) to allow comparison of pre-production estimates of grade and tonnage with final grade and tonnage for status 3 and 4 gold deposits. I suspect the disparity of the two is larger in gold than it is in other deposit types, because of the difficulty of economically and geologically evaluating gold deposits by diamond drilling.
(2) to allow the recording of grade and tonnage for status 2 deposits, i.e. developed prospects.

Note 6: In the file, both pre-production grade and tons for status 2 deposits and reserves for status 1 and 3 deposits were recorded. No meaningful numbers for this item in the sense described by (1) above were found for any of the deposits in the area.

Final grade and tonnage: This item is recorded for status 3 and 4 deposits.

Width, length, depth: All or any one of these items are recorded for specific mineralized zones when the information is available. In general, they cannot be recorded when the entity code is DEP in the case of deposits consisting of a number of individual mineralized zones.

Note 7: Although these dimensional data for different zones in specific deposits were recorded in the file, it is recommended that only "deposit" data be recorded; see Note 4.

Average grade: This item will be recorded when no tonnage figure is given. This will commonly be the case when only the "width" or "width and length" dimension is known in status 6 and 5 deposits.

Note 8: In a few deposits width, length, depth and grade were recorded but no total tonnage and grade were recorded in the literature. In these cases a "total ounces gold" item could be calculated (see below).

Best intersection grade and width: This item is recorded only in status 5 and 6 deposits, and commonly is the only economic data available on status 6 deposits.

Best grab sample: Many occurrences (status 6 deposits) are nothing more than showings from which samples returning gold assays were obtained. In assessing the significance of these, the best assay obtained is an important parameter, since virtually all sulphide-bearing rocks in gold camps contain some gold (e.g. trace, 0.01 oz/ton), but reasonably high assays (e.g. > 0.2 oz/ton) are not that common. If no assays are given, then in general, the "showing" is probably not worth trying to code, and may just represent a "location" property. Sometimes, however, assay data are not available, but there is evidence that gold occurs in the showing in significant amounts (e.g. very extensive drilling has been done, or Au is noted on the Ontario Geological Survey Data Series Maps or phrases like "scattered values were obtained", "visible gold occurs locally", occur in the descriptions) and the deposit should be coded. In this case, then, the follow

ing possible entries should be made in the "best grab sample" space:
VAU - visible gold reported
LOW - low gold values reported
HIH - scattered high values reported

LINES 12-14

References: References should be recorded as outlined in the MDIR coding instruction manual.

LINES 15-19

This line records the extent of exploration by drilling, trenching and underground development work. The entity code here will be DEP. In many cases the details of some of the exploration will be recorded but not all of it, the unrecorded part being referred to by a phrase like "previous to the present program, a number of holes were drilled by Hollinger in 1924 and McIntyre in 1920". In these cases add a + in the last column in the entry space for the appropriate item. If no + is added, then this space should remain blank.

Entity code: see Lines 04-06
(See Note 4)

Metres drilled: This is the total drilling done on the entity (either the entire deposit and/or specific mineralized zones within it). The last column remains blank unless there is a + entered for "greater than" the amount indicated.

DDH#: The total number of holes. The last column remains blank unless a + is entered for "greater than" the amount indicated.

Metres trenched: The total aggregate length of trenched exposure. Last column reserved for + as noted above.

Note 9: It was not found possible to obtain quantitative, meaningful data on this item.

Metres development: The aggregate length of underground development, including shafts and adits. Last column reserved for + as noted above.

Extent exploration: A subjective assessment of the exploration potential of the area covered by the record:
1. well explored
2. some potential
3. good potential
4. excellent potential
5. unknown

Note 10. It proved very difficult to assess this factor. It is recommended that the item be redefined as an "alarm" type item which would tag deposits which the compiler felt strongly had obvious unexplored potential. Thus the item could be termed: Exploration Potential with two possibilities: (1) Yes, and (2) Blank (i.e. no comment).

LINES 16-20

These lines record the lithological environment of the mineralization at the scale of the individual zone or deposit referred to by the entity code. In general, the entity referred to here will be either DEP (deposit) or a zone which is spatially distinct from other zones in the deposit. A separate and distinctive line 16-20 record should not be defined for each mineralized zone when all occur spatially together.

Entity Code: See Lines 04-06
(See Note 4)

Lithology class: Refers to the broadest subdivision of rock types:
I = Igneous
S = Sedimentary
M = Metamorphic
A = Alteration
N = Indeterminate

Note that the term metamorphic should only be used when the primary protolith of the rock is unrecognizable. The term A is used when the primary protolith is in doubt, but the rock has obviously been produced by the extensive chemical modification of some previous rock.

Lithology group: Refers to the major subdivisions within rock classes:

Rock Class	Rock Group
A	Use any of the following terms to indicate probable protolith, if this can be determined
I	VOLC - volcanic extrusive
	VLIN - intrusive-extrusive body
	INTR - intrusive
	VLCU - volcaniclastic; grain size unknown
	*VLCC - volcaniclastic coarse
	*VLCF - volcaniclastic fine
S	CSTC - clastic
	CHEM - chemical
	VLCH - volcaniclastic and chemical mixed
M	SHST - schist
	GINSS- gneiss
	SKRN - skarn
	UNKN - unknown

* Two grain size populations of volcaniclastic rocks are distinguished here so as to avoid a proliferation of terms in the data item "name" below (i.e. basalt tuff, basalt breccia, rhyolite tuff, breccia, etc.). The coarse volcaniclastic rocks include all breccias and agglomerates, and the fine volcaniclastics, all tuffs, lapilli tuffs and volcanic sandstones. The compositional type of volcaniclastic is recorded under "name". In the case of coarse polymictic volcaniclastics, only the predominating clast lithology is described under "name", or a combination name can be used, as indicated on the list below.

Lithology form: Refers to the geometrical form of the rock unit. Some possible forms are:
CONT = contact zone
LAYR = layer
DIKE = dike
SILL = sill
STCK = stock
BTHL = batholith
FLOW = flow
BED = bed
INCL = inclusion (xenolith)

Lithology name: This item is one of the most problematical, since a proliferation of names here would make it impossible to correlate the lithological data in the file. On the other hand, if a too simple terminology is used, important distinctive rock types of the gold-bearing environment may be missed. The following list should be adhered to as far as possible, keeping in mind that it may be worth adding more terms eventually.

ALBITE - Albitite
FLSAPL - Aplite
FLSAPH - felsic aphanitic: all rhyolites, dacites
TRCYTE - all trachytes and other light coloured undersaturated volcanic or dike rocks
FELSFP - felsic feldspar porphyry
FLSQFP - felsic quartz-feldspar porphyry
FELSQP - felsic quartz porphyry
FELSCG - all medium and coarse grained "saturated" felsic rocks such as granite, granodiorite
FELCGP - as above, but porphyritic
SYNITE - all medium and coarse grained "undersaturated" felsic to intermediate rocks such as syenite, monzonite, etc.
SYNITP - as above, but porphyritic
INTAPH - intermediate aphanitic. All andesites. Note, however, that rocks called andesite are usually basalt or altered basalt.
INTERP - intermediate porphyry
INTRCG - all medium and coarse grained intermediate rocks such as diorites, quartz diorites, but not the undersaturated rocks of intermediate silica content.
MFCAPH - Mafic aphanitic. All basalts and probably most andesites
MFFLAP - Mixed mafic-felsic volcaniclastic rock (e.g. felsic clasts in a mafic matrix, or mixture of mafic and felsic clasts)
LAMPRP - Lamprophyre (fine grained mafic dike or sill with abundant biotite and/or K-feldspar phenocrysts)
DIABAS - Diabase of Proterozoic type, i.e. post tectonic.
MAFCCG - Mafic medium and coarse grained: gabbro
ULTRAM - Ultramafic rocks of unknown grain size
ULTAPH - Ultramafic volcanic and subvolcanic
ULTACG - Ultramafic intrusions with medium and coarse grain size
MFUMCG - Mafic-ultramafic complex intrusion
QRTZTE - Quartzite
GRYCKE - Greywacke
ARKOSE - Arkose
CONGLM - Conglomerate
CONFEF - Conglomerate with iron-formation clasts
SEDBRC - Sedimentary breccia
SLTSTN - Siltstone or shale
CHERT - Chert
LIMEST - Limestone
SULFEF - Sulphide iron formation
OXDFEF - Oxide iron formation
SILFEF - Silicate iron formation
CARFEF - Carbonate iron formation
SOSFEF - Mixed silicate-oxide-sulphide iron formation
SOSCFF - Mixed silicate-oxide-sulphide-carbonate iron formation
SUXFEF - Sulphide-oxide iron formation
AMPHIB - Amphibolite

The names for other metamorphic rocks or highly altered rocks should be based on their mineralogical composition, using the following abbreviations for the common minerals. The minerals should be listed in the order of their abundance.
A - Amphibole
B - Biotite
C - Cordierite

D - Dolomite
E - Chert
F - Graphite
G - Garnet
H - Chlorite
K - K-feldspar
M - Muscovite
N - Ankerite
P - Plagioclase
Q - Quartz
R - Carbonate
S - Serpentine
T - Talc
X - Pyroxene
Y - Pyrite

Mineral: This item is to record the presence in unusual quantities of some particular mineral in the rock, and normally will be reserved for sulphide or oxide minerals, and graphite. For example, if a unit is uniformly pyritic (pyritic volcaniclastic) or graphitic (graphitic shale, etc), then enter the appropriate letter for the mineral. For mineral codes, see the list above.

Abundance: Refers to abundance on the deposit or mineralized zone scale. Either a percent figure can be entered (99 = 100 percent), or the equivalent terms:
MJ - major
IN - intermediate
MN - minor
UN - known

Relation to ore: The possibilities here are:
INDT = indeterminate
ISOR = is ore (e.g. the case where a dike or chemical sedimentary bed is the ore body)
UNHR = ore host rock, but importance as host, relative to other rocks is unknown
MJHR = major ore host rock
MNHR = minor ore host rock
NOHR = contains no ore, but appears to have been present at the time of ore formation
PSTO = contains no ore, but appears to have been emplaced after ore formation.

LINES 21-28

These lines record the shape, texture, and mineralogical characteristics of the mineralized zones and the associated alteration, as well their relationship to other geological features. Size and grade, which are economic, as well as geometrical characteristics, are recorded separately on Lines 07-11.

Entity code: This code is the same as that defined on Lines 04-06, and its use in both parts of the file serves to connect economic and geological characteristics. Note, however, that while an entire complex deposit comprised of a number of different ore types can be described economically (Lines 07-11) it cannot be described as a single geological unit here. In other words, all "entities" described here also are defined on Lines 04-06, but not all entities defined on Lines 04-06 will necessarily be described here (See Note 4).

Mineralized zone shape: This refers to the geometrical form of the specific mineralized zone being described.

The possibilities are:
INDT = indeterminate
ISOM = isometrical
TABU = tabuloid

CYLD = cylindroid
BLAD = blade-like
IRRG = irregular

Mineralized zone relation to stratigraphy: The possibilities here are:

COND = concordant
DISC = discordant
CNDS = both concordant and discordant
INDT = indeterminate

Mineralized zone relation to foliation: The possibilities are:

PARL = foliation-parallel
OBLQ = foliation-oblique
PRFD = foliation-parallel and folded
OQFD = foliation-oblique and folded
INDT = indeterminate

Note 11: *It was not possible to determine the value of this item in almost all deposits, therefore it should be dropped from the file.*

Mineralized zone relationship to non-penetrative structure: The possibilities are:

FALT - in fault
FOLD - in fold
FTFD - in fault and fold
INTR - in dike or stock (i.e. the mineralized zone is co-extensive with a dike or stock)
FRCT - in fracture across which there is no, or very little displacement .
SCHZ - shear zone
CONT - on rock contact
NAPL - not applicable, i.e. no control by non-penetrative structures
UNKN - unknown, i.e. probably a control by non-penetrative structures, but the nature of this control is unknown.

Dominant mineralization type: The possibilities are similar here to those used to define the "entity code", lines 04-06, except that reference is not made to the relationship of the mineralization to stratigraphy or structure. The possibilities are:

VEIN - simple vein
CMVN - complex vein (i.e. multiple re-opening, or a vein complex)
BXVN - breccia vein
VNLT - veinlets
SHVN - sheeted veinlets, i.e., subparallel small veinlets
STWK - stockwork veinlets
BXMX - breccia matrix disseminations
DISS - evenly disseminated
BNDS - banded disseminated (as in bedded sulphidic tuff)
INDT - indeterminate
Other terms for textural types of mineralization may be needed.

Note 12. *These possibilities covered all situations encountered .*

Subordinate mineralization type: Many individual ore zones consist of different textural types of mineralization. The possibilities are the same as in the previous record.

Dominant alteration: This is the most volumetrically significant alteration type. Unfortunately, there are very few deposits in which alteration has been properly defined. The commonly used terms like chloritization, silicification etc. are difficult to interpret, since "bleaching" (often called silicification) may involve loss of Fe-Mg, conversion of dark silicates to light Fe-Mg carbonates with no loss of Fe-Mg; or true silicification (i.e. addition of SiO_2 and loss of other constituents). Unfortunately, nothing much can be done to right this situation without restudying the deposits.

Therefore, these widely used terms will be retained here, as follows:
HEMT - hematization
KFEL - K-feldspathization
FELD - feldspathization
ALBT - albitization
SILC - silicification
BLCH - bleaching
CHLO - chloritization
CBTZ - carbonatization
SERC - sericitization
EPID - epidotization
PYRT - pyritization

Note 13: *It is recommended that the standard mineral mnemonic codes be used here.*

Subordinate alteration: These two records allow the description of the second and third most abundant alteration types.

Major host: This is the main host lithology of the mineralized zone.

Minor host: The minor, or subordinate host lithology of the mineralized zone.

Mineral 1. This is the most abundant mineral in the mineralized zone. Use the standard mnemonic mineral codes.

Abundance 1. Either a percentage (99 = 100%) or MJ = Major; MN = minor may be entered here.

Mineral 2-8 and Abundance 2-8 record the successively less abundant minerals in the zone.

Proportion of total mineralization: In contrast to the similarly titled data item on Line 04, Column 40-44, this item refers to the proportion of the total mineralization in the deposit which occurs in mineralized zones of the type being described, and not in the individual zone being described. Either a percentage may be entered (99 = 100 percent), or
MJ - major
MN - minor

Zones#: This refers to the number of zones in the deposit which are of a similar type to that being described.

Note 14: *These last two items would be unnecessary if the "entity definition" item were removed from the file, as noted in Note 4.*

REFERENCES

Hodgson, C.J.
1982: Gold Deposits of the Abitibi Belt, Ontario; p.192-197 in Summary of Field Work by the Ontario Geological Survey, edited by John Wood, Owen L. White, R.B. Barlow and A.C. Colvine, Ontario Geological Survey, Miscellaneous Paper 106, 235p.

Hodgson, C.J., and MacGeehan, P.J.
1982: A Review of the Geological Characteristics of "Gold-Only" Deposits in the Superior Province of the Canadian Shield, Canadian Institute of Mining and Metallurgy, Special Volume 24, p.211-229.

Knight, C.W.
1924: Lightning River Gold Area; Ontario Department of Mines, Annual Report, Volume 33, Pt. 3, p.41-49.

Price, P.
1948: Horne Mine; p.547-553 in Structural Geology of Canadian Ore Deposits, Canadian Institute of Mining and Metallurgy, Jubilee Volume, 948p.

Pyke, D.R.
1981: Relationship of Gold Mineralization to Stratigraphy and Structure in Timmins and Surrounding Area; p. 1-15 in Genesis of Archean, Volcanic-Hosted Gold Deposits, Symposium Held at the University of Waterloo, March 7, 1980, edited by E.G. Pye and R.G. Roberts, Ontario Geological Survey, Miscellaneous Paper 97, 175p.

Pyke, D.R., Ayres, L.D., and Innes, G.
1973: Timmins-Kirkland Lake, Cochrane, Sudbury and Timiskaming Districts, Ontario; Ontario Department of Mines, Map 2205, Geological Compilation Series, scale 1 inch to 4 miles.

Thomson, J.A., Charlewood, G.H., Griffin, K., Hawley, J.E., Hopkins, H., MacIntosh, C.G., Ogryzlo, S.P., Perry, O.S., and Ward, W.
1950: Geology of the Main Ore Zone at Kirkland Lake; Ontario Department of Mines, Annual Report for 1948, Vol. 57, Pt. 5, p.54-188.

The Role of Felsic Intrusions in Gold Mineralization

Soussan Marmont

Mineral Deposits Section, Ontario Geological Survey, Toronto

ABSTRACT

The spatial association of epizonal felsic intrusions with gold mineralization has been emphasised by several workers. However, the nebulous temporal and genetic links between the two have been subject to debate. Through field examination and literature review of several felsic bodies that are accompanied by peripheral gold and base metals mineralization, it became apparent that the emplacement of a felsic intrusion plays a multitude of roles in introduction, remobilization and concentration of metals. This composite function is subdivided as follows:

1. Magmatic effect, whereby the intrusion may be the source of metalliferous fluids.

2. Metamorphic/hydrothermal association, whereby the pluton, in metamorphosing adjacent country rocks, can dehydrate its contact zone, releasing fluids which may leach, transport and deposit metals in favourable sites.

3. Assimilation effect, whereby the passive emplacement of a magma can be accompanied by digestion and enclosure of metalliferous strata.

4. "Ground preparation", whereby the felsic intrusion, in fracturing caused by cooling, hydraulic pressure, brittle response to stress, propagating structural grains in the country rocks, and post-emplacement cataclastic deformation, will generate conduits for the circulation and deposition of ore forming fluids.

It is concluded that evaluation of a mineralized zone within, or in the vicinity of, a felsic intrusion is incomplete unless it is combined with several other pre-, syn-, and post-intrusion parameters, responsible for the mineralization. It is further suggested that comprehensive petrographic, fluid inclusion, isotope, radiometric dating and geochemical studies of several intrusions are needed, in order to characterize, and distinguish economically significant from insignificant plutons.

INTRODUCTION

In the course of investigating genetic and economic merits of "Archean porphyry" style of mineralization in Ontario (Marmont, in preparation), the close spatial, and possibly temporal, association of gold mineralization with epizonal, felsic intrusive bodies became evident. This study of some 120 copper-molybdenum-gold showings, in and/or adjacent to felsic intrusions (occurring as disseminations, stockwork, fracture-vein filling and breccias,

and accompanied by various types and degrees of hydrothermal alteration) included the documentation of characteristics of a number of felsic intrusions. It therefore led to a better grasp of the role played by the intrusive body in the generation of a gold deposit.

Hodgson (1982) in his compilation of 725 gold deposits, in the Ontario section of the Abitibi Belt, stated that 40 percent of the occurrences are associated with felsic alkalic suites of rocks (i.e. syenite, syenite porphyry or feldspar porphyry) and 14 percent with quartz porphyries. Outside of the main known gold camps, the association is equally apparent. The intrusions show a wide range of calc-alkalic (i.e. granodiorite, quartz monzonite, trondhjemite, etc.) and alkalic (i.e. syenite, quartz syenite, etc.) compositions and geometric forms (i.e. dikes, stocks, sills, cupolas, etc.). The role of the felsic intrusion in the generation and concentration of gold is manifested in several ways, some of which are the subject of this paper.

STYLES OF MINERALIZATION

In a broad sense, the relationship between felsic intrusions and gold can be divided into two general categories, based on the presence or absence of gold in the environment before the emplacement of the felsic body. In the first category, where gold is assumed to have been absent before the intrusion of the felsic magma, a magmatic source has been postulated. In the second category, where gold is assumed to have been present in some form before the intrusion of the felsic body, several possibilities for the deposition and concentration of the metal are proposed.

Table 1 shows the break down of the styles of gold mineralization in association with felsic intrusions, which have been studied in the Superior Province of Ontario.

Table 1. *Styles of gold mineralization associated with felsic intrusions.*

	Example
1. Magmatic association	—
2. Metamorphic/hydrothermal association	
2.1 Regional Metamorphism	Gutcher Lake
2.2 Contact Metamorphism	Terrace Bay
3. Assimilation association	High Lake, Chester Tp.
4. Volcanogenic Association	McIntyre?
5. Structural Association	Canadian Arrow

1. MAGMATIC ASSOCIATION

The close spatial association of gold with felsic stocks and dikes, which in several instances are the sole or the main host rock to the mineralization, has caused geologists to ponder over the genetic link between mineralization and the magma.

Mantei and Brownlow (1967) in a study of the Marysville stock, Montana, (producer of 1 million ounces of gold up to 1967) have suggested that the magma initially contained higher than background values of gold. During crystallization, the gold was concentrated in the residual phases, migrating towards the margins of the intrusion and was then deposited at or near the contact area. Tilling *et al.* (1973) have demonstrated that the gold content of unaltered igneous rocks is restricted and normally not higher than background levels. They emphasized that higher gold values result from secondary processes, rather than an initial magmatic abundance. This is better demonstrated by surface geothermal systems, in which both the thermal fluids and the country rocks are low in their gold content (0.05 ppb and less than 1 ppb, respectively), yet a long-lived hydrothermal system can increase the metal concentration to several hundred times background levels.

Kwong and Crocket (1978), in a study of the gold content of various rock types in the Kakagi Lake area of northwestern Ontario, concluded that primary gold content of igneous rocks does not play a role in the subsequent concentrations. They noted that quartz and feldspars are poor retainers of gold in comparison to ferromagnesian minerals, and that if gold does not separate from the melt along with the early-stage mafic minerals, it will not be retained in a residual felsic magma but will be lost to volatiles.

Wolfe (1976), after examining six felsic intrusions in locations across the Superior Province of Ontario, suggested that gold mineralization is correlated with "altered" sections of the felsic intrusions and the unaltered portions are barren, regardless of their primary gold content.

Ploeger (1980, 1981), in a study of gold associated with alkalic suites of the Kirkland Lake Break, noted that the original gold content of the syenitic rocks was not the factor responsible for the subsequent enrichment.

Detailed documentation and characterization of several felsic bodies is needed in order to clarify the genetic link between felsic magmas and gold mineralization. Of the occurrences investigated in the course of the study of "Archean porphyry" systems, no examples were found in which an "auriferous" felsic intrusion could be considered solely responsible for the associated mineralization (Marmont, in preparation).

2. METAMORPHIC/HYDROTHERMAL ASSOCIATION

The heat generated during regional or contact metamorphism has been considered significant in producing and circulating fluids which could carry and deposit gold.

2.1 REGIONAL METAMORPHISM

The role of regional metamorphism in the generation of metalliferous fluids is primarily effective on pre- or syn-metamorphic intrusions. The continuous permeation of externally derived fluids can hydrate an anhydrous intrusion and its contact aureole, and will then remobilize and redeposit metals in suitable sites. An example of this style of mineralization is the copper and gold mineralization associated with the Gutcher Lake stock, discussed as a Ph.D. topic by Studemeister (1982).

The Gutcher Lake body (Figure 1), situated about 30 km northeast of Wawa in Algoma District, is a semi-circular, epizonal stock which has been emplaced in a sequence of mafic and felsic metavolcanics, banded iron formation, and sulphidic mudstone interbedded with clastic metasediments. The dominant rock type of the stock is medium- to coarse-grained, massive, equigranular trondhjemite, which is undeformed in the core of the stock, but gradually grades into foliated, gneissic and schistose types near the margin of the stock. The contact area of the stock is irregular, containing numerous xenoliths, and porphyritic dikes extend as far as 3 km from the main mass of the stock into the country rocks. The north contact of the intrusion, where the most intense mineralization is found, coincides with the most deformed section of the contact area. Clastic breccia containing diverse fragments has been reported from this location (Studemeister 1982).

The emplacement of the Gutcher Lake Stock has metamorphosed the surrounding rocks to hornblende hornfels. The regional metamorphism is of lower greenschist facies, and has retrograded the contact aureole to biotite hornfels.

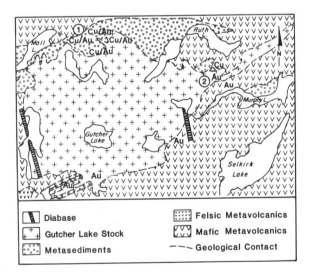

Figure 1. *Geology of the Gutcher Lake Stock (after Studemeister 1982).*

Mineralization is present in two forms.

1. Chalcopyrite and gold are found in parts of chemical metasediments consisting of quartz, chlorite, biotite, carbonate, epidote, magnetite, actinolite, pyrite and pyrrhotite. The mineralized sections appear to be concordant with the bedding/foliation of the metavolcanics.

2. Gold and sulphides, chiefly pyrite, pyrrhotite, chalcopyrite, arsenopyrite, sphalerite, galena and molybdenite, are found in quartz-carbonate-muscovite-chlorite veins. These veins crosscut the supracrustal rocks and transect the contact of the stock. The only difference between auriferous and barren veins is in their total sulphide content; sulphides are distinctly more abundant in the mineralized veins than in the barren ones. Sulphidic mud-flow units show a spatial association with the auriferous veins, and a temporal association has been inferred because the sulphide mineralogy and the organic carbon content of the mineralized veins and the mud-flow units correspond (Studemeister 1982).

Toward the veins, wall rock alteration intensifies. This is manifested by increases in the proportions of quartz, carbonate, chlorite, muscovite and pyrite and decreases in biotite, epidote and amphibole. Schistosity is most developed at the contact of the veins.

The main mineralized zone, at the northwestern corner of the stock (Ego Mines Limited property, No. 1 on Figure 1) consists of a cluster of gold-copper-bearing veins which fall within an east-trending shear zone. The veins are hosted by quartz-sericite schist and quartz porphyry. Graphite has also been reported from this zone. The mud-flow unit adjacent to these veins hosts pods and lenses of sulphides. Recent re-evaluation of the Ego Mines property indicated 348 000 tonnes of ore averaging 1.6 percent copper and 0.1 ounces gold per ton.

The Amherst Mine (No. 2, Figure 1), located at the east end of the stock, consists of massive quartz and ankerite veins containing as much as 20 percent sulphides in places. The sulphide content of these veins where hosted by the trondhjemite is lower than where they are hosted by mafic metavolcanics. The Amherst Mine produced 2533 ounces of gold between 1926 and 1940.

Studemeister (1982) proposed a two-stage model for the gold and copper mineralization. During the volcanic activity, "exhalative" base and precious metals were deposited as stringers and seams within the chemical sediments. The contemporaneous emplacement of the Gutcher Lake stock, in providing heat, recirculated the hot brines (seawater) which were focussed along conjugate sets of fractures near the top of the rising magma. The result of this process is seen at the Ego Mines Limited property.

The second stage of mineralization was caused by hydration of the contact aureole during regional metamorphism by fluids which then remobilized and reconstituted gold, in vicinity of pre-existing sulphides. The outcome of this stage of mineralization is seen at the Amherst Mine, at the deeper contact areas of the stock.

The actual existence, nature and origin of the second fluid is not substantiated by the fluid inclusion and oxygen isotope studies reported by Studemeister (1982), and the temporal relationships between the emplacement of the stock, the regional metamorphism and the mineralization, still poses some questions. A more extensive and thorough investigation of fluid inclusions, oxygen isotope studies complemented by hydrogen isotope studies, and age determinations using the U-Pb (zircon) method may decrease or eliminate these ambiguities.

2.2 CONTACT METAMORPHISM

The effect of contact metamorphism, through dehydration of the country rocks and generation of a convective cell at or near the margins of the intrusion, is another aspect to be considered in metamorphic/hydrothermal systems (Figure 2). In this case, the felsic intrusion acts as a heat "engine" giving rise to a contact aureole, in the process of which low grade mineral assemblages upgrade to hornfels or granulite facies. The fluid, released from the dehydration of the low grade assemblage, can leach and redeposit metals in preferred conduits. In addition to fluids generated in this manner, the convective cell may attract connate water from external sources or magmatic fluids from the intrusion itself. The contact aureole may locally be retrograded within the limits that the fluids have operated.

An example of this style of mineralization is present near the Terrace Bay Batholith, situated in the southern parts of Strey, Priske and Syine Townships, 225 km east of Thunder Bay and 85 km west of Marathon (Figure 3). Amygdaloidal, pillowed and variolitic iron-rich tholeiitic basalts dominate the metavolcanic sequence in the area. Intermediate tuff, lapilli-tuff, amygdaloidal and variolitic flows occupy a small portion of the volcanic pile and are

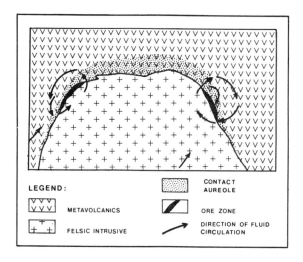

LEGEND:

METAVOLCANICS	CONTACT AUREOLE
FELSIC INTRUSIVE	ORE ZONE
	DIRECTION OF FLUID CIRCULATION

Figure 2. *Diagrammatic sketch of a metamorphic-hydrothermal system derived from dehydration of country rocks in the contact aureole of a stock.*

found at the northwestern margin of the batholith. The metavolcanics are interlayered with medium to finely bedded chert, wacke, coarse fragmental units and massive magnetite-pyrrhotite bands. The supracrustal rocks are folded along a synclinal axis plunging to the east. The Terrace Bay Batholith, intruding the supracrustal sequence, is an elongate body, approximately 19 by 5.6 km, with its long axis concordant with the surrounding metavolcanics.

The batholith is homogenous and represents a single intrusive event. The main rock type is massive, medium-grained, equigranular granodiorite, accompanied by minor biotite granite, hornblende-biotite granite, hornblende syenite and hornblende granodiorite. Granitic rocks containing more mafic minerals are normally found at or near the contact of the batholith, suggesting that assimilation of mafic wall rock during the emplacement of the intrusion enriched the melt in ferromagnesian constituents. The Terrace Bay Batholith is cut by aplitic and pegmatitic dikes varying in width from a few centimetres to 2 m. Offshoots from the batholith cut the metavolcanics and consist of pink to buff, fine-grained to aphanitic granophyric quartz-feldspar dikes and stringers. Alteration of the granodiorite consists of sericitization, chloritization and hematization, best seen in the areas where intense fracturing has occurred. A porphyritic granodiorite containing

plagioclase phenocrysts dusted by hematite occurs in the south-central section of the batholith. The general grade of regional metamorphism is greenschist facies, but the emplacement of the Terrace Bay Batholith has locally upgraded the country rocks to hornblende hornfels.

Mineralization in and around the Terrace Bay Batholith consists of two mineral assemblages:

1. Molybdenum-copper-bearing veins, which in places carry small amounts of precious metals, are hosted by granodiorite and/or aplite. These veins appear to have originated from a late-stage residual phase, enriched in molybdenum, which circulated through the outer/upper levels of the intrusion.

2. Polymetallic veins containing mainly pyrite, chalcopyrite, galena, molybdenite, sphalerite and gold are found at, or adjacent to, the contact zone of the batholith. Several gold-rich veins in the northwestern part (No. 2,3, Figure 3), as well as the North Shore Mine at the southwestern end (No. 10, Figure 3) and the Empress Mine at the northeastern contact of the batholith (No. 11, Figure 3), are examples of gold occurrences in close spatial association with the Terrace Bay Batholith.

Preliminary petrographic examination of a few samples from a gold-rich vein assaying as high as 25.82

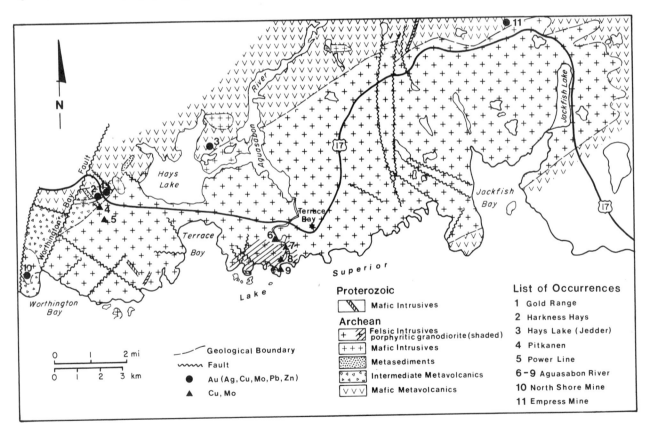

Figure 3. *Geology of the Terrace Bay Batholith (after Marmont and Colvine 1981).*

ounces gold per ton (No. 1, Figure 3) at the northwestern contact of the intrusion reveals that gold shows a distinct association with euhedral to anhedral, coarse- to very fine-grained pyrite. Coating and/or fracture filling of pyrite or other sulphides by gold have not been observed. The alteration halo around this auriferous vein consists of a chloritic zone of iron-rich chlorite grading to iron-poor chlorite away from the vein, and a sericitic halo, showing sharp contact with the amphibolite of the contact aureole. Unique enrichment in gold and large cubes of pyrite was observed where the vein is cut by a Middle to Late Precambrian lamprophyre dike. Detailed study of the Terrace Bay Batholith and the peripheral gold mineralization related to it is in progress (Marmont, in preparation).

In conclusion, the role of a felsic intrusive body in generating a metamorphic/hydrothermal system, regardless of the variations on the theme, lies in any one or a combination of the following factors:

1. Generating fluids within the contact aureole through dehydration of the supracrustal rocks.

2. Introducing some magmatic fluids.

3. Drawing supplementary fluids (connate, seawater, etc.) into the hydrothermal convective cell.

4. Giving rise to an anhydrous contact aureole, which if hydrated by externally derived fluids, can be a suitable media for gold concentration.

3. ASSIMILATION ASSOCIATION

The topics of contact facies, migmatization, hybridization and contamination of a melt are vast, in many respects ambiguous, and beyond the scope of this paper. Stated simplistically, passive emplacement of a rising magma can be accompanied by chemical reaction between the hot magma and the cold country rocks, leading to whole or partial digestion of the latter by the former. The extent of the reaction is dependent upon a multitude of factors, amongst which are the origin, temperature-pressure, composition, level and mode of emplacement of the magma, as well as the lithology and structures of the country rocks. The result of these reactions can give rise to enclosures which show significantly varied degrees of preservation. The enclaves range from "resisters" to "relicts", encompassing a spectrum of cases. The "resisters" are ghost structures or ghost stratigraphy which, at times, can be traced along horizons and seem to continue along the strike of their original strata. The "relicts" are aggregates of mafic minerals, indicating nearly complete assimilation and transformation of the country rocks. Between the two end members of the spectrum, xenoliths are found as random, disorderly arranged blocks of variable size, shapes and composition, near the margins or the top, where stoping has caused free fall from the roof into the uprising magma. In some instances, the contacts of the enclaves show concordance with the dominant structures of the intrusion, suggesting that they have been repositioned along the joints or foliation of the pluton.

The economic significance of xenoliths within a felsic body emerges when considering an intrusion which has been emplaced in a package of metalliferous strata, assimilating blocks and rafts of mineralized units (protore) (Figure 4). Clearly, the possibility of retention of gold and sulphides in the xenoliths should be judged against the extent of melting and deformation whereby highly metamorphosed terrains may have driven the metals out of the package. The emplacement of the intrusion and the enclosure of xenoliths may be contemporaneous with the mineralizing processes, in which case the enclosures and their adjacent sections of the intrusion can offer suitable channelways for ore-bearing fluids. Assimilation of metalliferous strata is illustrated by some of the gold and copper occurrences within the High Lake pluton and possibly within the hybrid zone of the Chester Township granitic body. Mackasey *et al.* (1974) referred to the Hammond Reef Mine, north of Atikokan, as a similar type of gold occurrence.

The High Lake area is located 48 km west of Kenora and 161 km east of Winnipeg (Figure 5). Massive and pillowed basaltic flows, are interbedded with andesitic flow breccias and pillows as well as fine-grained rhyolitic tuff, crystal tuff and quartz porphyritic rhyolite. Clastic metasediments, primarily arkose, arkosic greywacke and conglomerate beds, are intercalated with the metavolcanics. A graphitic mudstone containing massive to disseminated layers of sulphides, chiefly arsenopyrite, is interbedded with pillowed basalts. The High Lake pluton consists of a main mass of porphyritic trondhjemite to granodiorite with numerous peripheral dikes (the "North Phase") and a quartz diorite to granodiorite phase (the "South Phase"). Apart from differences in chemical composition, the main distinction between the North and the South Phases of the High Lake body is made on the basis of the degree of deformation, whereby the North Phase shows cataclastic deformation and penetrative cleavage (Davies 1965).

Erratic gold and copper mineralization is found at or

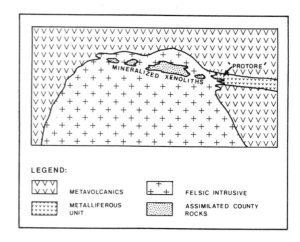

Figure 4. *Diagrammatic sketch of assimilation of metalliferous country rocks by a felsic intrusive body.*

near the eastern and southern margins of the North Phase, as well as in two gold and one copper showings that are situated well within the central part of the stock. It is believed that most of the gold mineralization associated with the contact zone of the High Lake Pluton is located along major shears or other linear structures (Davies 1965), leaving controversies over the origin and nature of the mineralizing fluids. However, the presence of gold and copper mineralization well within the body of the intrusion raises the possibility of assimilation of mineralized blocks (possibly of the graphitic, sulphidic mudstone unit) by the trondhjemite. A sample of this sulphidic mudstone, analysed by the Geoscience Laboratories, Ontario Geological Survey, Toronto, returned 1600 ppb Au and 9.2 percent As. The "porphyry copper" occurrence in the central part of the North Phase also seems to be the result of digestion, as the magnetite content and the sulphide mineralogy of the sulphidic chemical metasedimentary unit and the mineralized zone are compatible.

In the Chester Township area, Siragusa (1981) indicated that gold is specifically found in silicified shear zones and fractures within metavolcanic xenoliths. This observation is of guidance in the understanding of some of the gold-sulphide occurrences of Chester Township. However, the association of mineralization with shear and fracture zones, as well as silica-flooding and other alterations, leaves several other possibilities as to the genesis of mineralization of the area.

To conclude, it should be emphasised that although, in small-scale assimilation systems, the lateral and vertical extents of the mineralized zones may be of limited economic interest, in larger and multi-stage systems, the assimilation and hybridization of favourable supracrustal units may give rise to economically viable orebodies, hosted by felsic intrusions. These mineralized zones can also indicate the presence, in the surrounding volcano-sedimentary package, of protore which may be potentially economic.

4. VOLCANOGENIC ASSOCIATION

As observed in "black smokers", exhalation of lava on the seafloor can be accompanied by venting of metalliferous hydrothermal fluids, depositing sulphidic strata at the discharge site. Contemporaneous emplacement of a subvolcanic felsic intrusion will aid the circulation of seawater, leaching metals from surrounding rocks. These brines can then be focused along cooling fractures or other conduits, both within the felsic body and the adjacent volcanic rocks, depositing metals as sulphides or other minerals. Away from the *in situ* mineralization, distal chemical and clastic sedimentary layers, resulting from down-slope slumping, may also contain metallic enrichment. The shallow emplacement is usually expressed by a porphyritic texture, with an aphanitic or fine-grained matrix. Hence, in this geological setting, the intrusion

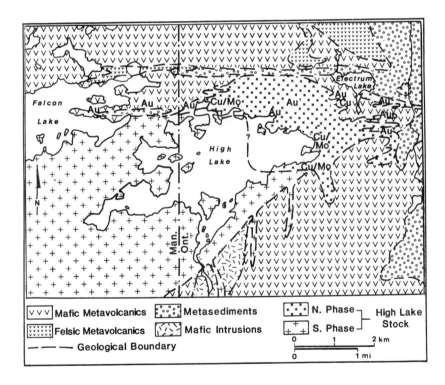

Figure 5. Geology of the High Lake Pluton (after Davies 1965).

forms an integral part of volcanism and unlike the felsic bodies that have been emplaced at greater depths before, during or after volcanism, parts or all of the hydrothermal fluids associated with it may vent. Accordingly, this hydrothermal system incorporates a large seawater component, causing pervasive alteration along with massive and/or disseminated mineralization at or near the water-rock interface (Figure 6).

Three genetic interpretations have been made for the McIntyre Mine (Schumacher Division of Pamour Porcupine Mines Limited, at Timmins), as follows:

1. The Pearl Lake Porphyry is an epizonal felsic intrusion (Griffis 1968, 1979). Based on this assumption a magmatic and/or metamorphic hydrothermal system would be responsible for alteration and mineralization of the intrusion and the surrounding country rocks.

2. The Pearl Lake Porphyry is a felsic intrusive unit which filled an irregular topographic surface (Davies and Luhta 1978, 1979).

3. The Pearl Lake Porphyry was a sub-volcanic mass, which through heat loss circulated seawater and created a hydrothermal system.

The last interpretation coincides with the volcanogenic association presently described.

In order to avoid repetition of lengthy descriptions, the reader is referred to Davies and Luhta (1978, 1979), Luhta (1974), Griffis (1962, 1968, 1979) and Pyke and Middleton (1970) for detailed accounts of the geology of the deposit. Luhta (1974) and Davies and Luhta (1978,

1979) argued against the intrusive origin of the Pearl Lake Porphyry. These workers suggested that due to absence of recognizable intrusive textures and intrusive contacts, the Pearl Lake Porphyry should be considered a metasomatized, post-deformational felsic volcanic unit. Supposing that the Pearl Lake Porphyry and equivalent felsic bodies in the Timmins area are high-level, sub-volcanic masses intruded along a major break (the Hollinger Fault?), the near surface level of emplacement and severe deformation may account for lack of definitive intrusive characteristics. Features such as disseminated sulphides hosted by a felsic porphyritic unit (compositionally comparable to a granitoid body), gold mineralization hosted by metavolcanics, incipient zoning of alteration consisting of sericitization, hematization and albitization, and alkali metasomatism coincide with some of the imprints of a sub-volcanic hydrothermal system. Since most of the data presented on Pearl Lake Porphyry is inconclusive, further petrographic, fluid inclusion and isotope studies are needed to better define the nature of the felsic schistose body and, thereon, to extrapolate the mineralizing processes.

5. STRUCTURAL ASSOCIATION

In this discussion, the implication of "structural" association is equated with processes of "ground preparation" (in or immediately adjacent to the intrusion) through which conduits allowing circulation and deposition of ore-forming fluids are formed. A few of these

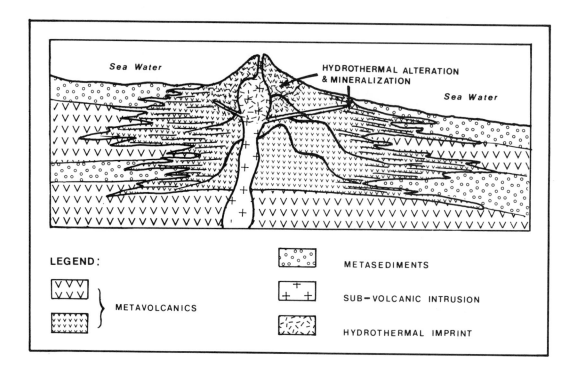

Figure 6. *Diagrammatic sketch of an extrusive-intrusive hydrothermal system.*

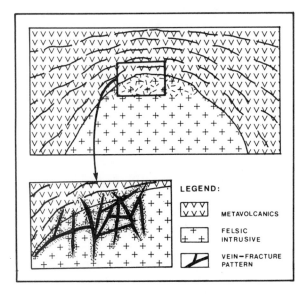

Figure 7. *Diagrammatic sketch of "ground preparation" in a felsic intrusive body through fracturing.*

processes include fracturing by several means and cataclastic deformation. Regional scale deformation is not considered in this discussion.

The difference in competency between a granitoid body, with a brittle deformational characteristic, and surrounding supracrustal rocks, with a ductile response to stress, can lead to development of a more extensive fracture pattern in the intrusion (Figure 7). This phenomenon is seen where veins and veinlets crossing the contact of a felsic body rapidly diminish into the metavolcanics. The alteration halo enveloping the veins also seems to decrease or change nature, where the border of the felsic mass is crossed. Such a case is seen at the Canadian Arrow Mines Limited gold deposit (see Cherry, this volume), where auriferous hematitic alteration halos to quartz veins are restricted to the monzonitic stock and die out where the veins enter the country rocks.

Cooling fractures are normally restricted to the upper and outer margins of an intrusion. These fractures result from the faster cooling of the peripheral zone of the magma, as the inner and deeper parts are still in the process of crystallization. Hydraulic fractures are due to high pressure of the fluids and volatiles in the magma and offer another possibility for fracturing of the felsic intrusion.

The seismic shocks generated as a result of the emplacement of a rising magma can reactivate old fractures, accentuate openings along lithological boundaries, dilate pre-existing structural grains, and expand brecciated zones.

Syn-plutonic deformation during passive emplacement of a magma can also create a more fissile and schistose fabric around the margins of the intrusive body. Cataclastic deformation (Figure 8) of intrusive and/or country rocks may create the appearance of a "porphyri-

tic" texture, within which the migration and circulation of fluids is facilitated. In this case the "porphyritic" texture is not of an intrusive origin, indicating the rapid cooling of the magma, rather, it is a secondary feature, which may be useful in delineating a zone of cataclastic deformation, i.e. shear or fault zones, etc.

The effect of regional deformation and tectonism on generation of conduits, whether in felsic intrusions or elsewhere, needs an extensive discussion of the structural parameters, and obviously falls outside the limits of this paper.

CONCLUDING REMARKS

As noted by Hodgson (1982), Riley *et al.* (1971) and numerous other workers, the spatial association of felsic intrusive bodies with gold mineralization is an apparent fact, whereas the temporal and genetic links between the two have been a matter of debate and controversy. In this paper, an attempt has been made to segregate and analyse individual processes involving the felsic intrusion, and then to place them in order of apparent occurrence with the other factors involved.

It should be emphasized that no single parameter can be solely responsible for the mineralization. Each of the examples cited is used to illustrate only one aspect of the role of a felsic intrusion in generation, deposition and concentration of gold, whereas in reality a multitude of elements are involved and the resultant setting is a composite model. Hence, the multiple effect, of an epizonal felsic body emplaced in a package of metavolcanics/metasediments, on associated gold mineralization will consist of the following:

1. Assimilation of blocks and xenoliths of country rocks, some of which may be mineralized.

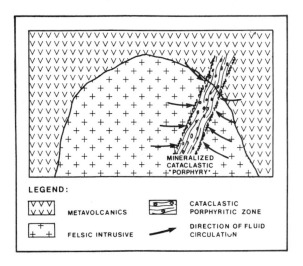

Figure 8. *Diagrammatic sketch of "ground preparation" in a felsic intrusion through cataclastic deformation.*

2. Contact metamorphism of the adjacent envelope, causing dehydration and release of fluids, which can then leach and remobilize metals from the country rocks.

3. Generation of a convective cell, through heat loss within the contact aureole, drawing in connate and other externally derived fluids, which can be metal-bearing or can leach metals in their paths.

4. Fracturing through cooling, hydraulic pressure, and competency difference with the surrounding supracrustal rocks, creating conduits for metal-bearing solutions.

5. Development of schistosity and gneissosity in the contact area, through syn-plutonic deformation, resulting in a more permeable and reactive contact zone.

6. Propagation of new and reactivation of pre-existing structural grains and openings, through seismic shocks during emplacement, producing further conduits.

7. Introduction of magmatic fluids that may be metalliferous.

8. Response to post-emplacement cataclastic deformation along shear/fault zones, giving rise to a "porphyritic" texture, which can facilitate permeation and localization of ore-bearing fluids.

Keeping these parameters in mind, assessment of a mineralized zone in or adjacent to a felsic intrusion will be invalid if other geological factors are ignored. Ambiguities on the timing and nature of regional metamorphism, alteration and deformation, hamper the evaluation of the role of a felsic intrusion in mineralization. Characterization of these epizonal bodies through petrographic, fluid inclusion, isotope, radiometric dating and geochemical studies can lead to a better understanding of compositional variations, mode and timing of emplacement and the paragenesis of hydrothermal events.

REFERENCES

Davies, J.C.
1965: Geology of the High Lake-Rush Bay Area, District of Kenora; Ontario Department of Mines, Geological Report 41, 57p. Accompanied by Maps 2068 and 2069. Scale 1 inch to ½ mile.

Davies, J.F. and Luhta, L.E.
1978: An Archean "Porphyry-Type" Disseminated Copper Deposit, Timmins, Ontario; Economic Geology, Vol. 73, p.383-396.

1979: An Archean "Porphyry-Type" Disseminated Copper Deposit, Timmins, Ontario – A Reply; Economic Geology, Vol. 74, p.697.

Gottfried, D., Rowe, J.J. and Tilling, R.I.
1972: Distribution of Gold in Igneous Rocks; United States Geological Survey Professional Paper 727, 42p.

Griffis, A.T.
1962: A Geological Study of the McIntyre Mine; Canadian Institute of Mining and Metallurgy, Transaction, Vol. 65, p. 47-54.

1968: McIntyre-Porcupine Mines Limited; p.122-130 in Geology and Ore Deposits of Tisdale Township, District of Cochrane, by Ferguson *et al.*, Ontario Department of Mines, Geological Report 58. Accompanied by Map 2075, Scale 1 inch to 1,000 feet.

1979: An Archean "Porphyry-Type" Disseminated Copper Deposit, Timmins, Ontario – A Discussion; Economic Geology, Vol. 74, p.695-696.

Hodgson, C.J.
1982: Gold Deposits of the Abitibi Belt, Ontario; p.192-197 in Summary of Field Work, 1982, by the Ontario Geological Survey, edited by John Wood, Owen L. White, R.B. Barlow and A.C. Colvine, Ontario Geological Survey, Miscellaneous Paper 106, 235p.

Kerrich, R., Gorman, B.E. and Fyfe, W.S.
1980: Geochemistry and Field Relations of Lode Gold Deposits in Felsic Igneous Intrusions; p.136-143 in Geoscience Research Grant Program, Summary of Research 1979-1980, Edited by E.G. Pye, Ontario Geological Survey, Miscellaneous Paper 93, 263p.

Kwong, Y.T.S. and Crocket, J.H.
1978: Background and Anomalous Gold in Rocks of an Archean Greenstone Assemblage, Kakagi Lake Area, Northwestern Ontario; Economic Geology, Vol. 73, p.50-63.

Luhta, L.E.
1974: A Petrographic and Mineralogic Study of the McIntyre Disseminated Copper Deposit; Unpublished M.Sc. Thesis, Department of Geology, Laurentian University, 97p.

Mackasey, W.O., Blackburn, C.E. and Trowell, N.F.
1974: A Regional Approach to the Wabigoon-Quetico Belts and Its Bearing on Exploration in Northwestern Ontario; Ontario Division of Mines, Miscellaneous Paper 58, 30p.

Mantei, E.J., and Brownlow, A.H.
1967: Variation in Gold Content of Minerals of the Marysville Quartz Diorite Stock, Montana; Geochimica et Cosmochimica Acta, Vol. 31, p.225-235.

Marmont, S.
in preparation: Gold, Copper and Molybdenum Mineralization Associated with Early Precambrian Felsic Intrusions in Ontario; Ontario Geological Survey.

Marmont, S., and Colvine, A.C.
1981: The Geology and Mineralization of the Terrace Bay Batholith, Mink Lake Stock and Cairo Stock; p.230-241 in Summary of Field Work, 1981, by the Ontario Geological Survey, edited by John Wood, O. L. White, R.B. Barlow, and A.C. Colvine, Ontario Geological Survey, Miscellaneous Paper 100, 255p.

Petruk, W. and Hodder, R.W. (eds.)
1982; Geology of Canadian Gold Deposits; Canadian Institute of Mining and Metallurgy, Special Volume 24, 286p.

Ploeger, F.R.
1980: Kirkland Lake Gold Study; p.188-190 in Summary of Field Work, 1980, by the Ontario Geological Survey, edited by V.G. Milne, O. L. White, R.B. Barlow, J.A. Robertson and A.C. Colvine, Ontario Geological Survey, Miscellaneous Paper 96, 201p.

1981: Kirkland Lake Gold Study, District of Timiskaming; p.248-250 in Summary of Field Work, 1981, by the Ontario Geological Survey, edited by John Wood, O. L. White, R.B. Barlow and A.C. Colvine, Ontario Geological Survey, Miscellaneous Paper 100, 255p.

Pyke, D.R. and Middleton, R.S.
1970: Distribution and Characteristics of the Sulphide Ores of the Timmins Area; Ontario Department of Mines, Miscellaneous Paper 41, 24p.

Riley, R.A., King, H.L. and Kustra, C.R.
1971: Mineral Exploration Targets in Northwestern Ontario; Ontario Department of Mines and Northern Affairs, Miscellaneous Paper 47, 72 p.

Siragusa, G.M.
1981: Precambrian Geology of Chester and Yeo Townships and Parts of Neville and Porter Townships, Sudbury District; Ontario Geological Survey, Preliminary Map P. 2449, Geological Series, Scale 1:15 840. Geology 1980.

Studemeister, P.A.
1982: An Archean Felsic Stock with Peripheral Gold and Copper Occurrences, Abotossaway Township, District of Algoma, Ontario; Unpublished Ph.D. Thesis, University of Western Ontario, 501 p.

Sutherland, I.G. and Colvine. A.C.
1979: The Geology and Mineralization of the Pickerel Arm, Canoe Lake, and High Lake Bodies; p.233-243 in Summary of Field Work, 1979, by the Ontario Geological Survey, Edited by V.G. Milne, O. L. White, R.B. Barlow and C.R. Kustra, Ontario Geological Survey, Miscellaneous Paper 90, 245p.

Tilling, R.I., Gottfried, D. and Rowe, J.J.
1973: Gold Abundance in Igneous Rocks, Bearing on Gold Mineralization; Economic Geology, Vol. 68, p.168-186.

Wolfe, W.J.
1976: Gold in Early Precambrian Superior Province Plutonic Rocks; Ontario Division of Mines, Geoscience Study 17, 11p.

The Association of Gold and Felsic Intrusions — Examples from the Abitibi Belt

M.E. Cherry

Mineral Deposits Section, Ontario Geological Survey, Toronto

ABSTRACT

A review of past production and estimates of reserves of gold in the Abitibi "greenstone" belt in Ontario shows that 70 percent of gold in the Kirkland Lake – Larder Lake mining camp and 60 percent of gold in the Porcupine mining camp occurs within or immediately adjacent to felsic intrusions. The contribution of felsic intrusions to the genesis of lode gold deposits, however, remains uncertain.

Preliminary results of studies of two such deposits, the Canadian Arrow Mine and the Murphy-Garrison Mine, indicate that:

1. gold mineralization is confined to pyritiferous alteration halos around quartz veins that fill fractures in both the intrusive rocks and their host basalts;

2. mineralization occurs in the intrusive rocks at the Canadian Arrow deposit and in the basalts at the Murphy-Garrison deposit;

3. at least two fluids precipitated quartz at the Canadian Arrow deposit: the early fluid also precipitated galena, and the later fluid also altered the monzonite and precipitated gold; and

4. fluid inclusions in vein quartz and primary mineral assemblages in the monzonite at the Canadian Arrow deposit are indicative of a high activity of CO_2.

The data indicate that mineralization occurred late in the development of both deposits and was structurally controlled, but are insufficient to distinguish between possible roles of the intrusions in the generation of the deposits.

INTRODUCTION

A close spatial association between felsic intrusions and lode gold deposits has long been recognized in Ontario in the Timmins and Kirkland Lake areas of the Abitibi Belt, in the Red Lake area of the Uchi Lake Belt (Pirie 1981), and in the Atikokan area of the Wabigoon Belt (Wilkinson 1982). The same association is present in the Malartic-Val d'Or gold camp of the Abitibi Belt in Quebec (Latulippe 1982). Despite recognition of the association and much speculation as to its importance, its implications to the genesis of and exploration for lode gold deposits are unresolved. Marmont (this volume) has discussed genetic interpretations of the association and Hodgson (this volume) has included a discussion of the association in his interpretation of a compilation of the characteristics of some 725 known gold deposits in the Abitibi Belt in Ontario. The frequency of the association and an illustration of its possible importance in the Abitibi Belt are given in the data of Figures 1 and 2. Figure 1 is a generalized geological map of the Abitibi Belt in Ontario upon which are located 95 gold deposits for which estimates of gold content are available. These data, from Hodgson's file (1982, this volume), include data for past gold production and estimated ore reserves. They are presented in Figure 2, in which the deposits have been grouped by location and arbitrarily classified, from published descriptions of their geology, into (1) deposits in which gold is hosted by or occurs immediately adjacent to a felsic intrusion and (2) all other deposits. The classification does not subdivide different styles of mineralization within an individual deposit and is current to 1982.

Despite this simplistic division, the data in Figure 2 point to the importance of felsic intrusions in the geology of Archean lode gold deposits, an association perhaps overlooked since hypotheses of syngenetic gold have become popular. Deposits with a strong association between mineralization and felsic intrusions contain 69.9 percent of the 24,820,090 ounces of gold in the Kirkland Lake – Larder Lake camp (17 of 33 deposits) and 60.3 percent of the 56,742,411 ounces of gold in the Porcupine camp (15 of 48 deposits). There is one large mine in each camp (Kerr Addison and Dome) that does not exhibit the association and contains over 50 percent of the gold not spatially associated with felsic intrusions. The association is particularly strong in the Kirkland Lake area, where all 10 deposits contain rocks of a syenitic intrusive suite.

A program to study this association was initiated by the Mineral Deposits Section of the Ontario Geological Survey in 1982, with the objective of defining characteristics of the intrusive rocks and their mineralization that might allow more efficient exploration for similar deposits. Because the geology of intrusion-associated deposits in the immediate Timmins and Kirkland Lake areas is complicated by the deformation and alteration of major structural zones, two deposits away from these zones were selected for the initial stage of the program with the hope that their apparent simplicity would allow easier interpretation that would be a foundation for subsequent studies of more complex deposits. These deposits are the Cana-

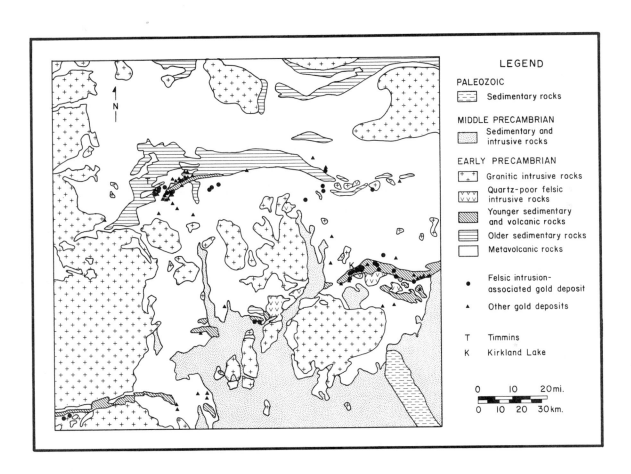

Figure 1. *Generalized geology of the Timmins — Kirkland Lake area. See text for explanation of the gold deposits shown.*

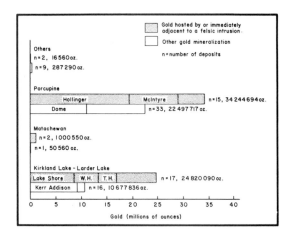

Figure 2. *Estimated gold content of 95 gold deposits in the Timmins — Kirkland Lake area. See text for explanation. WH = Wright-Hargreaves Mine, TH = Teck-Hughes Mine.*

dian Arrow Mine in Hislop Township and the Murphy-Garrison Mine in Garrison Township (see Figure 1). A summary of observations made during field studies in 1982 has been presented in Cherry (1982).

GEOLOGY OF THE DEPOSITS

CANADIAN ARROW MINE

The geology of the Canadian Arrow Mine (Figure 3) comprises an undeformed monzonite which has intruded deformed and metamorphosed basalts of the Kinojevis group. The pre-intrusion deformation history of the basalts is evident in their strong foliation, elongation of pillows and a narrow mylonite band with intrafolial folds. Dark grey-green basalt is composed of a fine grained, hypidiomorphic assemblage of plagioclase and chlorite with minor amounts of biotite and hornblende, pyrite, carbonate and oxides(?). Chlorite replaces biotite and hornblende. The carbonate, which locally is very abundant, is also secondary. Plagioclase is saussuritized by the development of epidote and sericite. Pyrite overgrows all other phases in the rock. The mineral assemblage is typical of lower greenschist facies of metamorphism.

The monzonite, which is grey with zones that are brick red, has a hypidiomorphic inequigranular, fine- to medium-grained texture which has none of the deformation present in the basalt. It is composed largely of plagioclase, potassium feldspar and quartz, with minor chlorite, remnant biotite and hornblende, carbonate, pyrite and oxides. There are scattered occurrences of primary muscovite. Accessory minerals include sphene, apatite, zircon, rutile and hematite. The euhedral to subhedral plagioclases have oscillatory and normal zoning (An$_{40}$-An$_{20}$; optical determinations) and cores that are altered with the development of epidote and sericite. The

potassium feldspars are anhedral and interstitial to the plagioclase, untwinned, and often have interiors that are clouded by very fine-grained red opaques. These are interpreted to be hematite, and it is their presence that gives the monzonite its red colour. These clouded grains are for the most part confined to alteration halos around quartz veins, but there are zones in the monzonite that are red, apparently because of similar hematitic alteration. Quartz is interstitial to both feldspars, commonly has undulatory extinction, and contains small, two-phase fluid inclusions. Carbonate often occurs as a primary interstitial phase, although there are veinlets and patches of secondary carbonate. Euhedral pyrite overgrows all other minerals and occurs in alteration halos around quartz veins.

The monzonite has a hiatal porphyritic texture in which much smaller grains of quartz and feldspar occur as trains and irregular interstitial patches among the coarser grains that comprise much of the rock. Although some occurrences of these fine-grained patches are vein-like and might be a result of grain reduction, their regular occurrence in the monzonite is interpreted to be indicative of a nucleation event that occurred late in the crystallization of the monzonite.

Both monzonite and basalt at the Canadian Arrow deposit are fractured into three regular, strong joint directions and several less well-developed, irregular fracture directions that branch from the strong joint sets. The joints in both lithologies are filled with quartz veins (not quartz-carbonate as stated in Cherry 1982); however, only those veins in the monzonite have visible alteration effects. The attitudes of these joint systems and their control of the vein directions are shown on the stereograms in Figure 3.

Field observations indicate that the joint set dipping shallowly northeast was the first to be filled by quartz veins, which contain galena and pyrite but do not visibly alter the monzonite. Veins of this set are cut by a dike of maroon, very fine-grained, flow foliated diorite; similar dikes cut the layering and the mylonite band in the basalts at a low angle. The early set of quartz veins and the diorite dike are cut by a set of steeply dipping quartz veins that strike northeast and have narrow red alteration halos where they occur in the monzonite. There is no galena and little pyrite in these veins, but their alteration halos are pyritiferous and the gold in the deposit is associated with this pyrite. The quartz in all vein systems has undulatory extinction and has undergone some polygonization. Vein quartz is choked with fluid inclusions, in contrast to the sparse inclusions in magmatic quartz of the monzonite. Preliminary petrographic studies also indicate a common occurrence of three phase fluid inclusions in the vein quartz; these have been suggested (A.J. Macdonald, Ontario Geological Survey, personal communication, 1982) to be H$_2$O liquid, H$_2$O gas and CO$_2$ gas.

Alteration and mineralization at the Canadian Arrow deposit are largely confined to the alteration halos around the latest set of quartz veins in the monzonite, although other veins occur in the monzonite and all vein sets also occur in the basalt. The mineralization is further

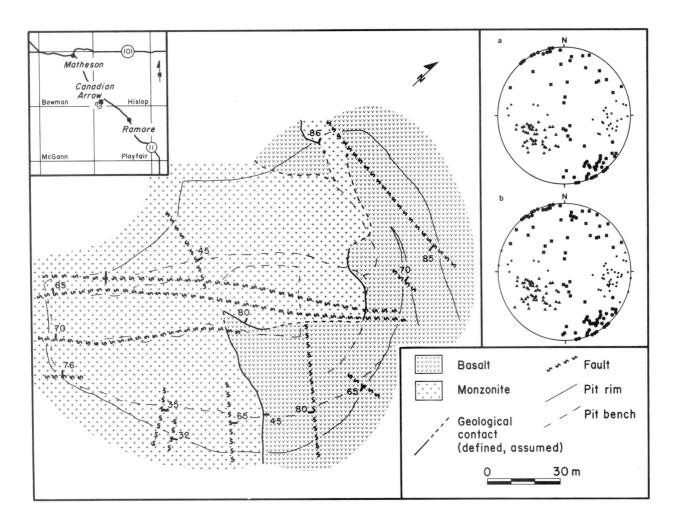

Figure 3. Geology of the Canadian Arrow Mine. The geological map is based upon one by the staff of Pamour Porcupine Mines Limited. Stereograms are equal area plots of poles to (a) veins and (b) fractures. Orientations are represented by: triangles — galena-bearing veins with NE dips; large circles — NE-striking veins with red alteration halos; small circles — veins with north-trending strike; squares — others. Diagram is from Cherry (1982).

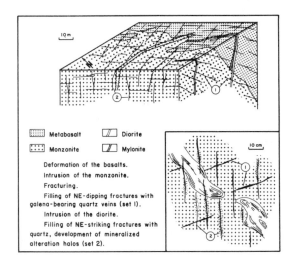

Figure 4. *Diagrammatic geological history of the Canadian Arrow deposit. The inset shows relationships among monzonite, diorite dike and two quartz vein sets.*

constrained between two shear zones that are subparallel to the haloed vein set. These shear zones are 1 to 2 m wide and comprise a mixture of quartz, chlorite and fragments of the monzonite. They can be traced across the pit in the monzonite, and appear as narrow quartz-filled fractures in the basalt.

These observations permit the development of a geologic history of the Canadian Arrow deposit, which is summarized in Figure 4. This history begins with the deformation and metamorphism of the basalt, followed by the intrusion and crystallization of the monzonite. Crystallization apparently occurred with some differentiation which generated aplite, probably as a fluid-saturated residual melt. This rock package cooled sufficiently to fracture in a brittle manner, after which the fracture set with northeast dips was filled by quartz from a fluid which also precipitated pyrite and galena, but not gold. A dioritic magma then intruded as dikes into both the basalt and the monzonite. Finally, the steeply dipping fracture set was filled with quartz from a fluid which caused hematitic alteration of the monzonite and the precipitation of auriferous pyrite in the altered intrusive rocks. Movement on major shear zones in the deposit apparently occurred with, or after, this vein filling. In any case, gold mineralization occurred late in the geologic history of the deposit.

MURPHY-GARRISON MINE

Work since publication of the summary of field work (Cherry 1982) has concentrated on the Canadian Arrow deposit and the present paper consequently adds little new information about the Murphy-Garrison deposit. The summary herein serves as a background to the ensuing discussion.

The geology of the Murphy-Garrison Mine (Figure 5) comprises fine-grained, dark grey metamorphosed basalts of the Kinojevis Group, intruded by several dikes of fine- to medium-grained pink monzonite. The monzonite is only a minor rock type in the open pit, in contrast to the relatively equal volumes of basalt and monzonite at the Canadian Arrow deposit. The foliated basalt includes variolitic, feldspar-phyric and massive varieties. Elongation of varioles and the presence of two mylonite bands, parallel to layering in the basalt, are evidence of deformation prior to intrusion of the monzonite, which is undeformed. Mesoscopic examinations, as yet unconfirmed by petrography, suggest that the basalt is composed largely of plagioclase, chlorite and some epidote; this assemblage is indicative of greenschist grade metamorphism. The foliation in the basalt is cut in several places in the pit by veins composed of quartz, epidote and garnet. These veins are boudinaged and therefore must have been emplaced before cessation of deformation.

The monzonite dike is apparently an apophysis of the Garrison stock, which is exposed about 1 km east of the pit. The monzonite is fine to medium grained, leucocratic and is composed of quartz, plagioclase and potassium feldspar with minor amounts of chlorite, hornblende and biotite.

As at the Canadian Arrow deposit, the basalt and the monzonite dike have been fractured, with the development of three preferred directions, and the fractures later filled with quartz veins. Fracture and vein orientations are shown on the stereograms in Figure 5. At least one of the three directions of fracture is present in the Garrison stock and these fractures are also filled with quartz. In contrast to the Canadian Arrow deposit, there is no mineralization associated with veins in the monzonite, although they do have narrow, bleached alteration halos. Veins in the basalt, however, have pyritiferous alteration halos which contain gold, apparently with the pyrite. These halos are brown to pale grey and are confined to the margins of the quartz veins except where vein sets intersect. In such cases, larger volumes of the basalt have been altered to a massive, pale grey rock with conspicuous pyrite cubes. The altered rock is hard and does not react with dilute HCl; the alteration is therefore assumed to be silicification.

In contrast to the vein sequence observed at the Canadian Arrow deposit, all of the fracture sets in the Murphy-Garrison pit apparently filled synchronously. It is obvious, however, that the fracture directions controlled the quartz veining and its accompanying alteration and mineralization of the basalts, in a similar manner to the structural control of mineralization at the Canadian Arrow deposit.

These field observations can be incorporated into a geologic history of the deposit (Figure 6) which begins with deformation and metamorphism of the basalt, followed by intrusion and crystallization of the Garrison stock and its apophyses. Aplite dikelets within and adjacent to the stock are indicative of some differentiation of the magma. Brittle fracturing of all rocks preceded the formation of quartz veins, alteration and gold mineraliza-

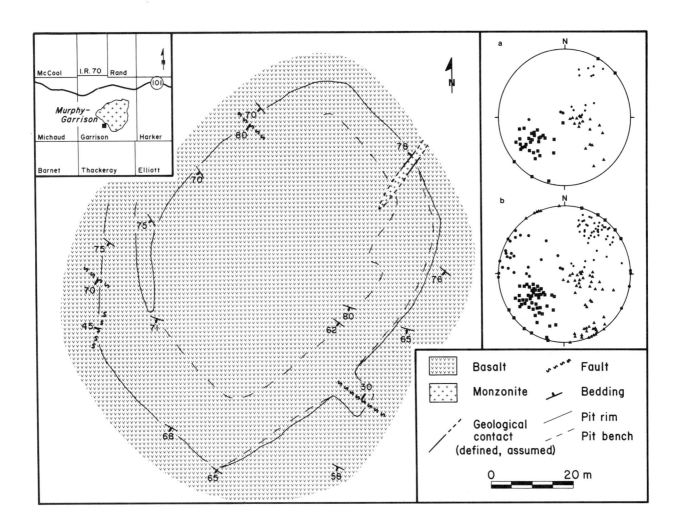

Figure 5. Geology of the Murphy-Garrison Mine. Stereograms are equal area plots of poles to (a) veins and (b) fractures. Vein directions are represented by: small circles — veins parallel to bedding; squares — veins with NE dips; triangles — veins with NW dips; large circles — others. Diagram is from Cherry (1982).

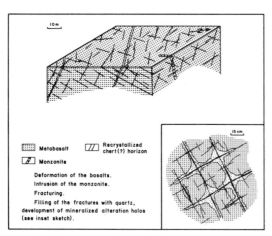

Figure 6. *Diagrammatic geological history of the Murphy-Garrison deposit. The inset shows the development of alteration halos about two directions of quartz veins.*

tion. As in the Canadian Arrow deposit, gold mineralization occurred late in the geologic history and was, at least in part, structurally controlled.

DISCUSSION

The objective of this study is to define characteristics of felsic intrusion-associated lode gold deposits that might serve as exploration criteria. Understanding the source of the magma, the mechanisms that controlled its emplacement and crystallization, the source of the gold and the controls of its movement and ultimate deposition are all important to this objective, as is a knowledge of the temporal relationships among these events.

The problem is most easily examined in terms of two possible cases: (a) gold was present in the country rocks before intrusion of the felsic magma, or (b) gold was absent from the country rocks before intrusion of the magma. If case (a) were true, the role of the intrusion in the formation of the gold deposit would be as a source of fluids and/or heat energy to remobilize gold from the protore and concentrate it in the country rocks and/or the intrusion. If case (b) were true, the gold might be: (1) carried by the intrusion and deposited in the country rocks and/or the intrusion, or (2) introduced from an unrelated source after crystallization of the magma and deposited in the country rocks and/or the intrusion.

If the last case were true, the gold would be neither derived from the felsic intrusion nor mobilized from the country rocks, and could have been introduced long after crystallization and cooling of the magma were completed. Localization of the gold in this case would be in a structurally and/or chemically preferred site.

Although only one of these cases suggests the magma to be the source of the gold, the intrusion may be important in all of them as a structurally or chemically preferred site for deposition of gold.

Observations from the Canadian Arrow and Murphy-Garrison deposits lead to the following speculations and suggestions for further work which may be pertinent to distinguishing between these possibilites or may prove useful as exploration criteria.

1. No evidence has yet been found at either deposit to prove whether gold was present in the supracrustal rocks before the intrusion of the magma, was introduced by the magma, or was introduced after intrusion and crystallization of the magma from some source unrelated to either the supracrustal or the intrusive rocks. Studies of the gold content of basalts and felsic intrusive rocks (see the discussion in Boyle 1979) have indicated that gold would have to be remobilized from very large volumes of these rock types to provide even the modest amounts present in these two deposits. There is no indication at either deposit (e.g. extensive alteration) that such remobilization has occurred. There are no other rock types exposed that might have been protore.

Studies of fluid inclusions in the vein quartz offer the best possibility of identifying the source of the mineralizing fluids and, hence, the source of the gold. Absolute ages of the country rocks, the intrusive rocks, the alteration, the vein quartz and the mineralization would be invaluable to understanding the gold-felsic intrusion association.

2. The monzonite at the Canadian Arrow deposit contains primary carbonate, indicative of a high CO_2 content in the magma which may prove characteristic of gold-associated felsic magmas. These CO_2-rich magmas are commonly interpreted to originate at deep crustal or mantle levels and to require deep-seated fracture systems for their emplacement high in the crust. This tectonic setting is present in both the Kirkland Lake – Larder Lake and Porcupine camps, where the felsic intrusions are spatially related to major fault systems.

3. The potassium feldspars in the monzonite at the Canadian Arrow deposit are untwinned, which suggests that they are monoclinic (orthoclase) and not triclinic (microcline). Alkali feldspars in felsic intrusions undergo an ordering process that results in inversion of the crystal structure from monoclinic to triclinic during post-solidification cooling. This process is promoted by slow cooling in the presence of peraluminous aqueous fluid and impeded by rapid cooling, an absence of fluids, or the presence of peralkaline fluids (Martin 1974). The effective temperature range of the process is from solidus temperatures to about 250°C. The aplite dikes at the Canadian Arrow deposit, which have not altered the monzonite, are indicative of a fluid phase that was present at least at the last stages of crystallization and there is no reason to suggest rapid cooling of the intrusion. The magmatic fluids of gold-associated intrusions may, therefore, have been peralkaline, reflecting a specific magma composition that may prove characteristic of felsic intrusions associated with lode gold deposits.

4. The vein systems at the Canadian Arrow deposit have cross-cutting relationships, alteration effects and mineralogy indicative of at least two different fluids. The older, which contains base metal mineralization but not gold,

did not alter the monzonite and this similarity to the lack of alteration around aplite dikelets raises the possibility that this vein set represents magmatic fluids. The younger set, which hematitized the surrounding monzonite and apparently precipitated auriferous pyrite, may result from a different fluid of uncertain origin.

5. The presence of CO_2-rich fluids in the vein quartz at the Canadian Arrow deposit, suggested by the fluid inclusions, is indicative of an environment with a high CO_2 activity during precipitation of the quartz and its associated sulphides and gold. This environment undoubtedly influenced the stabilities of complexes that might have transported gold in the hydrothermal fluids. Possible complexes include chloride (Helgeson and Garrels 1968, Henley 1973), thio (Seward 1972) and carbonate (Kerrich and Fyfe 1981) species, each of which has been suggested to have been derived from rocks undergoing metamorphism in the crust.

In such cases, the gold is derived from a source unrelated to the felsic intrusion, and is transported by and precipitated from fluids that also are unrelated to the intrusion. These fluids may have risen through the crust in the same structural zone that allowed the magma to rise and thus would encounter the crystalline intrusion and its host rocks, where precipitation of gold and its gangue minerals would be controlled by the chemistry and permeability of the intrusion and its host rocks.

6. There is a strong structural control, on the scale of a deposit, on gold mineralization at both the Canadian Arrow and Murphy-Garrison Mines. At the Canadian Arrow deposit, a competency contrast between monzonite and basalt may be responsible for localization of the mineralization. Alternatively, there may be a local chemical control; the fluids interacting with the monzonite and not the basalt at the Canadian Arrow deposit and with the basalt and not the monzonite at the Murphy-Garrison deposits. Reasons for this different interaction are not known.

CONCLUSIONS

The preceding discussion includes suggestions for research to increase understanding of the association between lode gold deposits and felsic intrusions and which may define exploration criteria for such deposits. Further work in this program will pursue these suggestions and will eventually include deposits in the Destor-Porcupine and Kirkland Lake – Larder Lake structural zones. These zones undoubtedly have an important role in the emplacement of the magmas and the circulation of mineralizing fluids and are hosts to the largest gold mines.

REFERENCES

Boyle, R.W.
1979: The Geochemistry of Gold and Its Deposits; Geological Survey of Canada, Bulletin 280, 584p.

Cherry, M.E.
1982: Felsic Intrusion Associated Lode Gold Deposits in the Matheson Area, Cochrane District; p.176-179 in Summary of Field Work, 1982, by the Ontario Geological Survey, edited by John Wood, O.L. White, R.B. Barlow, and A.C. Colvine, Ontario Geological Survey, Miscellaneous Paper 106, 235p.

Helgeson, H.C. and Garrels, R.M.
1968: Hydrothermal Transport and Deposition of Gold; Economic Geology, Volume 63, p.622-635.

Henley, R.W.
1973: Solubility of Gold in Hydrothermal Chloride Solutions; Chemical Geology, Volume 11, p.73-87.

Hodgson, C.J.
1982: Gold Deposits of the Abitibi Belt, Ontario; p.192-197 in Summary of Field Work, 1982, by the Ontario Geological Survey, edited by John Wood, O.L. White, R.B. Barlow, and A.C. Colvine, Ontario Geological Survey, Miscellaneous Paper 106, 235p.

Kerrich, R. and Fyfe, W.S.
1981: The Gold-Carbonate Association: Source of CO_2 and CO_2 Fixation Reactions in Archaean Lode Deposits; Chemical Geology, Volume 33, p.265-294.

Latulippe, M.
1982: An Overview of the Geology of Gold Occurrences and Developments in Northwestern Quebec; p.9-14 in Geology of Canadian Gold Deposits, edited by R.W. Hodder and W. Petruk, Canadian Institute of Mining and Metallurgy, Special Volume 24, 286p.

Martin, R.F.
1974: Controls of Ordering and Subsolidus Phase Relations in the Alkali Feldspars, p.313-336 in The Feldspars, edited by W.S. MacKenzie and J. Zussman, Manchester University Press, 717p.

Pirie, J.
1981: Regional Geological Setting of Gold Deposits in the Red Lake Area, Northwestern Ontario; p.71-93 in Genesis of Archean Volcanic-Hosted Gold Deposits, Symposium Held at the University of Waterloo, March 7, 1980, Ontario Geological Survey, Miscellaneous Paper 97, 175p.

Seward, T.M.
1973: Thio Complexes of Gold and the Transport of Gold in Hydrothermal Ore Solutions; Geochimica et Cosmochimica Acta, Volume 37, p.379-399.

Wilkinson, S.J.
1982: Gold Deposits of the Atikokan Area; Ontario Geological Survey, Mineral Deposits Circular 24, 54p.

Macassa Mine, Kirkland Lake
Production History, Geology, Gold Ore Types and Hydrothermal Regimes

G.P. Watson and R. Kerrich
Department of Geology, University of Western Ontario, London

ABSTRACT

The Macassa Mine is the only remaining gold producer of seven interconnected mines which constitute the Kirkland Lake mining camp. The camp has produced over 710 000 kg Au since 1913. The area is underlain by part of the Archean Timiskaming Group, a south-facing sequence of wacke, conglomerate, and trachytic flow and pyroclastic rocks intruded by a composite syenite stock.

At Macassa, there are three types of gold ore. (1) *Break ore* consists of native Au in chloritic fault gouge or small quartz lenses within a prominent, subvertical, thrust-fault system traversing the mine and the entire Kirkland Lake area. (2) *Vein ore* consists of gold-bearing quartz veins in both hanging and footwalls of this fault system. Veins consist of quartz, wallrock fragments, some dolomite and calcite, 2 to 3 percent disseminated pyrite, precious and base-metal telluride minerals and fine grained, native Au. Molybdenite with or without graphite coats fractures in the quartz. (3) *Breccia ore* occurs in several, relatively wide zones (up to 15 m) in the deep western part of the mine. The zones consist of very fractured, bleached, silicified and pyritized rock containing lenses and pods of quartz with native Au and telluride minerals. Molybdenite coats fractures throughout.

Oxygen isotope abundance in rocks and mineral separates from these ore types suggest the ore was precipitated from hydrothermal fluids of $+8$ to $+9.6$ ‰ $\delta^{18}O$, and at 420 to 490°C. These data are consistent with an initial fluid evolved by dehydration of volcanic and sedimentary rocks during accumulation and burial, which ascended and precipitated in open faults and fractures.

Isotopic data from rocks contained within the major faults suggest the initial fluid regime was followed by downward penetration of oxidising, sulphate-bearing fluids of probable marine origin, initially at temperatures of < 200°C and waning to 50°C or less. A third fluid regime is indicated in a quartz-magnetite-chlorite vein which has mineral pair fractionations corresponding to fluids of -4.0 to -0.5 ‰ $\delta^{18}O$ and 210 to 260°C. This fluid's isotopic composition is consistent with hydrothermal fluids of meteoric origin.

These three hydrothermal fluid regimes are interpreted to reflect a sequence of crustal compression, relaxation and uplift above sea level during the Archean.

INTRODUCTION

The gold deposit of the Macassa Mine is in Archean volcanic and sedimentary rocks which have been intruded by a composite syenite stock. The deposit consists of three ore types with distinct morphology, mineral association and relationship to complex fault and fracture systems.

This paper describes the history and geology of the mine and the nature of hydrothermal fluid regimes implicated in the formation of gold concentrations.

LOCATION AND ACCESS

The town of Kirkland Lake is in Teck Township, District of Timiskaming, in northeastern Ontario at Latitude 48°09′N and Longitude 80°03′W (Figure 1). The area is well served by Highways 11, 66, 112 and 624 along with many logging, concession and recreation roads that extend from these highways. The village of Swastika, 9 km southwest of Kirkland Lake, is on the Ontario Northland Railway line. A small commercial airport is situated immediately north of Kirkland Lake.

Teck Township is the west part of a gold producing area that extends east for 150 km into northwestern Quebec. The entire area is within the Abitibi "greenstone" belt, the largest continuous Archean greenstone belt in the Canadian Shield.

Lac-Minerals Limited (Macassa Division) is the only remaining operational mine of seven original gold producers of Kirkland Lake. Its holdings are 31 mining claims on the west edge of Kirkland Lake, immediately north of the village of Chaput Hughes.

HISTORY AND DEVELOPMENT OF THE KIRKLAND LAKE CAMP

The discovery and expansion of the Kirkland Lake gold camp has been well described in several publications (e.g. Burrows and Hopkins 1923, Todd 1928), and a historical synopsis and summary of development for each mine through 1947 appears in Thomson *et al.* (1948). Charlewood (1964) updated this report to 1962.

Gold was initially discovered in the vicinity of Larder Lake and at Swastika in 1906 by prospectors fanning out from Cobalt. Limited mining operations were carried out at the Swastika and Lucky Cross properties and small

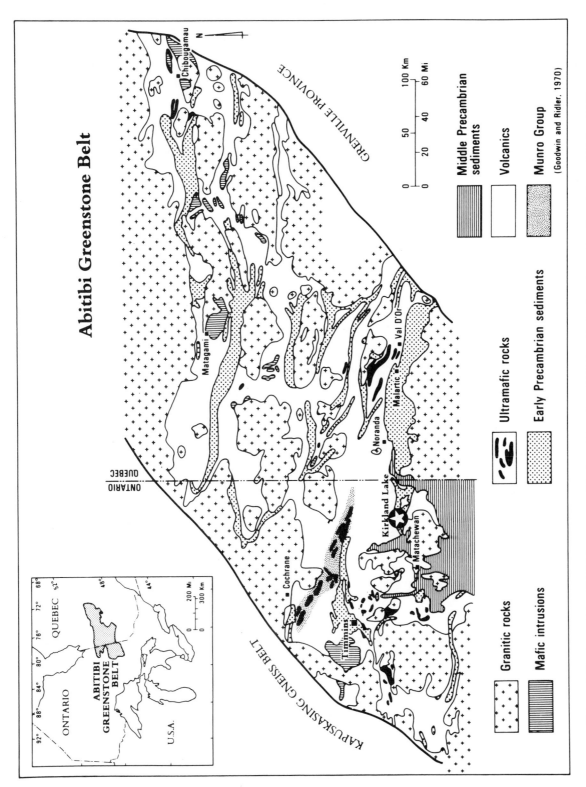

Abitibi Greenstone Belt

Figure 1. Geology of the Abitibi "greenstone" belt and location of Kirkland Lake (geology after Goodwin and Ridler 1970).

Legend:
- Granitic rocks
- Mafic intrusions
- Ultramafic rocks
- Early Precambrian sediments
- Middle Precambrian sediments
- Volcanics
- Munro Group (Goodwin and Ridler, 1970)

57

mills were erected which produced some gold (Thomson 1948b). It was not until 1911 that attention was focused on Kirkland Lake when W.H. Wright made the initial find of gold-quartz veins that later became the Wright-Hargreaves Mine . The development of mines resulting from this and subsequent discoveries over the next 30 years made the economic base for Kirkland Lake and other towns east to Larder Lake.

The operating mines of Kirkland Lake, from west to east along the 6 km main ore zone, were: Macassa, Kirkland Lake Gold (later Kirkland Minerals), Teck-Hughes, Lake Shore, Wright-Hargreaves, Sylvanite and Tough-Oakes Burnside (later Toburn) (see Figure 2, Ploeger and Crocket 1982). First production from the Toburn property was in 1913, from Teck-Hughes in 1917, from Lake Shore in 1918, from Kirkland Minerals in 1919, from Wright-Hargreaves in 1921, from Sylvanite in 1927, and from Macassa in 1933.

During the decade preceding World War II, Kirkland Lake flourished with the peak of production in the late 1930s to a population of 25,000, more than double the present population. To the end of 1948, the seven mines had milled 30 840 000 tonnes of ore and produced 480 000 kg of gold and 84 000 kg of silver, valued at $516,743,288 (Thomson *et al.* 1948).

Throughout World War II, operations were severely hampered by chronic labour shortage. After the war, steadily increasing production costs were not sufficiently offset because the price of gold was fixed at $35 per ounce. Additionally, all of the mines were forced to develop at deeper and deeper levels as more accessible ore zones were depleted. Faced with increased depth of mining with its attendant difficulties, and general decline of the size and average grade of orebodies at depth, six of the seven mines have ceased operations since 1948: Toburn in 1953, Kirkland Minerals in 1960, Sylvanite in 1961, Lake Shore and Wright-Hargreaves in 1965, and Teck-Hughes in 1968. Total production of all mines in Kirkland Lake since 1913 is over 710 000 kg of Au (Lovell and Ploeger 1980), second in North America to only the Porcupine district.

HISTORY AND DEVELOPMENT OF MACASSA MINE

The original Macassa Mines Limited was organized in 1926 and, in 1933, acquired the assets of United Kirkland Gold Mines Limited. Following this, the company was amalgamated in 1962 with Bicroft Uranium Mines Limited and Renabie Mines Limited to become Macassa Gold Mines Limited. Final amalgamation with Willroy Mines Limited and Willecho Mines Limited took place in November, 1970 with parent control by Little Long Lac Gold Mines of Toronto. From 1976 to 1979 management rights were optioned to Upper Canada Mines Limited.

The original Macassa Mines Limited property was made up of 11 claims but an additional 20 claims were acquired from Teck Corporation Limited and Oakdale Mines Limited (formerly Tegren Goldfields Limited) in

1977. In addition, short term options are presently in effect for mining of the old Kirkland Minerals and Teck-Hughes properties (Nemcsok 1980).

First underground work was conducted by Elliott Kirkland Gold Mines Limited which sank a shaft and performed limited development on several levels. Macassa Mines Limited undertook further work on the 500-foot level in 1926 and 1927 (Ward and Thomson 1948). The property was successfully developed in 1931 when arrangements were made to drive westward from the adjoining Kirkland Minerals property on their 2475-foot level. Ore was encountered along a major fault system and in subsidiary hanging-wall veins. In the meantime, No. 1 shaft was sunk to connect with the workings at this horizon. Since then, two additional internal winzes have been driven (No. 1 winze from 3000 to 4825-foot levels; No. 2 winze from 4825 to 6975-foot levels) (see Figure 3). A second surface shaft was sunk on the property some 1000 feet southwest of No. 1 and extends to a depth of 4625 feet. As of this writing, a third surface shaft is being developed at the far west end of the mine workings to a proposed depth of 6450 feet.

Currently, active workings begin at the 2300-foot level and extend to the lowest active level at 6450 feet. In a horizontal plane, these workings are spread from about 1 km east of No. 1 shaft to about 2.2 km west of No. 1 shaft.

A 200 ton-per-day mill was constructed and began operation in October, 1933. Later, this was increased to 425 tons per day and, during 1956, to a capacity of 500-525 tons daily. The present mill capacity is about 325-350 tons per day. To the end of 1981, 5 018 853 tonnes had been milled giving a total metal production of 72 970 kg (1937-1981) of gold. Ore reserves at the end of 1982 were 1 024 910 tonnes grading 14.28 grams Au per tonne.

PREVIOUS GEOLOGICAL STUDIES

The geology and mineral resources of the Kirkland Lake area have been described by geologists and engineers at intervals dating back to initial prospecting activity. The first geological reports of the Kirkland Lake area were by Burrows and Hopkins (1914, 1920, 1923), Tyrrell and Hore (1926) and Todd (1928). The earliest major study with detailed geology of Teck Township and the main ore zone of the Kirkland Lake camp was by Thomson (1948b) and Thomson *et al.* (1948). Gradually the descriptive work expanded to include general geological relations in the Matachewan area to the west (Dyer 1936; Marshall 1947; Lovell 1967; Ridler 1975) and the Skead area to the south (Hewitt 1949; Ridler 1969, 1970). Other important additions to the investigations of the Kirkland-Larder Lakes area were made by Hewitt (1963), Cooke (1966), Cooke and Moorhouse (1969), Jensen (1976, 1978a, 1978b), Tihor and Crockett (1977), Hyde and Walker (1977) and Hyde (1980). In 1975, field work was begun on a regional stratigraphic correlation of the Timmins-Kirkland Lake map area by Pyke and Jensen (1976) of the Ontario Geological Survey. Beginning in 1980, a three-year multi-disciplinary gold deposit study was initi-

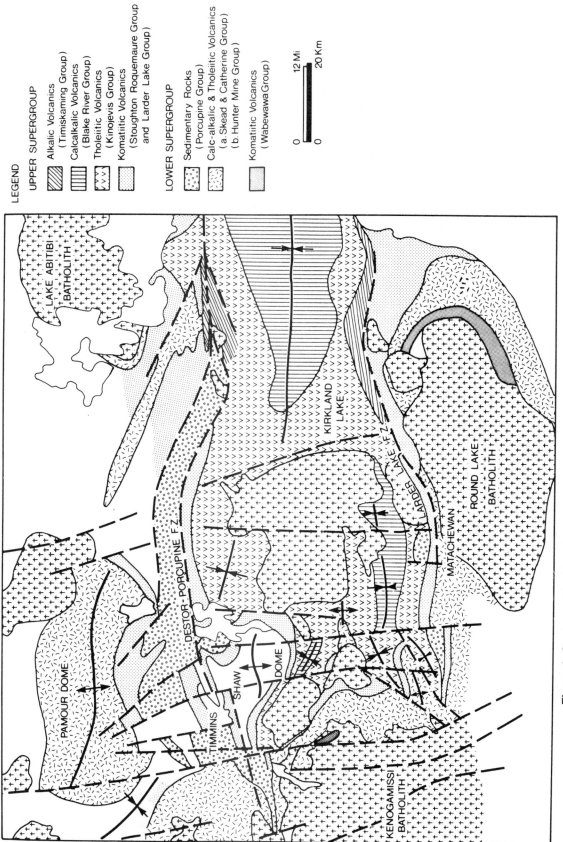

Figure 2. Geology of the Timmins-Kirkland Lake area (after Jensen 1978).

LEGEND

UPPER SUPERGROUP

Alkalic Volcanics (Timiskaming Group)
Calcalkalic Volcanics (Blake River Group)
Tholeiitic Volcanics (Kinojevis Group)
Komatiitic Volcanics (Stoughton Roquemaure Group and Larder Lake Group)

LOWER SUPERGROUP

Sedimentary Rocks (Porcupine Group)
Calc-alkalic & Tholeiitic Volcanics (a. Skead & Catherine Group) (b. Hunter Mine Group)
Komatiitic Volcanics (Wabewawa Group)

ated in the immediate Kirkland Lake area by the Ontario Geological Survey (Ploeger 1980).

To date, the only geological investigations dealing with the Macassa property have been those reported in Ward and Thomson (1948) and Charlewood (1964).

The geology of the Abitibi Belt has been described by Wilson *et al.* (1965) and Goodwin and Ridler (1970) (Figure 1). Recent detailed investigations include those dealing with stratigraphy (Hewitt 1963; Hyde 1978, 1980; Jensen 1978b, 1981), petrography (Bass 1961; Boutcher *et al.* 1966), metamorphism (Jolly 1974) and economic geology (Ridler 1969, 1970, 1976; Tihor and Crockett 1977; Lovell and Ploeger 1980; Ploeger 1980; Ploeger and Crockett 1982).

STRATIGRAPHY

In the Kirkland Lake district, the volcanic, sedimentary and associated intrusive rocks form part of a long, east-plunging synclinorium between the Lake Abitibi batholith and the Round Lake batholith (Figure 2). Two cycles of volcanism with associated sedimentary and intrusive rocks occur in the area. Each is composed of komatiitic rocks at the base, overlain in turn by tholeiitic and calc-alkalic rocks, and capped by an upper alkalic sequence. They are separated from each other by sedimentary rocks containing conglomerate, argillite, chert and iron formation. The gold mines of Kirkland Lake are within the Timiskaming Group, which is the upper, alkalic part of the second cycle. The Timiskaming Group includes both sedimentary and volcanic rocks, notably conglomerate, sandstone, siltstone, argillite, chert, iron formation, flows, agglomerate and tuff (Hyde 1980). Volcanic rocks are dominantly trachyte and phonolite. Cooke and Moorhouse (1969) identified leucite-bearing volcanic rocks within the Timiskaming Group. The maximum exposed thickness of the Timiskaming Group is about 5 km in east Lebel Township (Hewitt 1963). The Timiskaming Group unconformably overlies the Kinojevis, Blake River and Larder Lake Groups and has been intruded by a composite syenite stock.

STRUCTURE

The main structural elements of the district are two steeply inclined, east-trending structural discontinuities: the Destor-Porcupine Break in the north and the Larder Lake Break in the south. The Larder Lake Break extends from south of Kenogami Lake on the west to the Rouyn-Noranda area on the east where it is called the Cadillac-Bouzan Break. Where identified in the Kirkland Lake area, the Larder Lake Break is at or close to the south edge of the Timiskaming Group. To the east, the break is mainly within sedimentary rocks of the Timiskaming Group. The Larder Lake Break has been variously described as (1) a major thrust fault with attendant hydrothermal carbonatization (Thomson 1948a, b); (2) a sedimentary horizon of carbonate exhalite iron formation (Ridler 1969, 1975); and (3) a zone of ultramafic flows (Jensen 1976).

The Timiskaming Group forms an east-trending, narrow continuous belt 0.5 to 5 km wide northeast of the Round Lake batholith. It is a south-facing homoclinal sequence striking 065° and dipping 60 to 75° south. It is cut by strike faults, cross-faults and oblique faults. Parts of the older komatiitic sequence to the south have been faulted into the Timiskaming sequence in several places.

MACASSA MINE GEOLOGY
ROCK UNITS
TIMISKAMING GROUP

The Timiskaming Group is represented by sedimentary and volcanic rocks in the Macassa Mine workings. There are both pebble and boulder conglomerates exposed in widths up to 100 m along cross-cuts extending both north and south from the bottom of the No. 1 shaft (Figure 3), and to a lesser extent in drifts and drillholes to the west. Pebbles and boulders of massive and porphyritic syenite, granite, rhyolite, trachyte, diorite, gabbro, quartz, jasper and chert have been noted (Thomson 1948a, b). The matrix is normally fine- to medium-grained sandstone or greywacke. Hyde (1980) has interpreted these rocks as representing a resedimented marine facies.

Greywacke and tuff are common on the north and south margins of the composite syenite stock in the east and central part of the mine (Figure 3). Increasing amounts of these rocks are present in areas to the west, away from the main stock. Greywacke is typically a massive, medium- to fine-grained rock with 15 to 20 percent angular quartz fragments and 10 to 15 percent angular feldspar fragments in a matrix of quartz, chlorite, biotite, feldspar, and minor carbonate minerals. There are both fine-grained cherty tuff and a variety of medium- to coarse-grained volcaniclastic rocks including agglomerate, lapilli tuff and tuffaceous conglomerate. Tuffs contain up to 60 percent altered feldspar, apatite and secondary carbonate minerals. The essential difference between greywacke and tuff is the absence of clastic quartz in the latter.

In addition to these rocks, there are small amounts of arkosic greywacke, and massive and amygdaloidal trachytic flows exposed underground.

INTRUSIVE ROCKS

There are three main intrusive rock types in the Macassa Mine: augite syenite, syenite and porphyritic syenite. The long axes of all the surface exposures of intrusive rocks strike 060-080° and are generally parallel to the strike of the sedimentary and volcanic rocks of the Timiskaming Group. Intrusive rocks have dips which are steeper than those of adjacent sedimentary and volcanic rocks (Figure 3). A nearly vertical diabase dike averaging 2.5 m wide and striking 165° is located approximately 325 m west of No. 1 shaft; this dike cross-cuts all other rock types.

Augite syenite is the oldest and most widespread of the intrusive rocks. The main body intrudes Timiskaming

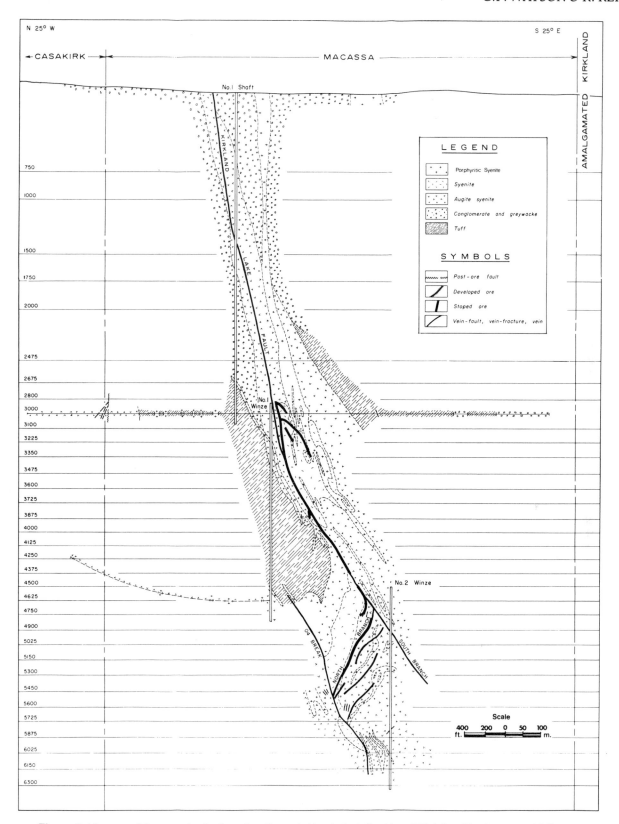

Figure 3. *Macassa Mine, geological section through No. 1 shaft (looking 65°) (after Charlewood 1964).*

conglomerate at surface in a narrow, elongate tabular mass, dips 75 to 85° south to about the 2000-foot level, and appears to bulge on its south side and generally flatten in dip (Ward and Thomson 1948). The fresh rock is dark-coloured commonly with a coarse, almost granitoid texture. The essential ferromagnesian mineral is augite, although this is generally pseudomorphed by chlorite, Fe-Mg carbonate, magnetite and actinolite. The feldspar is generally about $Ab_{90}An_{10}$ but is commonly replaced by fine mosaic orthoclase. Accessory minerals are magnetite, apatite and minor titanite.

The syenite occurs primarily as a westerly pitching pipe-like mass which enters the Macassa Mine from the Kirkland Minerals property on the 1300-foot level in the east. The rock has a granitic texture and consists mostly of orthoclase with 10 percent intergrown oligoclase. Chlorite, Fe-Mg carbonate, leucoxene and sericite occur as pseudomorphs after biotite, augite and feldspar. Accessory minerals are apatite, magnetite and ilmenite. In drill core and underground exposure, syenite is locally transitional into augite syenite with increasing augite content, and in other places has a sharp, well-defined intrusive contact. The age relationship between syenite and augite syenite is therefore ambiguous.

The main body of porphyritic syenite forms a central elongated plug that extends eastward 2.4 km from the Lake Shore Mine. To the west, in the Macassa Mine, porphyritic syenite occurs as dikes and small irregularly shaped sills which transect both syenite and augite syenite with well-defined intrusive contacts. The porphyritic syenite is therefore the youngest phase of the composite intrusive complex. This rock is red to grey in colour and distinctly porphyritic with plagioclase (Ab_{80-95}) as the dominant phenocrysts. Phenocrysts of orthoclase are rare but have been noted (Hawley 1948). Biotite, hornblende and chlorite are the common ferromagnesian minerals. Accessories are apatite, magnetite and ilmenite. Primary quartz is rare to absent. The matrix is a fine aggregate of plagioclase. The porphyritic syenite commonly has scattered xenoliths which are 0.5 to 10 cm in diameter.

FAULTING

The principal gold-producing mines of Kirkland Lake are disposed along one of several fault systems known as the Kirkland Lake Fault or the Main Break. The Main Break has been traced across Teck Township and a short distance into Lebel Township. The strike is about 067°, or approximately parallel to the long dimension of the composite intrusive stock and the regional trend of the Timiskaming Group. North and south of the Main Break there are other more or less parallel faults. Of these, the Narrows Break to the north and the Amalgamated Kirkland Break to the south are most prominent. There are two groups of faults and fractures: pre-ore and post-ore. Detailed analysis of the various forms and patterns of faulting and fracturing within the Kirkland Lake camp was given by Thomson *et al.* (1948) and Charlewood (1964).

The following synopsis for the Macassa Mine is taken largely from Nemcsok (1980).

PRE-ORE FAULTING

The Kirkland Lake Fault, or Main Break, traverses the entire 3.2 km length of the Macassa property. Thomson (1948b) has noted the relatively insignificant appearance of this structure on surface. The Main Break is exposed near the rear of the Macassa Mine office building where it is a shallow, drift-filled depression about 1 foot wide along the contact between augite syenite and Timiskaming conglomerate. Underground, the Main Break is generally a zone of cataclastic and sometimes brecciated wallrock, chloritic schist and mud or gouge, in which deformation is accomodated principally by transgranular fracturing. There is a vertical displacement across the Main Break of approximately 1,500 feet (450 m) in the west end of the Macassa Mine (Thomson *et al.* 1948) with the south (hanging wall) side up in relation to the north (footwall).

The Main Break strikes 065° on average and dips 80° south to above the 3475-foot level where it gradually rotates, flattening in dip to about 50°. The deeper levels of the mine have a branching fault system with an open split to the west below the 4125-foot level, forming a north and south branch to the Main Break (Figure 3). The south branch has a slightly flatter dip and is well south of the mine workings. It has been tested to about the 5300-foot level and is not known to be ore bearing below the 4750-foot level. The north branch is productive in the west part of the mine to the bottom of the present workings (6450-foot level).

Another fault of major importance, known as the '04 Break, is subparallel to the Main Break. The '04 is connected to the north branch of the Main Break via the S and R-2 Breaks (Figure 4). Striking about 060° and dipping 60-70° south, the '04 Break has been explored from the 4500-foot level to the 6500-foot level. Over the past 25 years, the '04 Break and its branches have been the main source of ore for the Macassa Mine.

Near the west end of the mine, commencing just west of the post-ore Tegren Crossfault, are two faults. One is called the '04 Break, although direct evidence is lacking that this is indeed the faulted extension of the '04 Break to the east, and the other to the south is called the South Break. The South Break is the more important of these and has been traced from just above the 5025-foot level down to the 5725-foot level, where it appears to recombine with the '04 Break. The Crossover Fault splits off the '04 Break at a low angle just west of the Tegren Crossfault and crosses over the South Break.

POST-ORE FAULTING

Major northerly striking faults in the Kirkland Lake area displace both sedimentary and volcanic units, along with the pre-ore structures. Three major post-ore faults of the

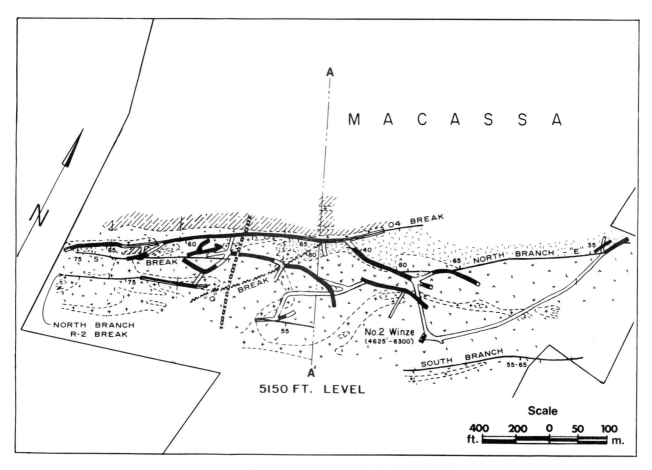

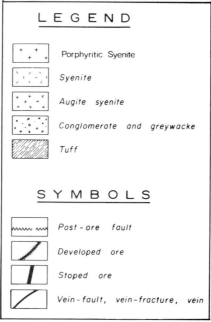

LEGEND

+ + +	Porphyritic Syenite
	Syenite
	Augite syenite
	Conglomerate and greywacke
	Tuff

SYMBOLS

wwww	Post-ore fault
	Developed ore
	Stoped ore
	Vein-fault, vein-fracture, vein

Figure 4. *Macassa Mine, geological plan of 5150-foot level illustrating relationship between the '04 and Main Breaks, S and R-Z Breaks (after Charlewood 1964).*

Macassa Mine are the Boundary Fault, the Tegren Crossfault system and the Amikougami Crossfault.

The Boundary Fault is a tight, west-dipping, brecciated fault striking due north near the west end of the old Macassa property boundary, approximately 0.65 km from No. 1 shaft. Movement on the Boundary Fault is unknown as most of the upper levels in the old Macassa workings are no longer accessible.

The Tegren Crossfault system occurs in two or three segments approximately 1.1 km west of No. 1 shaft. These segments strike approximately 016° and dip steeply to the east. As there are no definitive marker horizons which can be correlated across this fault system, only the relative displacement of the immediately adjoining ore segments can be used to indicate the sense of movement. There is an approximate displacement of 90 m vertically (west side up) and 60 to 75 m horizontally (west side south) (Nemcsok 1980).

The Amikougami Crossfault is a normal fault at the extreme west end of Macassa. It strikes approximately 165° and dips 85° east. This crossfault has recently been intersected by a westward drive on the 5725-foot level, the furthest underground development to the west. Movement is not known as there is only this one opening into the fault at present but slickensides on the hanging wall plunge 10° north, indicating a subvertical component of translation (G. Nemcsok, Willroy Mines Limited, personal communication, 1982).

In addition to these major, post-ore crossfaults there are several post-ore strike faults in the Macassa property which have separated different mineralized zones.

FRACTURING

Pre-ore fracturing is related to the major faults. On the upper levels, subsidiary fractures branch off the Main Break both vertically and laterally. Hanging wall subsidiary fractures generally parallel the strike and have dips 10-20° flatter than the main fault structure. These typically curl in toward the main fault going up dip. Other more steeply dipping hanging wall fractures make contact down dip with the fault plane. On lower levels in the east part of the mine, a widespread zone of fracturing occurs between the '04 and Main Breaks. Here these fractures typically extend between the major faults with relatively shallow dips to the north (Figure 5).

ORE TYPES

There are three proposed types of gold occurrences: (1) break ore, which is native Au in chloritic fault gouge or quartz lenses within sections of the major fault system, i.e. the Main Break and '04 Break; (2) vein ore, which is gold-bearing quartz veins in both the hanging and footwalls of this fault system; and (3) breccia ore, which is relatively wide, up to 15 m, zones in the deep western areas of the mine of highly fractured, bleached rock containing lenses and pods of quartz with native Au and tellurides.

BREAK ORE

Irregular and discontinuous lengths of the major branches of the Main Break ('04 Break) system have been mined for gold at Macassa. Gold commonly occurs associated with erratic lenses of grey and white quartz caught up within the fault gouge or mylonitized and cataclastically deformed rock bordering the fault. Occasionally, gold is found within the chloritic fault gouge itself with no quartz present. This ore type is generally of lesser grade than the other two, although it was the original motivation for developing Kirkland Lake.

VEIN ORE

Gold-bearing veins are quartz-filled fractures associated with the pre-ore fracturing described previously. Vein ore is in both the hanging and footwalls of the major faults. The Main Break in the east section of the mine has relatively more subsidiary veins associated with it than the '04 Break to the west. Vein ore occurs as single, well-defined quartz-filled fractures from 5 to 50 cm wide, and as intricately connected composite veins or lodes, sheeted vein zones, stockworks and vein breccias up to 10 m wide (Thomson 1948b). This change from relatively narrow, simple veins to wider, more complex zones typically reflects increasing proximity to major faults. Vein ore consists of several different generations of quartz, some Ca-Mg-Fe carbonate, calcite, 2 to 3 percent disseminated sulphide minerals (chiefly pyrite), precious and base metal tellurides and fine native gold. Sericite and chlorite occur in the ore and wallrocks. Molybdenite and/or graphite is confined to slips in fractured vein quartz. Gold appears to have been deposited late in the paragenetic sequence and is commonly found in fractures in vein quartz perpendicular to the vein contacts. Telluride minerals typically occur either as narrow bands parallel to and along the outer edges of veins, or alternatively disseminated in the vein-filling (G. Nemcsok, Willroy Mines Limited, personal communication, 1981) (Figure 6). The most common telluride minerals in the mine are altaite (PbTe) and calaverite ($AuTe_2$).

Some of the vein ore in the east part of the mine has distinctive mineral assemblages. The 'E'-vein system, a set of vertical to north-dipping quartz veins in the hanging wall of the Main Break near the Kirkland Minerals property, has co-existing actinolite, Ca-garnet, Mg-Fe carbonate, epidote and calcite as both vein-filling and within surrounding wallrocks. This vein set also has minor scheelite (less than 5 percent). Another vein set with distinctive mineral association is the 50-04 east quartz-magnetite-chlorite vein on the 5000-foot level of the mine. This set has minor to trace amounts of gold and appears to postdate other gold-bearing veins.

BRECCIA ORE

Breccia ore occurs principally in the deep, western third of the mine workings. Since 1980, over 40 percent of the unbroken ore reserves have been classed as breccia ore.

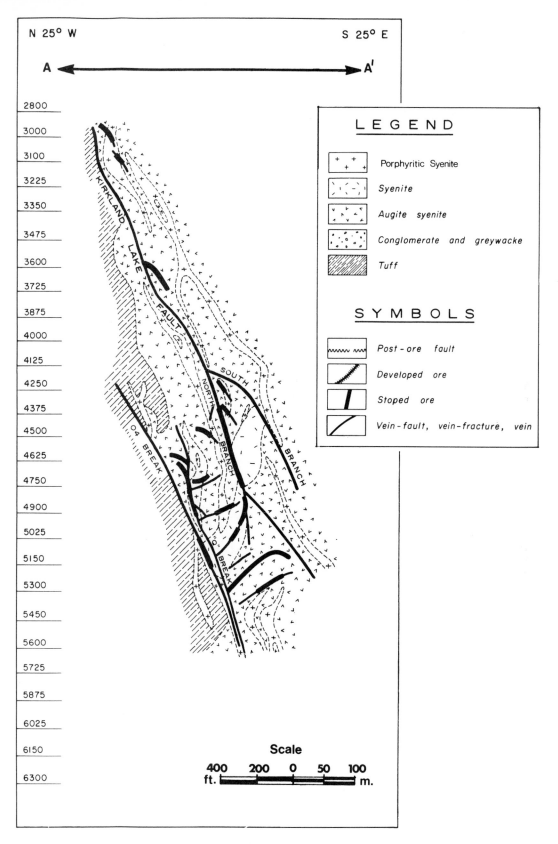

Figure 5. *Macassa Mine, geological section along A-A' (Figure 4) illustrating fracture pattern between the Main Break and '04 Break (after Charlewood 1964).*

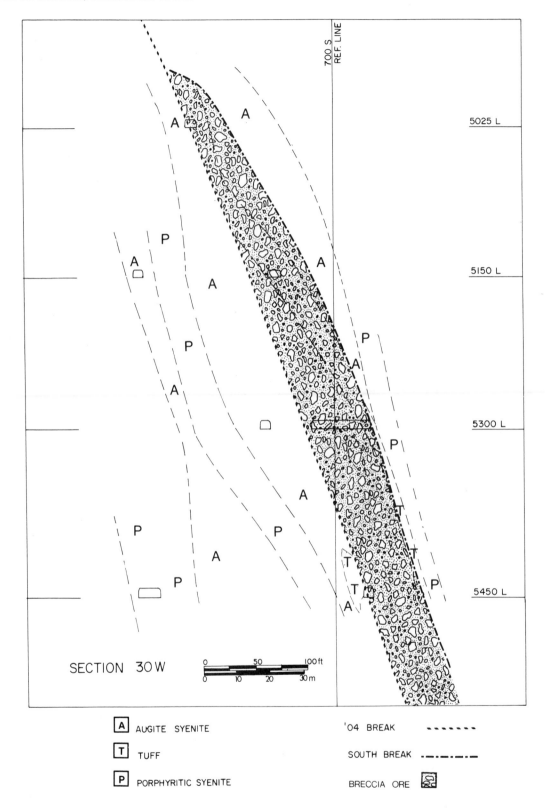

700 S
REF. LINE

5025 L

5150 L

5300 L

5450 L

SECTION 30 W

| 0 | 50 | 100 ft |
| 0 | 10 | 20 | 30 m |

A | AUGITE SYENITE   '04 BREAK

T | TUFF   SOUTH BREAK

P | PORPHYRITIC SYENITE   BRECCIA ORE

Figure 6. *Macassa Mine, geological section along 30W illustrating relationship of breccia ore to major faults.*

Breccia ore is in three major types of rock: (1) augite syenite, (2) tuff, and (3) porphyritic syenite. The major structural elements are the '04 and South Breaks, two steep, south-dipping faults striking approximately 065°. The South Break apparently recombines with the '04 below the 5725-foot level. Another structure of lesser importance is the Crossover Fault which traverses the ground between the two "Breaks" at a shallow angle. These geological relationships are illustrated in Figure 5 and 6.

The breccia ore is hosted by a mixture of augite syenite and tuff which have a complex, interfingering relationship and lesser amounts of porphyritic syenite. The ore is characterized by an erratic distribution of white and grey quartz pods and lenses which contain gold. Pyrite and sericite are abundant and molybdenite coats fractures in both host rock and quartz lenses. The breccia ore is confined on the north and south by the '04 and South Breaks respectively.

OXYGEN ISOTOPE STUDIES

The oxygen isotope compositions of the syenites and the three types of gold ore at the Macassa Mine, determined by the analytical methods outlined in Appendix 1, were used to interpret the possible sources of mineralizing fluids and the temperatures at which mineralization occurred.

$\delta^{18}O$ OF SYENITES

Syenite that is relatively fresh has a range of whole rock oxygen isotope compositions from 6.6 to 10 ‰ (Table 1). These values encompass the entire span of $\delta^{18}O$ for isotopically 'normal' felsic plutonic rocks, defined as +6 ‰ < $\delta^{18}O$ < +10 ‰ (Taylor 1978), and indicate that no significant component of high ^{18}O metasedimentary or hydrothermally altered igneous rocks participated in the source region melting, or contaminated a primary igneous syenitic magma. For syenites specifically, Taylor (1968) reported that whole rock δ-values are typically 6.0 to 7.0 ‰; K-feldspar, 6.5 to 8.8 ‰; and augite, 5.5 to 5.9 ‰. Hence the syenitic rocks at Kirkland Lake are isotopically similar to, or enriched by less than 3 ‰ relative to fresh counterparts.

Overall, the augite syenite is the lowest $\delta^{18}O$ member, as is expected from its greater proportion of mafic minerals and their lower ^{18}O content relative to coexisting feldspar at equilibrium. The highest recorded whole rock δ-values at 9.2 ‰ (felsic syenite), 10.0 ‰ (porphyritic syenite), and 9.6 ‰ (tuff) likely represent a trend of ^{18}O enrichment from primary igneous δ-values during sub-solidus, partial oxygen isotope exchange with a fluid reservoir. Various possible fluid regimes that would be consistent with the deduced trend of sub-solidus ^{18}O enrichment include pristine marine water ($\delta^{18}O \sim 0$ ‰) at 200°C, or an isotopically heavier reservoir such as evolved marine water, formation brines, or metamorphic fluids at greater temperatures. This multiplicity of possible fluid-alteration regimes is generally resolved by recourse to measuring $\Delta^{18}O$ quartz-feldspar, an avenue that is not tractable for the case of quartz-free syenitic rocks. However, the suggested partial sub-solidus oxygen isotope exchange is entirely in accord with the observed intermediate-temperature, secondary alteration products of primary igneous phases.

$\delta^{18}O$ OF ORES

BREAK ORE

Massive quartz from the breaks has a relatively narrow range of $\delta^{18}O$ at 12.2 to 12.5 ‰ (Table 1). Quartz isolated from the matrix of neighbouring wall rocks is isotopically similar to vein counterparts, signifying close isotopic equilibrium between fluids, vein quartz, and wall rock quartz; and in addition a fluid dominated system along fracture conduits occupied by veins.

On the other hand, minor quartz isolated from brecciated syenite at ~11.5 ‰ (samples C, H), and accessory quartz present in chlorite- or selenite-dominated break filling at 14 ‰ (sample A), are systematically lighter and heavier respectively than the massive variety of quartz in breaks. The isotopic composition of magnetite is highly variable in break-related rocks. Magnetite present in small quantities in rocks is known to undergo partial retrograde isotope exchange with coexisting minerals toward higher $\delta^{18}O$, and this effect may account for the observed spread of magnetite δ-values in break-related rocks, where the highest ^{18}O is recorded for rocks with ≤ 5 weight percent magnetite. Accordingly, only those samples with abundant magnetite have been utilised for computing isotopic temperatures from quartz-magnetite fractionations: these are 440°C (A) to 430°C (B). The calculated $\delta^{18}O$ of fluids in equilibrium with quartz and magnetite is 8.0 to 9.6 ‰ (Table 1). Such fluid isotopic compositions are commensurate with either magmatic or metamorphic hydrothermal solutions, but are isotopically heavy compared to meteoric or marine waters that had undergone high temperature isotope exchange with crustal rocks (c.f. Taylor 1974).

Quartz-chlorite fractionations of 11.3 and 9.4 ‰ for samples A and E correspond to isotopic temperatures of 200 and 250°C respectively, and a fluid in equilibrium with the chlorite of +0.5 and 2.2 ‰ for the specified temperatures (Table 1). This range of fluid $\delta^{18}O$ could plausibly reflect low-temperature evolved marine or meteoric water. The large differences in temperatures and fluid isotopic compositions deduced from Δquartz-magnetite and Δquartz-chlorite in sample A (Table 1) signify isotopic disequilibrium between the three minerals. Such relations are to be anticipated in view of the fact that the coexistence of selenite and pyrite in sample A indicates mineralogical and redox disequilibrium. Furthermore, two varieties of quartz are present in some samples which could have distinct isotopic signatures; for instance A contains white and citrine quartz, but white and rose quartz are present in sample H. Attempts to separate the different varieties of quartz are currently underway. Taking these features into consideration, along with the fact that whereas quartz does not readily undergo oxygen iso-

Table 1. Oxygen isotope composition of whole rocks and mineral separates from the Macassa Mine and environs, Kirkland Lake.

Sample description	Sample location	Sample number	$\delta^{18}O$ whole rock	$\delta^{18}O$ quartz	$\delta^{18}O$ chlorite	$\delta^{18}O$ amphibole	$\delta^{18}O$ magnetite	^{18}O quartz-mineral	Temperature °C	$\delta^{18}O$ fluid
PRINCIPAL IGNEOUS ROCK TYPES										
Felsic syenite	2475' level	G-80-70 / G-86	8.63 / 9.20							
Augite syenite	5450' level, 28 W	G-80-73	6.74							
Porphyritic syenite	3000' level, Casakirk X-cut / 7200' level, Wright-Hargreaves	G-80-143 / G-3475	9.96 / 6.56							
Tuff	3850' level, E / 4250' level, near S2 vein / 5300' level, by pass drift	G-80 / G-80-85 / G-80-124	9.60 / 7.74							
BREAK ORE										
Fault gouge: massive selenite with chlorite, minor quartz, + magnetite	5450' level (04 Break)	A		13.96*	27[+]		2.96*	12.3 (q-c) / 11.0 (q-m)	200 / 440	≤+0.5 / +9.6
Massive quartz from fault gouge		B		12.50 v / 12.21 m			0.82*	11.7 (q-m)	430	+8.0
Altered augite syenite, footwall to A,B		C		10.33 m			11.39			
Brecciated augite syenite	2000' level (Main Break)	D(G-80-113)		11.09 m			5.60			
Quartz fragments and fault gouge	3000' level, Casakirk (Narrows Break)	E		12.48 v / 12.61 m	3.09			9.4 (q-c)	250	≤+2.2
Fault gouge and breccia (selenite)	5725' level. 30 W. (04 Break)	H(G-80-125)		11.28*			4.26			
VEIN ORE										
High grade vein in felsic syenite	26-5A vein	F		12.63 v / 11.63 m						
Vein quartz	42-52 vein	G-80-82		13.64						
E VEIN SYSTEM (amphibole, garnet, W association)										
Altered augite syenite	5875' level, footwall of E vein	G-80-88		11.89		5.00	1.93	6.9 (q-a) / 10.0 (q-m) / 6.7 (q-a)	490	+8.5
Vein quartz	58-E vein	G-80-92		11.52 v / 11.56 m		4.81				
QUARTZ-MAGNETITE STRINGERS										
Vein quartz, with magnetite, biotite	58-X-17, 57-X-16 system	G-80-130		12.37 m						
Quartz-magnetite vein	50-04 E	G-82-150		12.12	-0.4[+]		-11.80	12.6 (q-c) / 23.9 (q-m)	260 / 210	-4.0 to -0.5

Table 1. Continued.

Sample description	Sample location	Sample number	$\delta^{18}O$ whole rock	$\delta^{18}O$ quartz	$\delta^{18}O$ chlorite	$\delta^{18}O$ amphibole	$\delta^{18}O$ magnetite	^{18}O quartz-mineral	Temperature °C	$\delta^{18}O$ fluid
BRECCIA ORE										
Quartz fragments from tuff horizon, with molybdorite	5475 drift. 31-5 W	G-80-8		12.56						
Tuff breccia ore	54-32 stope (50' above G-80-8)	G-80-38		12.91				7.58			
Pervasively microfractured augite syenite	5475' level, 32 W	G-80-32		12.57				0.54	12.0	420	7.9

(q-c) = quartz - chlorite; (q-a) = quartz-amphibole; (q-m) = quartz - magnetite

Isotopic temperatures and $\delta^{18}O$ fluid calculated from the fractionation equations reported by Clayton et al (1972) for quartz-water; Wenner and Taylor (1971) for chlorite-water; Javoy (1977) for quartz-amphibole, and O'Neil and Friedman (1977) for quartz-magnetite.

The postscript v signifies vein quartz, and m matrix quartz from the adjacent wall rock.

+ the $\delta^{18}O$ chlorite values have been estimated from isotopic analysis of ultrafine grained chlorite plus quartz mixtures and their relative proportions (see analytical methods)

* composite quartzes.

tope exchange at < 300°C chlorite may do so in the presence of high water/rock proportions, then the quartz-chlorite fractionations yield both maximum temperatures and fluid δ-values.

Hence the disequilibrium mineralogy and oxygen isotope fractionations of some break samples may reflect multi-stage fluid regimes: an earlier episode of discharge of high ^{18}O fluids of probable metamorphic origin implicated in the precipitation of Au, quartz, chlorite and magnetite, followed by a subsequent episode involving incursion of SO_4^{2-}-bearing oxidising fluids initially at < 200°C for an anhydrous sulphate-precursor to selenite, finally waning to ~50°C for stability of selenite itself.

VEIN ORE

Gold-bearing vein quartz in vein ore has a δ^{18}O of 12.6 to 13.6 ‰. In the absence of reliable mineral pair fractionations it is not possible to place constraints on the temperature or isotopic composition of fluids from which the veins were precipitated. Quartz in the matrix of wall rocks to veins is isotopically similar to that of neighbouring vein quartz, indicating close isotopic equilibrium between fluids, vein quartz and wall rock quartz, and in addition a fluid-dominated system in rocks bounding veins.

Quartz of the E vein system has a uniform isotopic composition of 11.5 to 11.9 ‰ (Table 1), or about 1.5 ‰ lighter than the characteristic values for gold-bearing vein ore discussed above (quartz-magnetite veins excluded). Quartz in the matrix of wall rocks is isotopically similar to vein quartz (c.f. sample G-80-92, Table 1). If the magnetite in G-80-88 is in isotopic equilibrium with coexisting quartz, then the mutual fractionation of 10.0 ‰ corresponds to precipitation temperatures for the veins of 490°C and a fluid isotopic composition of +8.5 ‰. In view of the fact that magnetite in other samples has undergone variable degrees of re-equilibration toward higher δ-values, the above Δquartz-magnetite should be considered as a minimum, thus yielding maximum estimates of temperature and fluid δ^{18}O.

The magnetite-bearing veins contain a coexisting amphibole which is actinolitic in composition and isotopically uniform at 4.8 to 5.0 ‰ (Table 1). No experimental mineral-water calibration exists for amphiboles, and thus it is difficult to establish whether or not the quartz, amphibole and magnetite are isotopically concordant. Javoy (1977) gives the equation Δ^{18}O quartz-hornblende = −0.30 + 3.15 x 10^{6}T^{-2} (°K), deduced on a combined theoretical-empirical basis for igneous rocks at high sub-solidus temperatures. Use of this equation yields temperatures of 400°C for the magnetite-amphibole-quartz veins which is not in close agreement with that deduced from quartz-magnetite. Such apparent isotopic disequilibrium has previously been reported for hydrothermal actinolite and cummingtonite (Costa 1980), and it seems likely either that extrapolation of the quartz-hornblende equation to lower temperatures is invalid, or that this equation is inappropriate for other amphibole compositions.

The quartz-magnetite-chlorite vein has distinctively low δ^{18}O chlorite and magnetite compared to any other

separates analysed (Table 1). In sample G-82-150 quartz, chlorite and magnetite approach triple concordancy, with the mineral pair fractions corresponding to temperatures of 210 to 260°C and fluids of -4.0 to -0.5 ‰. The fluid isotopic composition is consistent with a hydrothermal reservoir of meteoric origin (δ^{18}O < 0 ‰), and signifies downward penetration of surface groundwaters from terrain above sea level.

BRECCIA ORE

Vein quartz from the breccia ore is isotopically uniform at 12.6 to 12.9 ‰. This is in close compliance with what is believed to be single stage and isotopically least disturbed massive quartz samples from the break (Table 1). As for the case of rocks in the break, magnetite in breccia ore has a wide δ^{18}O spread; in this ore type, 7 ‰, from 0.5 to 7.6 ‰. If the quartz and abundant magnetite present in sample G-80-32 are assumed to be in equilibrium, then the quartz-magnetite fractionation of 12.0 ‰ corresponds to a temperature of 420°C and a fluid isotopic composition of 7.9 ‰.

SUMMARY AND DISCUSSION OF ^{18}O DATA

Break ore, vein ore, and breccia ore were all precipitated from hydrothermal solutions of +8 to +9.6 ‰, over the temperature interval 420 to 490°C (Figure 7). These fluids were probably evolved by dehydration reactions during accumulation and burial of the volcanic and sedimentary rocks, and released through permeable conduits provided by the faults. The δ^{18}O quartz, temperatures and fluid isotopic composition of Macassa gold veins are generally similar to other vein-dominated gold deposits (Table 2, after Kerrich 1983).

For all ore types, quartz in veins and bounding wall rocks is close to isotopic equilibrium, but heavy compared to the whole rock δ^{18}O of fresh syenite hosting the veins, or δ-values appropriate for their constituent feldspars. Hence lateral secretion of silica from wall rocks into veins is improbable. Rocks contained within the break locally record both isotopic and mineralogical disequilibrium. Isotopic relations are tentatively interpreted in terms of an early episode of discharge of high ^{18}O fluids of probable metamorphic origin implicated in the precipitation of quartz, gold, magnetite and chlorite. This was followed by incursion of oxidising, sulphate-bearing fluids of probable marine origin, initially at temperatures of ≤ 200°C, waning to 50°C or less: downward fluid penetration is likely in view of the negative temperature dependence of solubility for sulphate species.

The early fluid regime is interpreted to reflect crustal compression, with hydrothermal discharge during episodes of hydrofracturing under conditions of anomalously high hydraulic pressure, whereas the later fluid regime is considered to reflect fluid input at hydrostatic pressure during relaxation of crustal compression, with attendent dilation of both large and small scale structures creating permeability.

Arrays of quartz-magnetite stringer veins were precipitated over the temperature interval 210 to 260°C from hydrothermal fluids of meteoric origin ($\delta^{18}O = 2$ ‰). This in turn requires the existence of land above sea level, with downward penetration of groundwaters into fractured rock media. The timing of this meteoric water dominated fluid regime cannot be assessed with certainty in the absence of independent age determinations. However, inasmuch as the estimated temperatures of vein formation are close to ^{40}K-^{40}Ar blocking temperatures for muscovite of 250°C, and given ages of approximately 2.5 Ga for Abitibi belt rocks dated by this decay scheme (Purdy and York 1968), it is not unlikely that the meteoric water incursion was of Archean age.

For the Noranda district, Kennedy and Kerrich (1982) discussed the transition from marine water to meteoric water cooling of the Flavrian pluton, accompanying its emergence above sea level. Isotopic evidence for such emergence is commensurate with the presence of fluviatile sedimentary rocks high in the stratigraphic sequence. Hence emergence of land above sea level, with attendent meteoric water incursion, may not be uncommon for the late stages in development of greenstone belts.

ACKNOWLEDGEMENTS

This work forms part of a Ph.D. thesis currently being completed (by G.W.) at the University of Western Ontario, London, Canada. Supporting funds from Long Lac Mineral Exploration Limited are gratefully acknowledged. Particular thanks are due to G. Nemcsok, Chief Area Geologist, and the staff of the Macassa Mine.

Financial assistance for aspects of this study was provided by the Ontario Geological Survey. We are grateful to L. Willmore for analytical assistance. Mrs. G. McIntyre and Miss S. Hutchinson are thanked for typing the manuscript. R.W. Hodder read provisional drafts and is acknowledged for his valuable critical comments.

APPENDIX 1. Analytical Methods

Conventional procedures were employed for the extraction of oxygen from minerals with bromine pentafluoride and quantitative conversion to CO_2 prior to mass spectrometric analysis (Clayton and Mayeda 1963). Isotopic data are reported as $\delta^{18}O$ values in per mil (‰) relative to Standard Mean Ocean Water (SMOW). The overall repro-

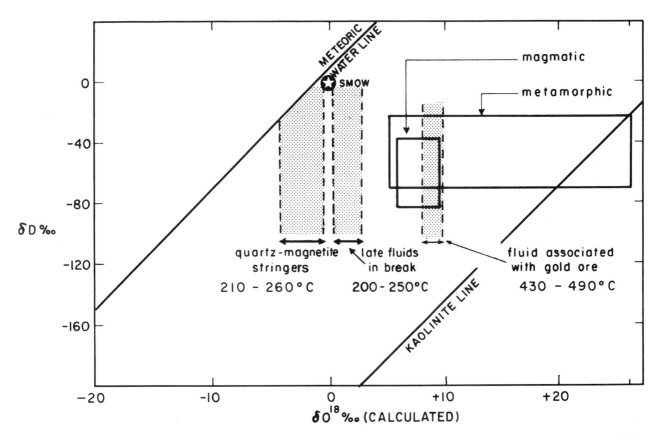

Figure 7. *Isotopic composition of natural terrestrial fluid reservoirs in δD, δ¹⁸O co-ordinate space, with calculated fields for hydrothermal solutions at Macassa superimposed.*

Table 2. Oxygen isotope composition of minerals separated from gold-bearing veins and their host rocks in mines from the Yellowknife, Timmins and Val d'Or districts, together with calculated isotopic temperatures and δ18O fluid (after Kerrich 1983).

		δ18O vein quartz	δ18O mineral	δ18O host quartz	Δquartz-mineral	temperature*°C	δ18O fluid
YELLOWKNIFE DISTRICT Campbell shear	gold-bearing quartz-carbonate veins, 2300 in sericite-chlorite schist	12.48		12.06			
		12.53	6.58 c		5.95	440	8.2
		11.50	5.97 c		5.53	480	7.9
		11.59	7.03 m		4.56	320	7.5
	4900	11.43		11.29			
	5100	10.80					
Con shear	gold-bearing quartz-carbonate veins, 250 in sericite-chlorite schist 1550	12.25					
		11.50	5.97 c		5.53	480	7.9
		12.06		12.13			
Giant shear-east zone H.G. zone open pit	gold-bearing quartz-carbonate veins in sericite chlorite schist	12.28					
		12.77		12.57			
		12.01					
Western granodiorite	gold-bearing quartz veins emplaced into shear zone within granodiorite	13.03		13.70			
Ptarmigan	gold-bearing quartz veins in metagreywacke	12.60	6.67 c		5.93	440	8.2
		13.16		13.91			
Surface	gold-bearing quartz-carbonate veins in metabasalts	13.51	6.70 c		6.81	370	7.6
		13.56	7.45 c		6.11	420	8.9
DOME MINE - TIMMINS	banded quartz-muscovite veins in ultramafic schist	14.74	10.98 m		3.76		
		14.41	11.28 m	14.66	3.13		
		14.37	10.78 m		3.59	430	9.8
		14.52	10.54 m		3.98	380	8.8
		14.63		15.17			
	banded quartz-tourmaline veins	15.07					
		15.24					
	veins in quartz-feldspar porphyry	14.97		15.31			
		13.93		13.87			
		14.19	8.05 c	14.26	6.14	420	9.6
	quartz-tourmaline veins in dacite	15.09	9.21 c		5.88	440	10.8
		15.17	9.38 c		5.79	450	11.1
	quartz veins in Timiskaming slates	14.65		14.10			
		14.52		15.77			
		14.76	11.26 m		3.50	440	10.5
	quartz-carbonate veins in metabasic schists	14.53	8.99 c	14.84	5.54	480	10.9
		15.20					
	quartz-carbonate veins parallel to auriferous stratiform carbonate	14.87	9.31 c	15.32	5.56	480	11.6
AUNOR MINE - TIMMINS	quartz veins parallel to auriferous stratiform carbonate	14.65					
		15.01					
MACINTYRE MINE	quartz-carbonate veins 1526 stope	15.02	10.62 m	14.86	4.40	340	8.2
		14.96					
	quartz-carbonate veins, 4675-5 vein	14.81	10.80 m	14.90	4.01	380	9.2
		14.74					
PAYMASTER	quartz-carbonate-chlorite veins. Mine dump	14.87	9.17 c		5.70	460	10.9
		14.89					
	silicified Au-bearing porphyry	14.80					
		14.62					
HOLLINGER	quartz-carbonate veins in altered ultramafic tuffs	13.5	7.7 c		5.8	440	9±1
CHADBOURNE	quartz-albite-carbonate veins in fractured basalt and andesite	12.0 to 13.5	6.1 to 6.9 c		5.9 - 6.8	380 to 450	8±1
			8.1 to 8.9 m		3.6 to 4.0		
KERR ADDISON MINE	quartz-muscovite - carbonate veins in carbonate sediment	14.48	10.54 m		3.94	390	9.0
	"flow ore" - albitic-pyrite tuffs and flows	14.4	12.0 ab 6.9 c		4.2	350	8
	"flow ore" - muscovite pyrite tuffs and flows	14.2	10.1 m				
LAMAQUE	quartz-tourmaline - carbonate veins. Main granodiorite	12.84	6.54 c		6.30	410	7.8
		12.71					
		12.79					
PASCALES	quartz-tourmaline - carbonate veins	11.86	5.71 c		6.15	420	8.1
		11.58					
BRAS D'OR	quartz-tourmaline - carbonate veins	11.61	5.61 c		6.00	430	8.2
		12.70					
EAST MALARTIC	albite-orthoclase-quartz-tuffaceous chert	13.4 to 21.7	10.4 to 12.3 (ab)			~200	0±1
			14.1 to 16.7 (or)			~150	0±1

c = chlorite; m = muscovite; ab = albite; or = orthoclase. Isotopic temperatures and fluid δ18O calculated from the mineral-water fractionation equations reported by Clayton et al., (1972) for quartz, O'Neil and Taylor (1967) for feldspars, O'Neil and Taylor (1969) for muscovite, and Werner and Taylor (1971) for chlorite.

ducibility of $\delta^{18}O$ values has averaged $\pm$ 0.18 ‰ (two standard deviations).

Fractionations, or differences in $\delta^{18}O$ among minerals, are quoted as Δ defined as:

$$\Delta_{A-B} = 1000 \ln \alpha_{A-B} \cong \delta_A - \delta_B$$

where α_{A-B} is the fractionation factor for the coexisting minerals A and B.

Mineral separates for isotopic analysis were obtained using standard techniques based on relative magnetic susceptibility, and utilising a Franz isodynamic separator. Pure quartz was recovered from quartz-feldspar mixtures by means of a selective digestion of the latter in hydrofluorosilicic acid (H_2SiF_6). Quartz and chlorite were intimately intergrown in samples A and G-82-150, such that pure chlorite separates could not be made. For these samples the $\delta^{18}O$ chlorite was estimated from that of the chlorite-quartz mixture, knowing their relative proportions and the $\delta^{18}O$ of quartz. In each case relative proportions were estimated from (a) XRD, (b) visual counting and (c) the oxygen yield of the mixture as compared to that of the two end members.

REFERENCES

Bass, M. N.
1961: Regional Tectonics of Part of the Southern Canadian Shield; Journal of Geology, Volume 69, p. 668-702.

Boutcher, S.M.A., Edhorn, A. S., and Moorhouse, W. W.
1966: Archean Conglomerates and Lithic Sandstones of Lake Timiskaming, Ontario; Geological Association of Canada, Proceedings, Volume 17, p.21-42.

Burrows, A. G., and Hopkins, P. E.
1914: The Kirkland Lake and Swastika Gold Areas; Ontario Bureau of Mines, Volume 23, pt. 2.
1920: The Kirkland Lake Gold Area (Second Report); Ontario Department of Mines, Volume 29, pt. 4, p. 1-48.
1923: Kirkland Lake Gold Area; Ontario Department of Mines, Volume 32, pt. 4, p. 1-52.

Charlewood, G. H.
1964: Geology and Deep Developments on the Main Ore Zone at Kirkland Lake; Ontario Department Mines, Geological Circular 11, 49 p.

Clayton, R. N., and Mayeda, T. K.
1963: The Use of Bromine Pentafluoride in the Extraction of Oxygen from Oxides and Silicates; Geochimica et Cosmochimica Acta, Volume 27, p. 43-52.

Clayton, R. N., O'Neil, J. R., and Mayeda, T. K.
1972: Oxygen Isotope Exchange Between Quartz and Water; Journal of Geophysical Research, Volume 77, p. 3057-3067.

Cooke, D. L., and Moorhouse, W. W.
1969: Timiskaming Volcanism in the Kirkland Lake Area, Ontario, Canada; Canadian Journal of Earth Sciences, Volume 6, p.117-132.

Cooke, D. L.
1966: The Timiskaming Volcanics and Associated Sediments of the Kirkland Lake area; Unpubublished Ph.D. Thesis, University of Toronto, 147 p.

Costa, U. R.
1980: Footwall Alteration and Ore Formation at Mattagami Mine, Quebec; Unpublished Ph.D. Thesis, University of Western Ontario, London, Canada. 289 p.

Dyer, W. S.
1936: Geology and Ore Deposits of the Matachewan-Kenogami Area; Ontario Department of Mines, Volume 44, pt. 2.

Goodwin, A. M., and Ridler, R. H.
1970: The Abitibi Orogenic Belt; p. 1-30 in Symposium on Basins and Geosynclines of the Canadian Shield, Geological Survey of Canada, Paper 70-40.
1977: The Abitibi Orogenic Belt; p.406-426 in The Archean, edited by G.J.H. McCall, Dowder, Hutchinson and Ross Inc., Pennsylvania, 508 p.

Freidman, I., and O'Neil, J. R.
1977: Compilation of Stable Isotope Fractionation Factors of Geochemical Interest; United Stated Geological Survey, Professional Paper 440-KK, Data of Geochemistry, 6th Ed.

Hawley, J. E.
1948: Mineralogy of the Kirkland Lake Ores; p. 108-124 in Geology of the Main Ore Zone of Kirkland Lake. Ontario Department of Mines, Annual Report for 1948, Volume 57, pt. 5, 188p.

Hewitt, D. F.
1949: Geology of Skead Township, Larder Lake Area; Ontario Department of Mines, Volume 58, pt. 6, 43 p.
1963: The Timiskaming Series of the Kirkland Lake Area; Canadian Mineralogist, Volume 7, pt. 3, p. 497-523

Hyde, R. S.
1978: Sedimentology, Volcanology, Stratigraphy and Tectonic Setting of the Archean Timiskaming Group, Abitibi Greenstone Belt, Northeastern Ontario, Canada; Unpublished Ph.D. Thesis, McMaster University, Hamilton, 422 p.
1980: Sedimentary Facies in the Archean Timiskaming Group and their Tectonic Implications, Abitibi Greenstone Belt, Northeastern Ontario, Canada; Precambrian Research, Volume 12, p. 161-195.

Hyde, R. S., and Walker, R. G.
1977: Sedimentary Environments and the Evolution of the Archean Greenstone Belt in the Kirkland Lake Area, Ontario; Geological Survey of Canada, Paper 77-1A, p. 185-190.

Javoy, M.
1977: Stable Isotopes and Geochemistry; Journal of the Geological Society, Volume 133, p. 609-636.

Jensen, L. S.
1976: Regional Stratigraphy and Structure of the Timmins-Kirkland Lake Area, Districts of Cochrane and Timiskaming and Kirkland Lake Area, District of Timiskaming; p. 82-95 in Summary of Field Work, 1976, by the Geological Branch, Edited by V. G. Milne, W. R. Cowan, K. D. Card, and J. A. Robertson, Ontario Division of Mines, Miscellaneous Paper 67, 183 p.
1978a: Archean Komatitic, Tholeiitic, Calc-alkalic, and Alkalic Volcanic sequences in the Kirkland Lake Area; in Toronto '78 Field Trip Guidebook, edited by A.L. Currie and W.O. MacKasey, Geological Association of Canada, 361 p.
1978b: Regional Stratigraphy and Structure of the Timmins-Kirkland Lake area, Districts of Cochrane and Timiskaming and the Kirkland-Larder Lake Area, District of Timiskaming; p.67-72 in Summary of Field Work, 1978, by the Ontario Geological Survey, Edited by V.G. Milne, O.L. White, R.B. Barlow and J.A. Robertson, Ontario Geological Survey, Miscellaneous Paper 82, 235p.

1981: Archean Gold Mineralization in the Kirkland Lake-Larder Lake Area; p.59-65 in Genesis of Archean, Volcanic-Hosted Gold Deposits, Symposium Held at the University of Waterloo, March 7, 1980, Edited by R. G. Roberts, and E.G. Pye, Ontario Geological Survey, Miscellaneous Paper 97, 175p.

Jolly, W. R.
1974: Regional Metamorphic Zonation as an Aid in Study of Archean Terrains; Abitibi Region, Ontario; Canadian Mining, Volume 12, p. 499-508.

Kennedy, L. P., and Kerrich, R.
1982: Transition from Marine to Meteoric Water Hydrothermal Regimes in an Emerging Archean Intrusive Complex: ^{18}O Evidence From the Morran Pluton; American Geophysical Union Abstracts, San Francisco, Dec. 1982.

Kerrich, R.
1983: Geochemistry of Gold Deposits in the Abitibi Greenstone Belt: Parts I through III; Canadian Institute of Mining and Metallurgy, Bulletin (in press).

Lovell, H. L.
1967: Geology of the Matachewan Area; Ontario Department of Mines, Geological Report 51, 61 p.

Lovell, H. L., and Ploeger, F. R.
1980: 1979 Annual Report of the Kirkland Lake Resident Geologist; p. 77-96 in Annual Report of the Regional and Resident Geologists, Ontario Geological Survey, Miscellaneous Paper 91, 143p.

Marshall, H. I.
1947: Geology of Midlothian Township. Ontario Department of Mines, Annual Report, Volume 56, Part 5: 24 p.

Nemcsok. G.
1980: Geology of the Macassa Gold Mine; Unpublished Company Report.

Ploeger, F. R.
1980: Kirkland Lake Gold Study, District of Timiskaming; p. 188-190 in Summary of Field Work, 1980, by the Ontario Geological Survey, Edited by V. G. Milne, O. L. White, R. B. Barlow, J. A. Robertson, and A. C. Colvine, Ontario Geological Survey, Miscellaneous Paper 96 201, p.

Ploeger, F. R., and Crocket, J. H.
1982: Relationship of Gold to Syenitic Intrusive Rocks in Kirkland Lake; p.69-72 in Geology of Canadian Gold Deposits, Canadian Institute of Mining and Metallurgy, Special Volume 24, 286p.

Purdy, J. W., and York, D.
1968: Rb-Sr Whole Rock and K-Ar Mineral Ages from the Superior Province Near Kirkland Lake, Northeastern Ontario, Canada; Canadian Journal of Earth Sciences, Volume 5, p. 699-705.

Pyke, D. R., and Jensen, L. G.
1976: Preliminary Stratigraphic Interpretation of the Timmins-Kirkland Lake Area, Ontario; Program with Abstracts, Geological Association of Canada, Volume 1, p. 71.

Ridler, R. H.
1969: The Relationship of Mineralization to Volcanic Stratigraphy in the Kirkland Lake area, Northern Ontario, Canada; Unpublished Ph.D. Thesis, University of Wisconsin.

1970: Relationship of Mineralization to Volcanic Stratigraphy in the Kirkland Lake-Larder Lake Area, Ontario; Proceedings, Geological Association of Canada, Volume 21, p. 33-42.

1975: Regional Metallogeny and Volcanic Stratigraphy of the Superior Province; p. 353-358 in Report of Activities, Part A, Geological Survey of Canada, Paper 75-1A.

1976: Stratigraphic Keys to the Gold Metallogeny of the Abitibi Belt; Canadian Mining Journal, Volume 97, No. 6, p. 81-87.

Taylor, H. P.
1968: The Oxygen Isotope Geochemistry of Igneous Rocks; Contributions to Mineralogy and Petrology, Volume 19, p. 1-17.

1974: The Application of Oxygen and Hydrogen Isotope Studies to Problems of Hydrothermal Alteration and Ore Deposition; Economic Geology, Volume 69, p. 843-883.

1978: Oxygen and Hydrogen Isotope Studies of Plutonic Granite Rocks; Earth and Planetary Science Letters, Volume 38, p.177-210.

Thomson, J. E.
1946: The Keewatin-Timiskaming Unconformity in The Kirkland Lake District; Transactions, Royal Society of Canada, Series 3, Volume 40, p. 113-124.

1948a: Regional Structure of the Kirkland Lake-Larder Lake Area; p. 627-632 in Structural Geology of Canadian Ore Deposits, Canadian Institute of Mining and Metallurgy, Special Volume.

1948b: Geology of Teck Township and Kenogami Lake Area, Kirkland Lake Gold Belt; Ontario Department of Mines, Volume 57, pt. 5, p. 1-53.

Thomson, J. E., Charlewood, G. H., Griffin, K., Hawley, J. E., Hopkins, H., MacIntosh, C. G., Ogrizio, S. P., Perry, O. S., and Ward, W.
1948: Geology of the Main Ore Zone at Kirkland Lake; Ontario Department of Mines, Volume 7, pt. 5, p. 54-196.

Tihor, L. A., and Crocket, J. H.
1977: Gold Distribution in the Kirkland Lake-Larder Lake Area with Emphasis on Kerr Addison Type Ore Deposits - a Progress Report; p. 363-369 in Report of Activities, Part A, Geological Survey of Canada, Paper 77-1A.

Todd, E. W.
1928: Kirkland Lake Gold Area; Ontario Department of Mines, Volume 37, pt. 2.

Tyrrell, J. B., and Hore, R. E.
1926: The Kirkland Lake Fault; Transactions, Royal Society of Canada, 3rd series, Volume 20, pt. 1, Section 4.

Ward, W., and Thomson, J. E.
1948: Geology of the Macassa Mine; p.125-132 in Geology of the Main Ore Zone of Kirkland Lake. Ontario Department of Mines, Annual Report for 1948, Volume 57, pt. 5.

Wenner, D. B. and Taylor, H. P.
1971: Temperatures of Serpentinization of Ultramafic Rocks Based on $^{18}O/^{16}O$ Fractionation Between Co-existing Serpentine and Magnetite; Contributions to Mineralogy and Petrology, Volume 32, p. 165-185.

Wilson, D. B., Andrews, P., Moxham, R. L., and Ramel, K.
1965: Archean Volcanism in the Canadian Shield; Canadian Journal of Earth Sciences, Volume 2, p. 161-175.

The Iron Formation – Gold Association Evidence from Geraldton Area

A.J. Macdonald

Mineral Deposits Section, Ontario Geological Survey, Toronto

ABSTRACT

Gold mineralization in the North Zone of the MacLeod-Cockshutt and Hard Rock Mines at Geraldton, is hosted by a large Z-fold in Archean iron formation on the northern limb of a synclinorium, part of an isoclinally folded (F1) "greenstone" assemblage within the Wabigoon Subprovince. A cleavage was developed throughout the Geraldton area in response to this folding event. Ore-bearing structures include veins, shear zones and replacement sulphide bodies in iron formation, metamorphosed wacke and porphyry sills. The replacement bodies in iron formation are spatially associated with veins that are subparallel to axes of minor Z-shaped folds (F2). The F1 cleavage is deformed by the small Z-folds, implying that veining postdates F1 cleavage development and F2 folding. Mineralization is also spatially associated with secondary iron-bearing carbonate that has altered both sedimentary and intrusive rocks. Three hundred metres along strike from the gold deposits, secondary carbonate is rare to absent in iron formation.

INTRODUCTION

The stratabound nature of many Archean lode deposits has led researchers in economic geology to propose a syngenetic origin for the mineralization; i.e. ore formed more or less in situ and contemporaneously with the enclosing host rock (e.g. Karvinen 1981). The contrasting epigenetic theory postulates that hydrothermal gold mineralization was introduced along structurally favourable zones at some period after the host rock was lithified. That the late introduction of hydrothermal fluid often postdated structural deformation, in which originally horizontal units were deformed into the vertical, would, in the epigenetic theory, account for the coincidence of structurally prepared zones and specific lithologies. Archean iron-formation-hosted lode gold deposits have been particularly caught up in this debate. It is the aim of this study to attempt to provide insight into the problem through interpretation of detailed field mapping with subsequent petrological and geochemical investigations. Preliminary field observations and interpretations of a gold deposit near Geraldton are described in this report.

GLOBAL DISTRIBUTION OF PRECAMBRIAN GOLD DEPOSITS ASSOCIATED WITH IRON FORMATION

Gold deposits hosted by iron formation have been mined since prehistorical time in Zimbabwe (Foster *et al.* in preparation). The deposits have only been adequately described, however, during the last half century (Boyle 1979).

The association is most marked in Archean volcanic belts, such as the Kolar goldfield in the Dharwar metavolcanics of Mysore Plateau, India (Narayanaswami *et al.* 1960), over 125 deposits in the Sebakwian and Bulawayan Groups of Zimbabwe (Fripp 1976), in banded iron formation near Jardine, Montana, USA (Hallager 1982), the Central Patricia and Pickle Crow Mines in Kenora District of Ontario (Barrett and Johnston 1948; Corking 1948) and the MacLeod-Cockshutt and Hard Rock Mines (Figure 1) south of Geraldton, Ontario (Ferguson 1967). Precambrian (possibly Archean) iron formation related gold deposits include the Homestake Mine in South Dakota, USA (McLaughlin 1931), similar deposits near Contwoyto Lake such as the Lupin Mine in the Northwest Territories, Canada (McConnell 1964), several mines in the 'Quadrilatero Ferrifero' of the Minas Gerais District, Brazil (Matheson 1956), the Mount Magnet, Lennonville and Bougardi deposits of Western Australia (Lambert *et al.* 1982; Finucane 1953) and the Geita and Musoma Goldfields of Tanzania (Harris 1961; Basu 1982).

Two possible genetic models have been proposed for gold lodes in general and are applicable to the iron formation association.

1. Epigenetic Model. The "magmatic or metamorphic differentiation theory", maintains that gold is derived from a crystallizing magmatic body, or by a metamorphic process at depth, concentrated in a siliceous, hydrothermal fluid and injected into a structurally prepared host rock (Figure 2a).

2. Syngentic Model. The "metamorphic or lateral secretion theory" suggests that the associated lithologies, such as iron formation, were the metal source, or protore, from which the gold was mobilised and concentrated as a result of regional metamorphism (Figure 2b)(modified from Saager and Meyer 1982).

75

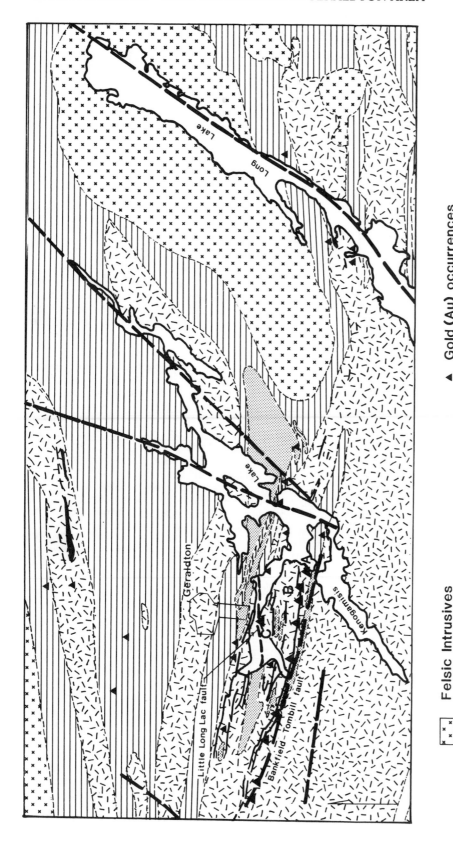

Felsic Intrusives

Mafic Intrusives

Clastic Metasediments

Mafic to Intermediate Metavolcanics

Iron Formathion

A Hard Rock mine
B MacLeod-Cockshutt mine
C Little Long Lac mine

▲ Gold (Au) occurrences
▲ Major Producing Mines
– – Fault

Figure 1. Geology and gold deposits in the Geraldton area.

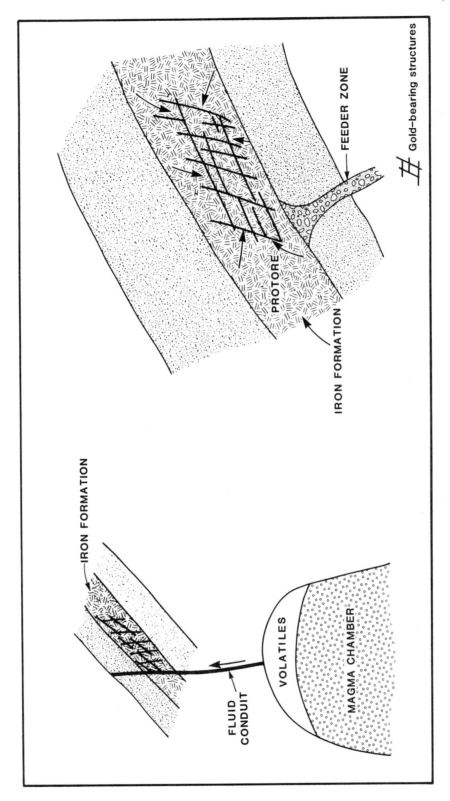

Figure 2. Possible models for gold mineralization in iron formation: **a.** (left) epigenetic, **b.** (right) syngenetic.

Of those deposits for which a process of ore formation has been proposed, the syngenetic model, or metamorphic secretion theory, is most favoured. For example, Fripp (1976), after detailed mapping, suggested that several dozen gold deposits in iron formation in Zimbabwe had formed as a result of sea-floor volcanic exhalation. Hallager (1982) suggested that iron-formation-hosted gold near Jardine, Montana, was deposited by submarine hot springs. Ladeira (1980) similarly interpreted the gold-bearing sulphide bodies and the host iron formation in the Minas Gerais district of Brazil to be chemical precipitants on the sea floor, formed as a result of the mixing of the ascending reduced hot aqueous fluids and seawater. Rye and Rye (1974) considered that the gold and other constitutents of the Homestake deposit in South Dakota were indigeneous to the Homestake Formation, which has been interpreted to be a metamorphosed iron formation, and were of syngenetic, exhalative origin, based upon studies of light stable isotopes.

A small number of researchers in the field have raised a note of caution: Foster *et al.* (in preparation) stated that perhaps not all the deposits in Zimbabwe formed syngenetically but may have had epigenetic components in the mineralizing process(es). R. Shegelski (Newmont Exploration of Canada Limited, personal communication, 1982) has suggested that the gold deposits associated with iron formation near Pickle Lake are epigenetic.

GOLD DEPOSITS IN THE GERALDTON AREA

In late summer of 1982, a study commenced on the North Zone of the MacLeod-Cockshutt and Hard Rock Mines (Figure 3) 5 km south of Geraldton in the Wabigoon Belt.

The mines are located in Ashmore Township, which was mapped by Horwood and Pye (1951). Both mines

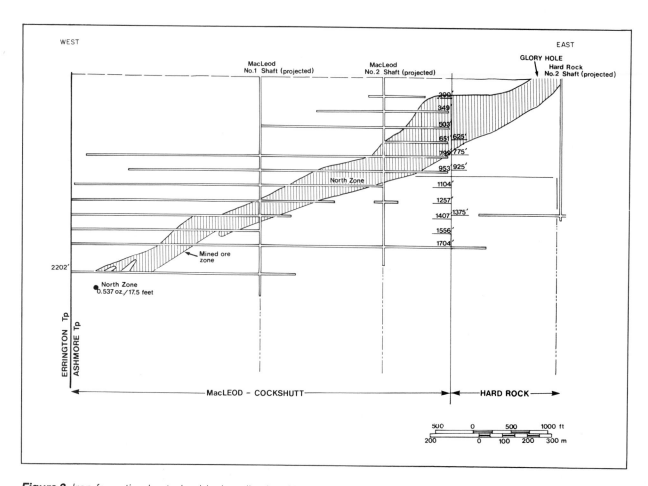

Figure 3. *Iron-formation-hosted gold mineralization, North Zone, MacLeod-Cockshutt and Hard Rock Mines, Geraldton.*

78

(and the Consolidated Mosher Mine immediately to the west) worked the 4.7 km strike extensions of several ore zones. All three mines are presently owned by Lakeshore Mines Limited. Both mines commenced production in 1938 and apart from brief closures in late 1945 and early 1946 due to labour shortages were in steady production until the Hard Rock closed in 1951 and the MacLeod-Cockshutt in 1970. The Hard Rock Mine produced 269,081 ounces of gold and the MacLeod-Cockshutt, 1,475,728 ounces.

It would be misleading, however, to infer that production from the Geraldton camp has solely been from iron-formation-hosted ore. For example, Figure 4 shows one of the largest orebodies in the camp, the F zone on the Consolidated Mosher property, directly to the east of the MacLeod-Cockshutt Mine. The F zone is located along a porphyry-wacke contact and is estimated to have contained (on both the Mosher and MacLeod-Cockshutt properties) in excess of 10,000,000 tons at approximately 0.15 ounces of gold per ton. In fact less than 30 percent of the production from Geraldton has been from iron-formation-hosted ore, the bulk of the ore being hosted by metamorphosed wacke or arkose alone, such as in the Little Long Lac Mine, or as in the F zone, along intrusive rock-wacke contacts.

GEOLOGICAL RELATIONSHIPS

Four prominent lithologies are exposed in the North Zone Glory Hole:
1. banded iron formation;
2. metasediments, principally siltstone and wacke;
3. porphyry sills;
4. felsite sills and dikes.

The banded iron formation has three sub-units: (a) 'lean' iron formation, consisting of discrete beds of magnetite (typically up to 1 cm thick) in wacke and siltstone; (b) magnetite iron formation, consisting of alternating beds (typically 1 cm) of magnetite (with minor hematite) and silicified mudstone or dark chert; and (c) magnetite-jasper iron formation, consisting of alternating 1 cm beds of magnetite and jasperitic quartz or red chert. All sub-units locally contain varying amounts of iron-bearing carbonate.

The wacke and siltstone show gradational contacts with both the northern and southern flanks of the iron formation. All rock types are locally carbonate-rich and structurally disturbed. The brown-weathering secondary carbonate is present within all rock types, suggesting that the carbonate was introduced following intrusion of felsite and porphyry. Carbonate is absent to rare in iron formation containing no mineralization, 300 m along strike to the west. Considerable shear strain has been localized by the finer grained material, disrupting and rafting apart wacke layers to form an intraformational breccia. The breccia contains apparently randomly distributed but uniformly aligned clasts of wacke (typically 5 cm in long dimension, but up to 50 cm) in siltstone. Commonly, all primary bedding has been destroyed; the principal planar feature is a shear-related cleavage.

The porphyry sills rarely exceed 1 m in thickness and are feldspar-phyric with minor quartz phenocrysts. The feldspar is altered by chlorite and sericite. Although concordant on a large scale, in detail the porphyry sills cut sedimentary contacts and may have chilled margins up to 10 cm in thickness. The felsite intrusions (very fine grained), which are similar to the matrix of the porphyry sills, may be concordant or may cut sedimentary contacts at angles up to approximately 40 degrees.

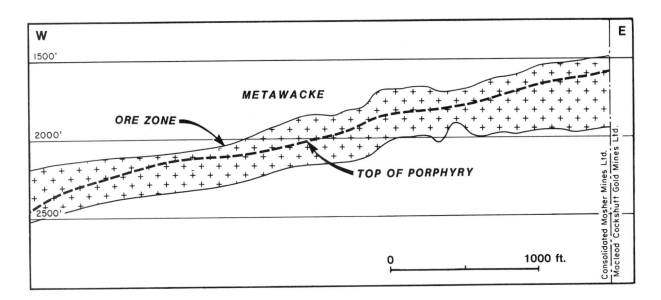

Figure 4. Gold mineralization along contact of porphyry and metawacke, F-Zone, Consolidated Mosher Mine, Geraldton.

STRUCTURAL RELATIONSHIPS OF THE ROCK TYPES

The North Ore Zone is located in a Z-shaped drag fold on the north limb of the approximately west-northwesterly striking Hard Rock Synclinorium (section no. 1, Ferguson 1967). The synclinorium is located in the footwall of a major break, the Bankfield-Tombill Fault, which dips steeply to the south. Indicated motion of the fault is a combination of reverse faulting and dextral strike-slip. Both the major and minor fold structures and the contained ore zone plunge to the west at 28 to 29 degrees (Horwood and Pye 1951). A regional cleavage formed in response to the isoclinal F1 folding that gave rise to structures such as the Hard Rock Synclinorium in the Geraldton area.

On an outcrop scale, extensive asymmetric minor folds are present within the iron formation and porphyry, and have amplitudes up to 5 m. The mean strike of the minor fold axis is 83 degrees (one standard deviation is 7 degrees, Table 1). The minor folds deform and hence are later than the original cleavage developed in response to F1 folds. The minor folds are suggested therefore to be manifestations of F2 folding.

Shear zones, up to 1 m in thickness and sub-parallel to fold axes, are commonly located along the porphyry-iron formation and metasediment-iron formation contacts but may also cut across stratigraphy in the iron formation. Where evidence is unequivocal, dextral shear is indicated. On a hand specimen scale, extremely delicate kink structures are present in the iron formation in response to the drag folding event. Feldspar phenocrysts in the porphyry sills are stretched parallel to the fold axes and the direction of the shear. This foliation has been unaffected by the outcrop-scale folds, suggesting that final penetrative shear post-dates minor folding. Felsite sills behave structurally in a manner similar to the porphyry sills. Where felsites cut stratigraphy they have been deformed, in places, into complex asymmetric folds and have been characteristically truncated by shear zones in the iron formation.

Table 1. *Summary of structural data for North Zone, Hard Rock Mine.*

VEINS	MEAN STRIKE	1σ	N
(a) Type 1 in Iron Formation	91°	18°	59
(b) Type 1 in Porphyry: Major Set	96°	10°	76
(c) Type 2 in Porphyry: Minor Set	64°	13°	41
MINOR FOLD AXES	83°	7°	23

MINERALIZATION AND VEIN STRUCTURE

Metal and metal-sulphide mineralization are found in three structural types:

1. relatively undeformed quartz-carbonate-sulphide veins striking approximately west-northwest, often localized by shear faults;

2. deformed quartz-carbonate-sulphide veins, striking obliquely (east-northeast) to the major structures; and

3. quartz-carbonate-sulphide replacement ore, after iron formation, spatially associated with type (1) veins.

The mineralogy of all three types is essentially identical. Gangue minerals include quartz, ankerite, calcite, tourmaline, and scheelite. In addition to pyrite, sulphides include, in decreasing order of abundance, arsenopyrite, pyrrhotite, sphalerite, chalcopyrite, and galena.

The structural attitude of type (1) veins is shown in Figure 5 and summarized in Table 1. Veins in porphyry and iron formation have been subdivided. Note that both sets strike in approximately the same direction, while veins in the porphyries tend to dip less steeply. Type (1) veins in porphyry units locally comprise a sheeted vein system of subparallel veins striking west-northwest and dipping steeply to the north; vein frequency reaches 4 or 5 per metre. Typical vein widths vary between 2 and 10 cm. Where the sills are thickened in fold hinges, widths of about 7 or 8 m are attained. The sheeted veins commonly terminate at contacts with enclosing iron formation.

The three mineralization types are relatively undeformed (indicating that vein formation postdates folding), except in the wacke unit where a pervasive east-trending cleavage has developed, destroying original bedding. Late motion along cleavage planes has deformed type (1) and (2) veins (type 3 mineralization is absent in wacke). Type (1) veins have been subjected to small scale Z-folding and boudinage parallel to the cleavage direction; type (2) veins, which strike obliquely to the other veins, are often highly folded due to approximately west-northwest shear, producing shortenings of considerable magnitude, e.g. a type (2) vein may be attenuated by up to 80 percent of its original strike length by tight isoclinal folding in response to shear within the host rock. These structures have led Horwood and Pye (1951) to refer to type (2) veins as "wiggly" veins. The same veins are seen throughout the McLeod-Cockshutt and Hard Rock Mines. For this reason structural attitudes of type (2) veins have not been recorded in wacke.

Figure 6 summarizes in cartoon form, the inter-relationships of deformed lithologies and mineralized structures described in this and the preceding section. Relative ages of the three vein types are equivocal. Type (2) veins are seen to both cut and be cut by mineral selvages in type (1) veins. In places, both have been displaced by type (3) shear related structures, although this motion may only reflect late stage adjustment along shear planes.

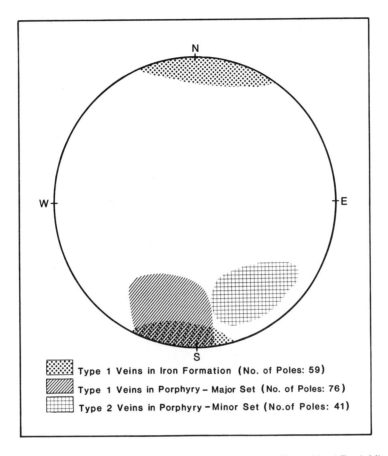

Figure 5. *Equal-area stereographic projection of π-poles to veins, North Zone, Hard Rock Mine, Geraldton.*

SUMMARY

Gold-bearing mineralization associated with iron formation on the MacLeod-Cockshutt and Hard Rock properties is found in quartz veins and as replacement of the ferruginous metasediments. The ore-bearing structures are controlled by lithological contacts and localized strain deformation. There is a spatial association between mineralization, a Z-shaped fold, and secondary iron carbonate. Further structural analysis of vein, shear, cleavage and fold axis attitudes will permit determination of the total deformation sequence and in particular the timing of the formation of structures hosting ore. Geochemical evidence is being sought to define the origin of the components of mineralization, including gangue minerals, sulphides and metallic gold. Present data suggest that gold mineralization is confined to veins and sulphide replacement zones that post date or are coeval with asymmetric F2 folding. The origin of the F2 event is not apparent, although the effects of motion on the spatially associated Bankfield-Tombill Fault and related parallel structures cannot be eliminated. Elsewhere in the Wabigoon Subprovince, vein-hosted gold mineralization is genetically associated with structures produced by large transcurrent fault systems that possibly act as fluid conduits (Poulsen, this volume). The lithostratigraphic zone in the Geraldton area containing the bulk of the mineralization (see Figure 1) has also undergone considerable deformation in response to motion along a series of extensive faults that strike subparallel to stratigraphy. For example, in the Geraldton area, the Bankfield-Tombill Fault is seen in outcrop on the Bankfield Consolidated Mine property in the west of Errington Township (Pye 1951). The fault zone, up to 70 m in width, has been a locus for considerable quartz flooding and in places carries small quantities of gold, e.g. the McLellan property (Figure 7) contains approximately 85,000 tons of pyritiferous gold mineralization with a mean grade of 0.17 ounces of gold per ton over 100 feet in two separate bodies, based upon data available to Pye (1951, p.117). The Little Long Lac Mine is spatially associated with a major fault (see Figure 1).

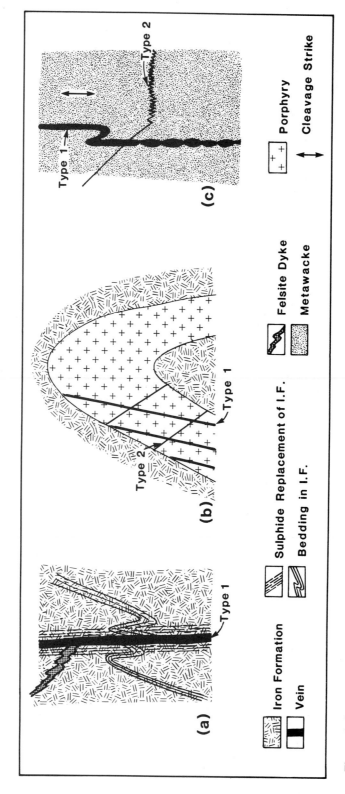

Figure 6. Structure and mineralization, North Zone, Hard Rock Mine, Geraldton: (a) Iron Formation; (b) Porphyry Sill; (c) Metawacke.

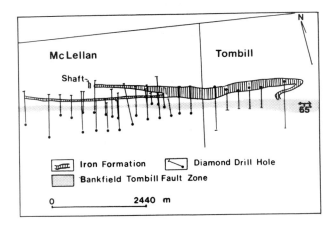

Figure 7. *Gold mineralization within the Bankfield-Tombill Fault Zone, McLellan property, Geraldton.*

Pye (1951, p. 43) reported that all lithologies in the mine contain auriferous quartz stringers and that gold content of the stringers increases towards the fault. Current research in the Geraldton area indicates that iron-formation-hosted gold mineralization is epigenetic. The role of faults, such as the Bankfield-Tombill Fault and the Little Long Lac Fault, as possible ore fluid conduits is also under investigation.

REFERENCES

Barrett, R.W., and Johnston, A.W.
1948: Central Patricia Mine; p.368-372 in Structural Geology of Canadian Ore Deposits, Canadian Institute of Mining and Metallurgy, Volume 1.

Basu, N.K.
1982: Mesoscopic Structures in the Nyanzian Rocks and Its Relation to the Localization of Gold-Sulphide Veins; Abstract, in Gold '82, Zimbabwe, p.26.

Boyle, R.W.
1979: The Geochemistry of Gold and Its Deposits; Geological Survey of Canada Bulletin 280, 584p.

Corking, W.P.
1948: Pickle Crow Mine; p.273-376 in Structural Geology of Canadian Ore Deposits, Canadian Institute of Mining and Metallurgy, Volume 1.

Ferguson, S.A.
1967: MacLeod Mosher Gold Mines Limited, Cross Sections of Parts of Errington and Ashmore Townships, District of Thunder Bay; Ontario Department of Mines and Northern Affairs, Preliminary Geological Map, P.437.

Finucane, K.J.
1953: The M.U.S.O. Gold Mine, Bougardie; p.231-235 in Geology of Australian Ore Deposits, 5th Empire Mining and Metallurgy Congress, Australia and New Zealand, Volume 1.

Foster, R.P., Mann, A.G., Stowe, C.W., and Wilson, J.F.
in preparation: Archaean Gold Mineralization in Zimbabwe; Manuscript Submitted for Publication in "Ore Deposits of Southern Africa", Geological Society of South Africa, 88p.

Fripp, R.E.P.
1976: Stratabound Gold Deposits in Archean Banded Iron Formations, Rhodesia; Economic Geology, Volume 71, p.58-75.

Hallager, W.S.
1982: Geology of a Stratiform Archean Gold Deposit Near Jardine, Montana; Abstract in Gold '82, Zimbabwe, p.29.

Harris, J.S.
1961: Summary of the Geology of Tanganyika, Pt. 4, Economic Geology; Tanganyika Geological Survey, Memoir 1, 143p.

Horwood, H.C., and Pye, E.G.
1951: Geology of Ashmore Township; Ontario Department of Mines, Annual Report, Volume 60, Part 5, 105p.

Karvinen, W.O.
1981: Geology and Evolution of Gold Deposits, Timmins Area; p. 29-41 in Genesis of Archean, Volcanic-Hosted Gold Deposits, Symposium held at University of Waterloo, March 7, 1980, Ontario Geological Survey, Miscellaneous Paper 97, 175p.

Ladiera, E.A.
1980: Metallogenesis of Gold at the Morro Velho Mine and in the Nova Lima District, Quadrilatero Ferrifero, Minas Gerais, Brazil; Unpublished Ph.D. Thesis, University of Western Ontario, 272p.

Lambert, I.B., Phillips, G.N., and Groves, D.I.
1982: Sulphur Isotope Compositions of Archean Gold Deposits and Their Significance; Abstract, in Gold '82, Zimbabwe, p.22.

Matheson, A.F.
1956: The St. John Del Ray Mining Company Limited, Minas Gerais, Brazil; Canadian Institute of Mining and Metallurgy Bulletin, Volume 525, p.400-413.

McConnell, G.W.
1964: Notes on Similarities Between Some Canadian Gold Deposits and the Homestake Deposits of South Dakota; Economic Geology, Volume 59, p.719-720.

McLaughlin, D.M.
1931: The Homestake Enterprise - Ore Genesis and Structure; Engineering Mining Journal, Volume 132, No.7, p.324-329.

Narayanaswami, S., Ziandlin, M., and Ramachandra, A.V.
1960: Structural Control and Localization of Gold Bearing Lodes, Kolar Goldfield, India; Economic Geology, Volume 55, p.1439-1459.

Pye, E.G.
1951: Geology of Errington Township, Little Long Lac Area; Ontario Department of Mines, Annual Report, Volume 60, Part 6, 140p.

Rye, D.M. and Rye, R.O.
1974: Homestake Gold Mine, South Dakota: I Stable Isotope Studies; Economic Geology, Volume 69, p.293-317.

Saager, R., and Meyer, M.
1982: Gold Distribution in Archean Sedimentary, Volcanic and Acidic Plutonic Rocks from Southern Africa: Clues to the Source of Gold in Archean Gold Quartz Veins?; Abstract in Gold '82, Zimbabwe, p.23.

Gold Mineralization in the Beardmore-Geraldton Area

John K. Mason and Craig D. McConnell

Resource Geologists, Ontario Ministry of Natural Resources, Thunder Bay

THIS PROJECT WAS FUNDED EQUALLY BY THE GOVERNMENTS OF CANADA AND ONTARIO UNDER THE NORTHERN ONTARIO RURAL DEVELOPMENT AGREEMENT (NORDA).

ABSTRACT

Production from the Beardmore-Geraldton "greenstone" belt has exceeded 4.1 million ounces of gold and ¼ million ounces of silver. Gold deposits have been subdivided on the basis of stratigraphic location and host rock lithology:

1. southern mafic volcanic dominated;
2. southern sedimentary dominated; and
3. northern felsic volcanic dominated.

As over 94 percent of the production in the area is from the southern sedimentary belt, deposits within this group are further subdivided into those hosted by (a) metasediments, (b) intrusive rocks, both mafic and felsic, (c) metasediment-minor intrusive contacts, (d) mafic metavolcanics. The bulk of the known mineralization appears to be structurally controlled. No auriferous primary sulphide ironstone-hosted gold deposits have been identified to date.

INTRODUCTION

The Beardmore-Geraldton area is located east of Lake Nipigon, 160-275 km northeast of Thunder Bay, Ontario. The area has a history of gold production in the past 50 years from 18 mines; the larger of these include the MacLeod-Cockshutt, Leitch, Little Long Lac, Consolidated Mosher, Hard Rock, Magnet Consolidated and Northern Empire Mines. The Beardmore-Geraldton gold camp rates among the top five gold camps in the Canadian Shield with production of 4.12 million ounces of gold and ¼ million ounces of silver (Table 1).

HISTORY

Gold was originally discovered in the Beardmore area at the Beardmore (Northern Empire) Mine in 1925, now the Pan-Empire Joint Venture. The Orphan (Dik-Dik) Mine and Northern Empire Mine commenced production in 1934. At Geraldton, gold was first reported by Tony Oklend during World War I on Kenogamisis Lake but not until 1931, did T. Johnson and R. Wells discover gold on

Magnet Lake and W. Smith discovered a gold-bearing quartz vein on what became the Hard Rock Mine. In 1932, Johnson and Oklend discovered gold in quartz veins on Barton Bay. In 1934, this property was to become the Little Long Lac Gold Mine, the first gold producer in the Geraldton area.

The Pan-Empire Joint Venture, Consolidated Louanna Gold Mine, Crooked Green Creek Mine and the Greenoaks Prospect recorded gold production in 1982. Exploration within the Beardmore-Geraldton area in the early 1980s has been primarily for gold.

GENERAL GEOLOGY AND STRUCTURE

The Beardmore-Geraldton area lies at the southern boundary of the east-trending, isoclinally folded Early Precambrian metavolcanic-metasedimentary sequence of the Wabigoon Subprovince (Figures 1, 2). It is not clear whether lithological contacts in the Beardmore-Geraldton area represent depositional, facies changes or are tectonically transposed, as has been demonstrated elsewhere in the Wabigoon Subprovince (Poulsen 1981). All lithofacies reconstructions (Figure 2) are therefore, necessarily, conjectural. A unit of fine-grained metasediments (wacke, siltstone, argillite) bounded on the south by a laterally extensive mafic to intermediate metavolcanic unit (basalt, mafic tuff) appears to be disconformably overlain by a coarser grained metasedimentary unit in the Geraldton area (conglomerate, wacke, argillite, ironstone) (Mackasey 1970c; Pye 1951). Both metasedimentary units thin to the north, and are overlain by a mafic to intermediate unit in an area north of Beardmore (Mackasey 1975). Further north and up-section, in the Paint Lake area, felsic pyroclastic rocks interfinger with coarse clastic metasediments (Mackasey 1970c). The metavolcanic-metasedimentary sequence has been intruded by felsic batholiths, stocks and sills, and lenticular mafic intrusions. Late Precambrian diabase dikes and sills intrude all rock types. The regional metamorphic grade is greenschist facies.

Folding has been about east-trending axes at Beardmore and Geraldton. Ironstone, spatially related to many gold deposits in the Beardmore-Geraldton area, can be

Table 1. Gold and silver production in the Beardmore-Geraldton area.

Mine	Years	Ounces Gold	Ounces Silver	Tons of Ore Milled	Average Gold Grade-ozs./T	Average Silver Grade-ozs./T
Bankfield	1937-42 1944-47	66,417	7,590	231,009	0.29	0.03
Beardmore (Northern Empire)	1934-41 1949	149,493	19,803	425,866	0.35	0.05
Brengold	1941, 1949	134	-	46	2.91	-
Hard Rock	1938-51	269,081	9,009	1,458,375	0.18	0.01
Jellicoe	1939-41	4,238	145	10,620	0.40	0.01
Leitch	1936, 1968	847,690	31,802	920,745	0.92	0.03
Little Long Lac	1934-54 1956	605,499	52,750	1,780,516	0.34	0.03
MacLeod-Cockshutt	1938, 1968	1,475,728	101,388	10,337,229	0.14	0.09
Magnet Consolidated	1938-43 1946-52	152,089	16,879	359,912	0.42	0.05
Maloney Sturgeon Prospect	1937	73	16	1	73.00	16.00
Maylac	1946-47	792	46	1,518	0.52	0.03
Mosher Long Lac	1962-66	330,265	34,604	2,710,657	0.12	0.01
Orphan (Dikdik)	1934-35	2,460	1,558	3,525	0.70	0.44
Sand River	1937-42	50,065	3,628	157,870	0.32	0.02
Sturgeon River	1936-42	73,438	15,922	145,123	0.51	0.11
Talmora-Long Lac	1942, 1948	1,417	36	6,634	0.21	0.01
Tashota-Nipigon	1935, 1938	12,356	14,527	51,200	0.24	0.28
Theresa	1935-38 1941-43, 1945 1950-53, 1955	4,785	202	26,120	0.18	0.01
Tombill	1938-42, 1955	69,120	8,595	190,622	0.36	0.05

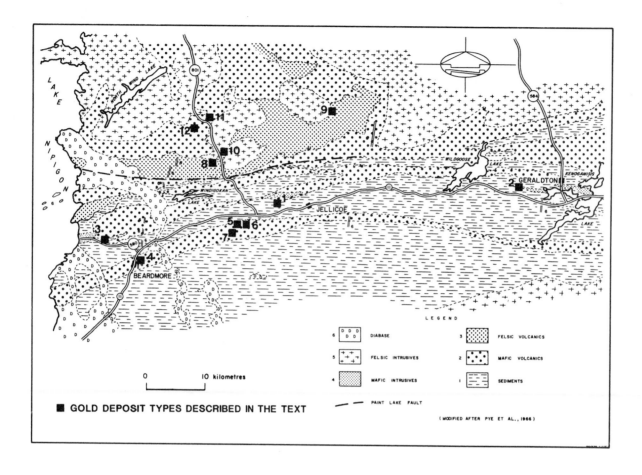

Figure 1. Geology of the Beardmore-Geraldton area.

1. Solomon's Pillars Prospect (Oremond Prospect)
2. Magnet Consolidated Gold Mine
3. Leitch Gold Mine
4. Pan-Empire Joint Venture (Northern Empire Mine)
5. Maki Property
6. Pichette Occurrence
7. Craskie-Vega Occurrence
8. Quebec Sturgeon River Mines Limited
9. Orphan (Dik-Dik) Gold Mine
10. Mitto Prospect (Kengate Resources Limited)
11. Greenoaks Prospect
12. Crooked Green Creek Mine (Northern Concentrators Limited)

traced in outcrop and from aeromagnetic data, from southwest of Lake Nipigon to east of Geraldton. The iron-stone is situated at the north boundary of the most southerly metasedimentary unit (coarse metasedimentary unit). Regional or east-trending faults, i.e. Paint Lake Fault, can mark changes in lithology or structural style. "South of the fault, interbedded metasediments and mafic metavolcanic flows are folded along east-trending axes, but to the north, intermediate to felsic pyroclastic rocks predominate and fold axes trend north and north-west" (Mackasey 1970c, p.74).

The Bankfield-Tombill Fault (strike 100-110°, dip 60-70° south) and the east-trending Little Long Lac Fault appear to have been important in determining the location of most of the Geraldton area gold deposits. Motion on the faults is complex. Underground mapping by Pye (1951, p. 42-45) indicates that thrusting to the north is dominant with minor rotational and translational adjustments. Faulting commenced prior to mineralization but subsequent to felsic intrusion and continued after mineralization.

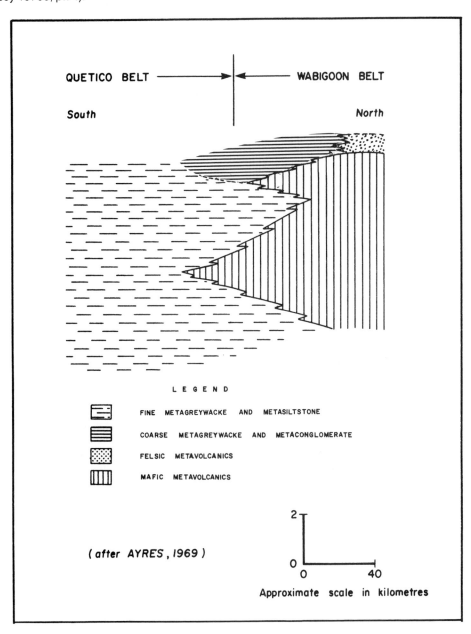

Figure 2. *Diagrammatic cross-section showing possible relationship between Quetico and Wabigoon belts at Beard-more-Geraldton.*

GOLD DEPOSITS

Gold mineralization in the Beardmore-Geraldton area has been subdivided into 'belts' on the basis of stratigraphic location and host rock lithology.

1. Southern mafic volcanic dominated belt

e.g. Northern Empire Mine, Maki property and the Pichette and Craskie-Vega occurrences.

2. Southern sedimentary dominated belt

a. Metasedimentary host rock

e.g. (i) quartz veins and stringers in fracture zones in clastic metasediments — the Little Long Lac, Magnet Consolidated, Leitch, Sand River, Hard Rock, Jellicoe and Talmora Mines; (ii) in quartz vein stringers, and replacement sulphide zones in ironstone (chemical metasediment with limited clastic component) — MacLeod-Cockshutt and Hard Rock Mines and Solomon's Pillars prospect.

b. Felsic and mafic intrusive host rocks

e.g. (i) quartz veins and stringers in folded albite porphyry — MacLeod-Cockshutt, Hard Rock Mines; (ii) mineralized zones of shearing and albite porphyry — Consolidated Mosher Mine; (iii) quartz veins in shear zones in hornblende diorite or gabbro — Talmora Mine.

c. Localized at the contact between minor felsic intrusive rocks and metasediments

e.g. (i) shear zone between metawacke and albite porphyry — Bankfield, MacLeod-Cockshutt, Hard Rock and Consolidated Mosher Mines; (ii) sulphide zones in fracture or shear zones in the contact between ironstone and quartz diorite — MacLeod-Cockshutt Mine.

d. Mafic volcanic host rock

e.g. veins cutting mafic metavolcanics — Wods Mac Property.

3. Northern felsic volcanic dominated belt

e.g. Orphan (Dik-Dik) Mine and the Mitto and Greenoaks Prospects.

The three belts are shown in Figure 1. It should be noted that the subdivisions do not necessarily reflect different origins for gold mineralization. Of the gold produced in the Beardmore-Geraldton camp, 94 percent is from the southern sedimentary dominated belt. The deposits in this subdivison have been further subdivided for clarity into four types based upon host rock lithology (modified from Pye 1951; Horwood and Pye 1951). It should be noted that individual deposits may exhibit one or more type of mineralization.

Polyphase deformation is a major factor in determining the location of economic gold deposits. Examples of several deposit types (Figure 1) are presented including detailed geology and structure.

1. SOUTHERN MAFIC VOLCANIC DOMINATED BELT

The most southerly unit in the Wabigoon Subprovince is an intermediate to mafic metavolcanic sequence, forming an east-trending lenticular belt up to 3 km wide. It consists of massive, pillowed and amygdaloidal flows (chlorite schist), mafic tuffs, felsic to mafic intrusions, and/or coarse flow rocks. Pillow structures suggest younging directions to the north (Peach 1951); the south metasedimentary unit overlies the south metavolcanic unit, although the contact may be structural.

Auriferous chemical metasediments (ironstone) and post-ironstone quartz (± carbonate) veins are hosted by the volcanic rocks. The ironstone units are east-trending, steeply dipping regional features, present as discontinuous lenses (Peach 1951, p.3). They are magnetite-silicate-carbonate ironstone consisting of alternating ferruginous recrystallized chert, magnetite, iron carbonate, and iron amphibole (grunerite) members. Fracturing has allowed vein quartz to be injected with arsenopyrite, pyrrhotite, magnetite, chalcopyrite and gold. Quartz (± carbonate) veining has intruded the mafic metavolcanics disconformably to foliation. Gold is associated with chalcopyrite, galena and pyrrhotite.

Pan-Empire Joint Venture (Northern Empire Mine). The Pan-Empire Joint Venture (former Northern Empire Mine) is located 1.5 km northeast of Beardmore, Ontario. The Northern Empire Mine produced 149,493 ounces of gold and 19,803 ounces of silver from 1934 to 1941 at an average grade of 0.35 ounces gold per ton and 0.05 ounces silver per ton. Since March 1982, Pan-Continental Mining (Canada) Limited, has been processing dump material through a 200-ton per day gold mill on the site.

The Pan-Empire Mine is the only gold producer in the southern metavolcanic belt. The property lies in a narrow east-trending unit of Early Precambrian mafic to intermediate metavolcanics. The composite quartz-carbonate production vein, the Power Vein, intrudes the metavolcanics and is almost concordant to foliation. Within the composite vein, gold was mined from a relatively persistent boudinaged single vein. The vein strikes 72° and dips 80°S. Average width of the vein is 0.6 m within a 1.2-3.0 m wide shear zone. The metavolcanics are fine-grained pillowed basalt and massive medium-grained basalt, with some mafic tuffaceous rocks. Granitic dikes and steeply dipping diorite sills, up to 4.5 m wide, intrude the metavolcanics (Benedict and Titcombe 1948).

A relatively flat-lying diabase sheet, the youngest rock type present, intrudes all lithologies. The diabase sheet cross-cuts bedding at 75° and locally dips shallowly to the west. The sheet cuts off the vein, with no lateral displacement, at a depth of 198 m and is 172 m thick. The metavolcanics have been contact metamorphosed for 15 m on either side of the sheet. Chloritic alteration has been noted up to 61 m above and below the diabase.

The gold-bearing "Power Vein", which includes en echelon veins, is mineralized with gold, arsenopyrite, pyrrhotite, pyrite and minor chalcopyrite, galena, and tourmaline. The metavolcanic wallrocks marginal to the vein contains sulphides with no gold values. Relatively pervasive carbonate alteration occurs subparallel to the vein.

Maki Property. The Maki gold property is situated in Vincent Township, 17 km east-northeast of Beardmore. The property is underlain by mafic metavolcanics, represented by chloritic schists, massive basalt and mafic tuffs. Quartz-carbonate veins, containing chalcopyrite, galena, pyrrhotite and gold intrude the metavolcanics. The quartz is milky white, massive to saccharoidal and locally contains epidote, tourmaline, chlorite and hematite. Veins are up to 5.0 m wide.

Gold also occurs in a magnetite-silicate-carbonate ironstone of regional extent, striking 95°. Mineralization within the ironstone consists of discordant quartz-carbonate veinlets, arsenopyrite, pyrrhotite and grunerite. The silica member of the ironstone is recrystallized chert rhythmically layered with magnetite and lesser amounts of iron carbonate. Gold is associated with sulphides within the ironstone and the post-ironstone quartz-carbonate veins.

Values in the quartz-carbonate veins range up to 0.81 ounces gold per ton and 5.89 ounces silver per ton for selected grab samples. Selected grab samples from the ironstone assayed up to 0.40 ounces gold per ton. (Assays by the Geoscience Laboratories, Ontario Geological Survey, Toronto).

Pichette Occurrence. The Pichette occurrence is located in the north-central portion of Vincent Township, 20 km east-northeast of Beardmore. Mineralization consists of pyrite and gold in easterly trending sheared and carbonatized mafic metavolcanics (Figure 3). The mafic metavolcanics are made up of pillowed and massive basalts. The shear zone may be up to 90 m wide. First documentation of the large shear zone was by P.A. Peach (1951). Highly contorted, saccharoidal, quartz veins contain pyrite, minor chalcopyrite and gold within the same shear zone. The veins are narrow and mainly discordant.

Grab samples assayed up to 0.22 ounces of gold per ton in the shear zone and up to 0.16 ounces of gold per ton across 71.0 cm from one vein. (Assays by the Geoscience Laboratories, Ontario Geological Survey, Toronto).

Craskie-Vega Occurrence. The Craskie-Vega occurrence is located in the Townships of Vincent and McComber, 15 km east-northeast of Beardmore. The property is underlain by mafic metavolcanics with foliation striking 75-90° and dipping vertically, except in the southwest portion of the claims where the rock dips steeply to the south. Chloritic schists predominate to the south and massive mafic flows and diorite outcrop to the north. Narrow ironstone units occur throughout the entire sequence. They consist of alternating ferruginous recrystallized chert, iron carbonate and magnetite members. Medium-grained, quartz porphyry sills, 0.5-1.5 m wide, intrude many of the ironstones and appear related to a small stock 183 m by 3.5 m which straddles the eastern boundary of the property.

Gold mineralization is associated with two persistent subparallel chert-magnetite-carbonate ironstones. The ironstones are 37.5 m apart and strike 75° and dip 85° north. Surface prospecting and diamond drilling have traced the ironstones 600 m along strike and they average 2.0-2.5 m wide. Arsenopyrite occurs in quantities up to 2 percent. Up to 20 percent magnetite has been noted in the ironstones.

Pyrite occurs as euhedral crystals and as disseminations within siliceous chlorite schist. Pyrrhotite is fairly ubiquitous on the property as disseminated "blebs" and stringers mainly in diorite and quartz stringers.

Tombill Gold Mines (Annual Report, 1952), owner of the Craskie Gold Mines Limited, have outlined four gold-bearing zones within the ironstone on the property. Dimensions and grade are as follows:

430 feet by 6.6 feet at 0.17 ounces gold per ton;
350 feet by 6.9 feet at 0.19 ounces gold per ton;
150 feet by 6.8 feet at 0.18 ounces gold per ton; and
200 feet by 4.8 feet at 0.25 ounces gold per ton.

2. SOUTHERN SEDIMENTARY DOMINATED BELT

Eleven gold mines of this deposit type recorded production. Gold mineralization is associated with the east-trending coarse metasedimentary unit which includes conglomerate, wacke, argillite and magnetite-hematite-chert (± jasper) ironstone. Gold mineralization occurs in shear zones, quartz veins and breccia zones hosted in clastic metasediments, felsic intrusions, gabbro intrusions, sulphides within oxide ironstone, and minor mafic metavolcanics.

Isoclinal folding and tight drag folding, in the Beardmore area (Leitch and Sand River Mines) and the Geraldton area, specifically observable in the ironstone, appear to be necessary controls for ore structure developments. Drag folds and ore-bearing structures throughout the belt plunge westward at 35-40°. In the Geraldton camp, most gold production has come from the rocks adjacent to, and north of, the Bankfield-Tombill Fault, situated on the south limb of the Little Long Lac Syncline, south of the Little Long Lac Fault – Portage Shear Zone. The Bankfield-Tombill Fault may be the resultant structure after "the limit of drag folding had been reached" (Horwood and Pye 1951, p.29). The 70 km distance between the Beardmore and Geraldton camps is marked predominantly by a linear ironstone, within the metasedimentary package, and which has supported no gold production.

Due to the deformation and failure characteristics of the albite porphyry, wacke and ironstone units, brittle fracturing has provided a plumbing system for hydrothermal auriferous fluids (Horwood and Pye 1951, p.48; Macdonald, this volume). In the Geraldton camp, there is a trend of diminishing total gold production from mines west of the MacLeod-Cockshutt Mine.

The granitic stock in Croll Township, east of Geraldton, is thought to underlie much of Ashmore Township,

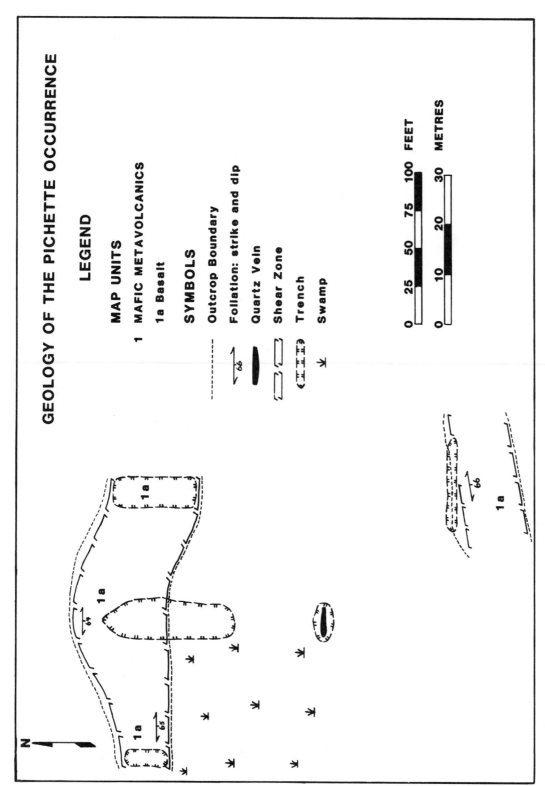

Figure 3. *Geology of the Pichette occurrence.*

and it has been postulated to be the magmatic source of heat and a possible source of the auriferous hydrothermal fluids (Horwood and Pye 1951, p.47).

In the Geraldton and Beardmore areas, alteration adjacent to veining consists of narrow zones of sericitized, carbonatized and silicified metasediments and albite porphyry. At Geraldton, gold occurs in two of five generations of quartz (Horwood and Pye 1951). Pyrite, arsenopyrite, galena, scheelite, pyrrhotite, calcite and tourmaline occur with gold in the Beardmore–Geraldton area. Galena appears to be an indicator mineral for gold and gold tellurides. At Beardmore, specifically the Leitch Mine, pyrite was considered the indicator mineral for gold.

METASEDIMENTARY HOST ROCK

Clastic Metasediments

Magnet Consolidated Mine. The Magnet Consolidated Gold Mine is situated in Errington Township, 8 km west-southwest of Geraldton. In the years 1938-1943 and 1946-1952, the mine produced 152,089 ounces of gold and 16,879 ounces of silver at a grade of 0.42 ounces gold per ton and 0.05 ounces silver per ton.

The property is underlain by conglomerate, wacke, argillite and ironstone intruded by diorite, diorite porphyry, albite porphyry and diabase (Pye 1951, p.101). The ironstone is typically composed of magnetite and hematite layers interbedded with argillite (chloritic mudstone) or greywacke. Bedding strikes 110° and dips 75-80° south. The unit is on the south limb of the Ellis Syncline (Pye 1951, p.103). Z-shaped folds plunging 30-45°W are overprinted on the fold. The Magnet Vein, the main production vein, and other auriferous quartz veins are parallel to the Bankfield-Tombill Fault Zone (105°). The fault zone is a silicified and carbonatized zone up to 30 m wide and traverses the property 345 m south of the shaft. The initial rupture along the fault zone occurred previous to the formation of the ore bodies, since at the Magnet Mine, the minor folds are cut by the ore-bearing structures (Pye 1951, p.44).

The Magnet Vein is a persistent composite vein with one main vein up to 0.3 m wide. Parallel quartz stringers give the composite vein a maximum width of 4.5 m. The near vertical Magnet Vein exhibits roll structures. The vein intersects the ironstone at 5-10°.

Carbonate, pyrite, arsenopyrite, chalcopyrite, sphalerite, galena and gold occur in the vein. Gold is present as blebs and fracture fillings in pyrite and arsenopyrite, as irregular grains within a grey quartz and as fracture fillings along contacts between quartz and the host rock (within the crack-seal vein texture). Later quartz and calcite veining contains gold along cleavage planes (Pye 1951). Wallrock alteration adjacent to veins typically exhibits sericitization, carbonatization and silicification within the wacke, and chloritization in the ironstone.

Leitch Mine. The Leitch Mine is located in Eva Township, 7 km northwest of Beardmore. Between 1936 and 1968, the Leitch Mine produced 847,291 ounces of gold and 37,775 ounces of silver. The average grade was 0.92 ounces gold per ton.

Metasediments which host the Leitch orebody are a portion of the east-trending fold belt, locally trending east-northeast. Metasediments are overturned to the north (Mackasey 1970 a, b). Interbedded wacke, sandstone, siltstone, argillite and minor conglomerate are present on the property. Ironstone is intercalated with the other lithologies and attains a maximum thickness of 25 m. The ironstone is a portion of the east-trending regional ironstone. Jasper, hematite and magnetite are interbedded with argillite. Margins of the ironstone unit are marked by thinner jasper-hematite beds associated with thick beds of ferruginous wacke and argillite. Some diorite dikes are present. A 180 m thick diabase sheet (post-ore) intrudes the metasediments. This is the same sheet that cuts the Pan-Empire Joint Venture and Sand River Mine auriferous veins.

The mine workings follow westerly and southwesterly plunging fissure-type quartz veins in fractured metasediments. This structure is mimicked at outcrop scale by west-plunging drag folds. Production veins range up to 0.6 m in width and are crack-seal type veins; portions of the altered wallrock now represented by sericite and chlorite seams have been incorporated within the generating vein. Gold, pyrite, scheelite and minor amounts of tetrahedrite, sphalerite, and bournonite occur in the veins. Veins exhibit sericitization and carbonatization.

Ironstone

The major gold producer from ironstone, on the Hard Rock and MacLeod-Cockshutt properties, is described elsewhere (Macdonald, this volume).

Solomon's Pillars Prospect (Oremond Prospect). The Solomon's Pillars gold property straddles the Walters-Leduc Township line, 7.0 km west-southwest of Jellicoe, Ontario. Magnetite-chert (± jasper) ironstone is interbedded with wacke, siltstone and slate. The ferruginous chemical metasediments are portions of the regional east-trending ironstone near the north boundary of the most southerly metasedimentary unit of the Wabigoon Subprovince (Figure 4). Siltstone and slate display cleavage subparallel to bedding. Refractive cleavage was noted in some wackes (Mackasey 1976, p.32).

Gold on the Solomon's Pillars property is associated with quartz-pyrite-arsenopyrite veins that replace and cut magnetite-chert (± jasper) ironstone. Initial exploration and development by Oremond Gold Mines Limited (1936) identified auriferous sulphide lenses. A 100 m shaft, with levels at 45 and 85 m, was developed, but no gold was mined from the property. Assays of selected grab samples ranged up to 0.92 ounces of gold per ton. Pyrite, the most prevalent sulphide, is medium to coarse-grained and typically equant. Gold fills fractures and occurs as irregular blebs with the pyrite and arsenopyrite.

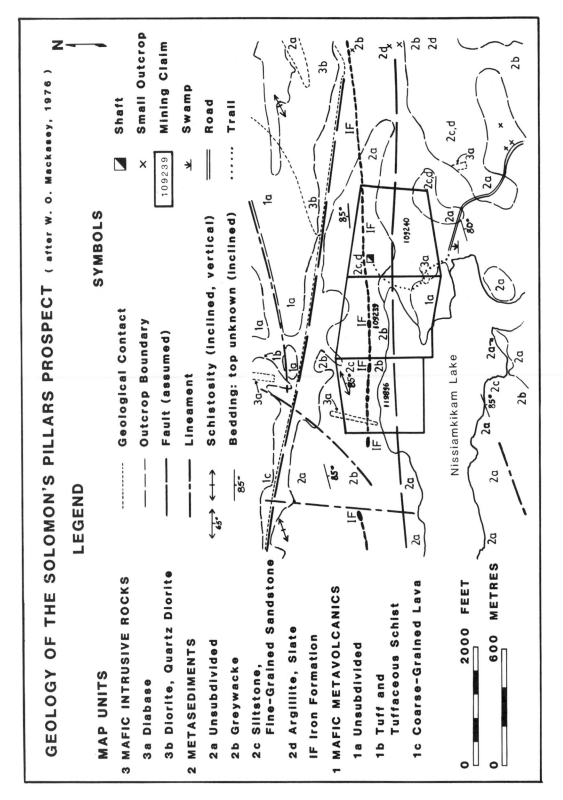

Figure 4. *Geology of the Solomon's Pillars prospect.*

Other Host Rocks

Zones of mineralization hosted by minor porphyry intrusive rocks and their contacts with enclosing metasediments have been described by Pye (1951) and Horwood and Pye (1951).The final deposit type within the southern metasedimentary dominated belt to be described, is that hosted by mafic metavolcanics, such as the Wods Mac property between Eldee Lake and Highway 11, in the southeast quadrant of Ashmore Township (Horwood and Pye 1951). Quartz vein mineralization cuts mafic metavolcanics in the vicinity of albite porphyry intrusions. Vein mineralization contains pyrite, pyrrhotite, chalcopyrite, native copper and coarse visible gold. There is no production recorded from this deposit type.

3. NORTHERN FELSIC VOLCANIC DOMINATED BELT

The stock-related, metavolcanic-hosted gold deposit type is typically high grade, low tonnage. The deposits are auriferous quartz (± carbonate) veins and fracture-filled sulphide associated gold deposits in mafic to felsic metavolcanics, often marginal to felsic intrusive stocks. Veins are sigmoidal or lenticular products of ductile failure. Three principal stocks occur in the west-central portion of the belt: the Coyle Lake Stock, the Elmhirst Lake Stock, and the Kaby Lake Stock. Most of the veins that were mined are hosted in the metavolcanics around the intrusions and include the Quebec Sturgeon River Mine and the Orphan (Dik-Dik) Mine. Few gold occurrences have been located within the stocks. Wolfe (1971), noted no anomalous gold concentrations within the Coyle Lake Stock where a detailed geochemical survey was undertaken (Mackasey and Wallace 1978, p.50).

The Kaby Lake Stock, south of Onaman Lake, is a "massive pink to light grey granodiorite to trondhjemite with local occurrences of granite and quartz monzonite" (Mackasey and Wallace 1978, p.38). The east and south contact of the stock are well defined. This is clearly illustrated at the Orphan Gold Mine. To the west, where exposure is poor at the contact, inclusions of porphyritic metavolcanics were noted. Biotite, hornblende, quartz (up to 40 percent) and microcline or perthite (up to 25 percent) make up the stock (Mackasey and Wallace 1978, p.39).

The Coyle Lake Stock is mainly composed of "massive, medium-grained, bright pink or dark grey", granodiorite (Mackasey and Wallace 1978, p.36). Porphyritic granodiorite occurs within the stock. The contact zone is represented by an irregular narrow porphyritic diorite which intrudes silicified metavolcanics. The Elmhirst Lake Stock is a granodiorite-quartz diorite complex. The contact zone, although variable in composition and up to 0.8 km wide, is typically porphyritic diorite.

The Coyle Lake and Elmhirst Lake Stocks are composed of up to 15 percent hornblende and 15 percent biotite. Quartz (up to 35 percent) is present "as highly strained anhedral grains and granular aggregates inter-

stitial to feldspar" (Mackasey and Wallace 1978, p.38-39). Up to 3 percent microcline is present in a texture similar to quartz and in a myrmekitic texture with quartz.

Alteration occurs with all three stocks. Chlorite, epidote and muscovite are alteration products of hornblende. Plagioclase feldspar has been sericitized and saussuritized. Quartz and potassium feldspar are unaltered (Mackasey and Wallace 1978).

Quebec Sturgeon River Mine. The Quebec Sturgeon River Gold Mine, located in Irwin Township 18 km northwest of Jellicoe, produced 72,438 ounces of gold and 15,922 ounces of silver at a grade of 0.51 ounces gold per ton and 0.11 ounces silver per ton between 1936 and 1942. The mine is the largest producer of the "Stock Related" type.

The geology has been described by Mackasey (1975, p.62):

The area is underlain by intermediate to felsic metavolcanics that have been intruded by granodiorite, mafic dikes, quartz veins and diabase dikes. The metavolcanics are medium grey to dark green and vary from massive to foliated. Fine-grained quartz-eye porphyry is present in the vicinity of the mine and may be the result of silicification related to the intrusion of the granodiorite stock to the east. Tuffaceous volcanic rocks and minor tuff breccia outcrop along the north half of the western boundary of the property.

The Elmhirst Lake Stock (granodiorite and quartz diorite) outcrops to the north and the Coyle Lake Stock (granodiorite) outcrops to the east of the Quebec Sturgeon River Mine. Massive equigranular granodiorite was intersected in the underground development. A large lamprophyre dike cuts the granodiorite northeast of the shaft (Bruce 1936, p.28). The youngest rock type present is a flat lying post-quartz vein diabase dike intersected at 343.0 m vertically in the mine. At least two sets of fissure type quartz veins have been mapped. One set strikes northeast and the second set, which includes the No. 3 vein, strikes just east of north.

The ore in No. 3 vein is associated with a dominant northeasterly trending shear zone which attains widths of up to 15.0 m. The No. 3 vein has an average strike of 13°, a dip of 70°W and an average width of 22 cm. Vein minerals include calcite, pyrite, chalcopyrite, sphalerite, gold and gold tellurides. Gold is found only in the vein, in pyrite and between pyrite and gangue minerals, but predominantly in fractures and associated with alteration products, chlorite, and sericite near the walls (Mackasey 1975).

Orphan (Dik-Dik) Mine. The Orphan (Dik-Dik) Gold Mine is situated 15 km north-east of Jellicoe. The property is underlain by porphyritic basalt, crystal and laminated tuff of felsic to intermediate composition which have been intruded by grey coarsegrained granodiorite (Mackasey and Wallace 1978) (Figure 5). The porphyritic

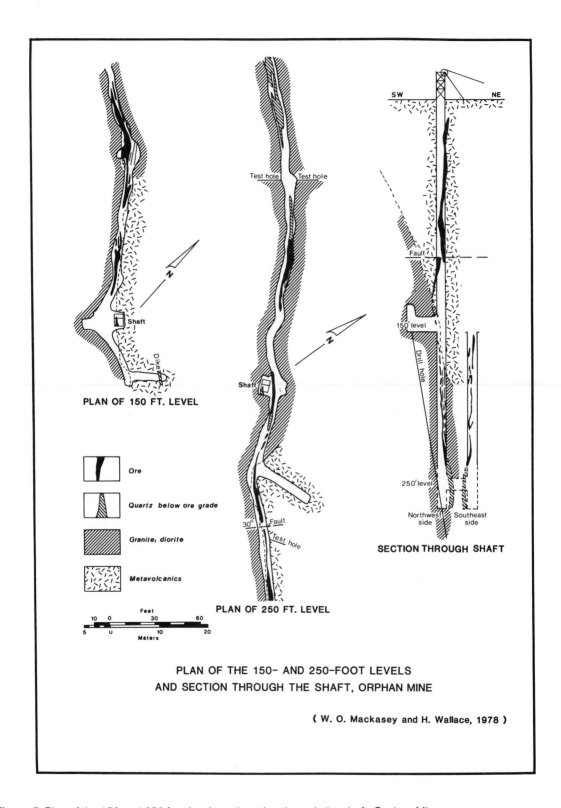

PLAN OF 150 FT. LEVEL

Ore

Quartz below ore grade

Granite, diorite

Metavolcanics

PLAN OF 250 FT. LEVEL

SECTION THROUGH SHAFT

PLAN OF THE 150- AND 250-FOOT LEVELS
AND SECTION THROUGH THE SHAFT, ORPHAN MINE

(W. O. Mackasey and H. Wallace, 1978)

Figure 5. *Plan of the 150 and 250 foot levels and section through the shaft, Orphan Mine.*

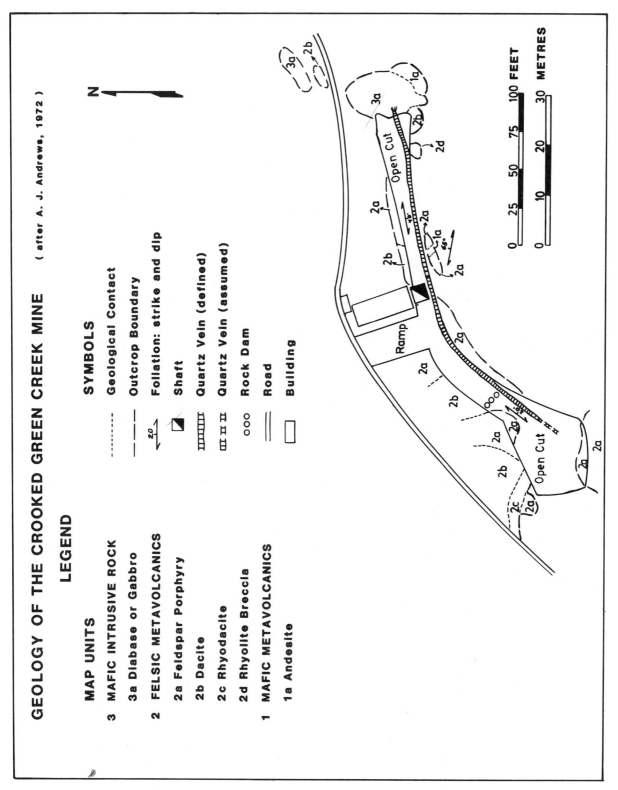

GEOLOGY OF THE CROOKED GREEN CREEK MINE (after A. J. Andrews, 1972)

LEGEND

MAP UNITS

3 MAFIC INTRUSIVE ROCK
3a Diabase or Gabbro

2 FELSIC METAVOLCANICS
2a Feldspar Porphyry
2b Dacite
2c Rhyodacite
2d Rhyolite Breccia

1 MAFIC METAVOLCANICS
1a Andesite

SYMBOLS

Geological Contact
Outcrop Boundary
Foliation: strike and dip
Shaft
Quartz Vein (defined)
Quartz Vein (assumed)
Rock Dam
Road
Building

N

Figure 6. Geology of the Crooked Green Creek Mine.

basalt is fine grained, massive, dark green, and contains abundant anhedral plagioclase phenocrysts. The grano-diorite represents the eastern portion of the Kaby Lake Stock. Commonly epidote, chlorite, and sericite are now present in the granodiorite.

The contact between the felsic intrusive rock and metavolcanics is sharp. Quartz lenses in a shear zone cross the contact between the mafic metavolcanics and the granodiorite and form the orebody at the Dik-Dik Mine. The zone strikes 140° and dips vertically. The quartz lenses attain a maximum width of 2.7 m. The quartz is mineralized with pyrite, chalcopyrite, pyrrhotite, sphalerite, galena, gold and minor arsenopyrite and tetrahedrite.

Alteration in the granodiorite is intense. Plagioclase has been altered to sericite and has also been saussuritized. Hornblende has been altered to chlorite, epidote and muscovite. Chlorite and epidote alteration is noted in the metavolcanics.

The Dik-Dik was the initial gold and silver producer of the BeardmoreGeraldton area. From 1934 to 1935, 2,460 ounces of gold and 1,558 ounces of silver were produced. Average grade mined was 0.70 ounces gold per ton.

Mitto Prospect. A. Mitto holds a gold-silver property in the northwest corner of Elmhirst Township, 22 km northeast of Beardmore. Four en echelon veins striking 30-35° are hosted in andesite and dacite marginal to granodiorite and quartz diorite of the Elmhirst Lake Stock possibly within a ductile shear zone. The veins contain breccia zones of angular and sub-angular quartz clasts cemented in a sulphide matrix of fine-grained pyrite, sphalerite, galena and chalcopyrite. Coarser-grained euhedral pyrite and sphalerite occur in the breccia zones. Rare aggregates of pyrite and amphiboles are present. Sericitization and chloritization have locally altered the metavolcanics. Values up to 0.52 ounces of gold per ton were obtained from selected grab samples. (Assays by Geoscience Laboratories, Ontario Geological Survey, Toronto).

Greenoaks Prospect. The Greenoaks Prospect is situated in the Townships of Elmhirst and Pifher, 27 km northeast of Beardmore. To the east of the property, andesite, dacite and feldspar porphyry have been intruded by granodiorite-quartz diorite of the Elmhirst Lake Stock. A series of quartz veins and fracture fillings strike 110° and discontinuously follow the contact between the porphyry and the flow rocks. Veins and fractures contain chalcopyrite, pyrrhotite and gold. Metavolcanics are silicified.

Crooked Green Creek Mine. The Crooked Green Creek Mine is located in Pifher Township 24.0 km northeast of Beardmore, Ontario. The property is underlain by andesite, dacite and related feldspar porphyry, and minor rhyodacite and rhyolite breccia (Figure 6). Three quartz

veins are mineralized with gold. The No. 1 vein, which has seen the bulk of exploration and development, is a sigmoidal, northwest-trending quartz vein cutting a feldspar porphyry hosted in dacite and minor rhyodacite. The vein dips 45° to 70° south and is 0.3 to 0.6 m wide near the abandoned shaft; to the west the vein dips 70° and narrows to 5 cm. The mineralization consists of chalcopyrite, pyrrhotite and gold in massive, blue-black quartz.

The metavolcanics are silicified. Nine hundred and fifteen tons of ore at 0.265 ounces of gold per ton have been mined at surface, and milled, from the No. 1 vein (1980-1982) (George Cross News Letter, No. 238, 1982, p.2).

CONCLUSIONS

Over 94 percent of the gold produced from the Beardmore-Geraldton camp is spatially related to folded ironstone and occurs in veins, breccia and shear zones hosted in metasediments, intrusive rocks and metavolcanics. Replacement sulphides in ironstone also contain gold. No auriferous primary sulphide ironstone-hosted gold deposits have been identified in the Beardmore-Geraldton camp. Gold appears to be structurally controlled although chemical "trapping" of gold by ironstone (presently being studied) may be an additional variable in the mineralizing process. Detailed analytical studies of gold in ironstone at and away from known gold mineralization will determine if anomalous gold values occur in the ironstone and therefore if syngenetic gold existed prior to reconcentration.

REFERENCES

Andrews, A.J.
1972: Unpublished Report on Geology of the Crooked Green Creek Gold Mine; Resident Geologist's Files, Ontario Ministry of Natural Resources, Thunder Bay, Ontario, 34p.

Ayres, L.D.
1969: Early Precambrian Stratigraphy of Part of Lake Superior Provincial Park, Ontario, Canada, and its Implications for the Origin of the Superior Province; Unpublished Ph.D. Thesis, Princeton University, 399p.

Benedict, P.C., and Titcombe, J.A.
1948: The Northern Empire Mine; p. 389-399 in Structural Geology of Canadian Ore Deposits, Canadian Institute of Mining and Metallurgy.

Bruce, E.L.
1936: The Eastern Part of the Sturgeon River Area; Ontario Department of Mines Volume 45, Pt. 2, p.1-59. Accompanied by Map 45A, scale 1 inch to 1 mile.

Davies, R.
1974: Unpublished Report on the Geology, Geophysics and Geochemistry of the Nezah Property; Resident Geologist's Files, Ontario Ministry of Natural Resources, Thunder Bay, Ontario, 7p.

Ferguson, J.A., Groen, H.A., and Haynes, R.
1971: Gold Deposits of Ontario; Ontario Divison of Mines, Mineral Resources Circular 13, 315p.

Horwood, H.C. and Pye, E.G.
1951: Geology of Ashmore Township, Little Long Lac Area; Ontario Department of Mines, Annual Report, Volume 60, Pt. 5, 105p. Accompanied by Map 1951-2, scale 1 inch to 1000 feet.

Karvinen, W.O.
1982: Geology and Evolution of Gold Deposits, Timmins Area, Ontario; p.101-112 in Geology of Canadian Gold Deposits, Canadian Institute of Mining and Metallurgy, Special Volume 24, 286p.

Laird, H.C.
1936: The Western Part of the Sturgeon River Area; Ontario Department of Mines, Annual Report, Volume 45, Pt. 2, p.60-117. Accompanied by Map 45A, scale 1 inch to 1 mile.

Macdonald, A.J.
1982: The MacLeod-Cockshutt and Hard Rock Mines, Geraldton: Examples of an Iron-Formation Related Gold Deposit; p.18-191 in Summary of Field Work, 1982, by the Ontario Geological Survey, edited by John Wood, Owen L. White, R.B. Barlow, and A.C. Colvine, Ontario Geological Survey, Miscellaneous Paper 106, 235p.

Mackasey, W.O.
1970a: Eva Township, District of Thunder Bay; Ontario Department of Mines, Preliminary Geological Map, P.601, scale 1 inch to 1/4 mile.
1970b: Summers Township, District of Thunder Bay; Ontario Department of Mines, Preliminary Geological Map, P.602, scale 1 inch to 1/4 mile.
1970c: The Beardmore-Geraldton Belt; 16th Annual Institute on Lake Superior Geology, p.69-84.
1975: Geology of Dorothea, Sandra and Irwin Townships, District of Thunder Bay; Ontario Division of Mines, Geoscience Report 122, 83p. Accompanied by Map 2294, scale 1 inch to 1/4 mile.
1976: The Geology of Walters and Leduc Townships, District of Thunder Bay; Ontario Division of Mines, Geoscience Report 149, 60p. Accompanied by Map 2356, scale 1:31,680 (1 inch to 1/2 mile).

Mackasey, W.O., Blackburn, C.E. and Trowell, N.F.
1974: A Regional Approach to the Wabigoon-Quetico Belts and its Bearing on Exploration in Northwestern Ontario; Ontario Division of Mines, Miscellaneous Paper 58, 29p.

Mackasey, W.O. and Wallace, H.
1978: Geology of Elmhirst and Rickaby Townships, Ontario Geological Survey, Geoscience Report 168, 120p. Accompanied by Map 2373, scale 1:31,680 (1 inch to 1/2 mile).

ODM-GSC
1974: Jellicoe Project, Thunder Bay District; Ontario Division of Mines – Geological Survey of Canada, Geophysical Series (High Resolution Aeromagnetic), Map 30 002G, scale 1:125 000.

Patterson, G.C, Mason, J.K. and Schnieders, B.R.
In Press: Annual Report of Regional and Resident Geologists, 1982, Ontario Geological Survey Miscellaneous Paper.

Peach, P.A.
1951: Preliminary Report on the Geology of the Blackwater-Beardmore Area; Ontario Department of Mines, Preliminary Report 1951-7, 6p.

Poulsen, K.H.
1981: The Geological Setting of Mineralization in the Mine-Centre-Fort Frances Area, District of Rainy River; p.190-195 in Summary of Field Work, 1981, by the Ontario Geological Survey, edited by J. Wood, O. L. White, R.B. Barlow, and A.C. Colvine, Ontario Geological Survey, Miscellaneous Paper 100, 255p.

Pye, E.G.
1951: Geology of Errington Township, Little Long Lac Area; Ontario Department of Mines, Annual Report, Volume 60, Pt. 6, 140p. Accompanied by Map 1951-7, scale 1 inch to 1,000 feet.

Pye, E.G., Harris, F.R., Fenwick, K.G., and Baillie, J.
1965: Tashota-Geraldton Sheet, Thunder Bay and Cochrane Districts; Ontario Department of Mines, Geological Compilation Series Map 2102, scale 1 inch to 4 miles (1:253,440).

Wolfe, W.J.
1971: Geochemical Surveys in Northern Ontario; p.107-109 in Summary of Field Work, 1971, by the Geological Branch, edited by E.G. Pye, Ontario Department of Mines, Miscellaneous Paper 49, 109p.

The Carshaw and Malga Iron-Formation-Hosted Gold Deposits of the Timmins Area

J.A. Fyon, J.H. Crocket, and H.P. Schwarcz

Geology Department, McMaster University, Hamilton

ABSTRACT

The Carshaw and Malga iron formations, southeast of Timmins, are hosted by Archean calc-alkaline basalts of the Deloro Group. Steeply dipping ultramafic and felsic dikes cut the mafic flows and the iron formation. Quartz veins cut all rock types including the iron formations. Where cut by quartz veins, the iron formations are replaced by auriferous pyrite. No pyrite replacement accompanies the veins which cut igneous rock. The veins consist dominantly of quartz with traces of dolomite and chlorite. All rocks except a late diabase dike have been metamorphosed to greenschist facies. The igneous rocks and the banded iron formation units have been subjected to the following sequence of alteration events: (1) silica dumping in vesicles and amygdules; (2) intense dolomitization; and (3) quartz veining. These events may have been consanguineous and may represent the progressive evolution of a mega-hydrothermal system.

The gold mineralization of the banded iron formations is epigenetic and resulted from sulphurization of iron-rich mesobands. Sulphurization is most intense adjacent to late quartz veins where magnetite-rich mesobands are preferentially replaced by pyrite, containing gold. Sulphurization is much less intense away from the quartz veins where pyrite and pyrrhotite occur as disseminated grains and as replacements after magnetite and ferroan dolomite. Laminated pyrite of possible syngenetic origin, hosted in chlorite mesobands, contains 1-2 ppm gold, but contributes little to the overall gold tenor due to its volumetrically small proportion.

INTRODUCTION

In Archean volcano-sedimentary sequences throughout the world, there is an association between gold and banded iron formations. Much debate surrounds the nature of this association and both syngenetic and epigenetic models are evoked. Evidence favouring a syngenetic origin for iron-formation-hosted gold deposits is given by Fripp (1976) for several Zimbabwe deposits and by Fleischer and Routhier (1973) for the Passagem de Mariana deposit in Brazil. Page (1979) suggested that the Cullaton Lake gold deposit in the Northwest Territories is also a syngenetic, iron-formation-hosted gold deposit. Less certainty is associated with the origin of the iron-formation-hosted gold deposits of the Hard Rock Mine in the Long Lac area of Ontario (Matheson and Douglas 1948) although the iron-formation-hosted gold deposit of the adjacent MacLeod-Cockshutt Mine (Macdonald 1982) appears to be epigenetic. Similarly, the Opapimiskan Lake gold discovery appears to be a structurally controlled gold deposit in an iron formation (Andrews *et al.* 1981). Three occurrences of iron-formation-hosted gold mineralization are known to exist in the metavolcanic-metasedimentary belts of Archean age in northeastern Ontario. The Carshaw deposit, held by Gowganda Resources Limited, and the Malga deposit (Ferguson *et al.* 1971, p.89) are located southeast of Timmins in the Abitibi Belt whereas the New Golden Rose Mine (Gordon *et al.* 1979, p.48) is located 40 kilometres northeast of Sudbury in the Temagami "greenstone" belt.

The exploration philosophy with which iron-formation-hosted gold deposits are sought is dependent in part on the genetic models ascribed to. Hence it is of fundamental importance to understand the nature of this gold mineralization. To this end, the surface geology of the Carshaw and Malga iron formations in the Timmins area (Figure 1) was mapped and the underground exposure of the gold mineralization on the Carshaw property was examined in detail. The Carshaw deposit is reported to contain approximately 167,000 tons at 6 g/ton Au (0.205 ounces per ton) between surface and 200 feet (Willars 1982), whereas the Malga deposit contains approximately 80,000 tons grading 10.7 g/ton (0.34 ounces per ton, Malga Porcupine Gold Mines Limited 1944). While these are not large tonnages relative to the Porcupine Camp proper, the properties have only been explored to shallow depths.

GEOLOGY

The iron formations exposed on the Carshaw and Malga properties are hosted by calc-alkaline basalts of Formation II, Deloro Group (Pyke 1981) and lie south of the inferred anticlinal axis of the Shaw Dome (Pyke 1981, Fig. 1) These basaltic rocks are slightly older than 2725 ± 2 my, the age of felsic volcanic rocks which mark the top of Formation III of the Deloro Group (Nunes and Pyke 1980).

Local stratigraphy trends 000° to 035° and dips 30° to 70° easterly (Figure 2). Ultramafic and felsic dikes cut the mafic flows and the iron formation. A late diabase dike trends 110° across the Carshaw property. All dikes appear to dip vertically or steeply. No folding is evident in the volcanic stratigraphy.

The classification of typical rock types on a cation plot is illustrated in Figure 3. The felsic dikes are dacitic and calc-alkaline in composition, whereas the ultramafic dikes are komatiitic. The basaltic flows have compositions which are scattered through the calc-alkaline and magnesian tholeiitic fields. This scatter is attributed to rock alteration.

ROCK ALTERATION

The volcanic rocks and iron formations have been subjected to the following sequence of alteration events, listed chronologically: (1) filling of primary porosity by silica (quartz) and possibly calcite; (2) intense dolomitization; and (3) quartz veining.

SILICA PRECIPITATION IN PRIMARY POROSITY

Some vesicles and amygdules in the basalt flows have been filled by granular quartz, texturally similar to the iron formation chert (Figure 4a). In a given outcrop area, approximately 25 percent of the vesicles have been filled by silica. This quartz has been recrystallized to yield a polygonized quartz array with grain size increasing from 0.01 mm at the vesicle wall to 0.1 mm at the vesicle core (Figure 4a). Rarely primary colloform textures are preserved (Figure 4b). The average diameter of the silica-filled voids is less than 1 cm, except within 10 m of the iron formation footwall, where circular silica balls have diameters exceeding 5 cm (Figure 4c).

Some vesicles are filled by both polygonized quartz and granular calcite (Figure 4d). Although the temporal relationships between the quartz and quartz-calcite balls are ambiguous, there is a tendency for quartz-calcite vesicle fillings to occur only on the outer fringes of intense dolomitic alteration zones, whereas the pure quartz vesicle fillings are found in both carbonate-free and dolomitized lithologies. This relationship suggests that the intense dolomitization has been superimposed upon those domains bearing silica-filled vesicles and that the quartz-calcite fillings may be consanguineous with the intense dolomitization.

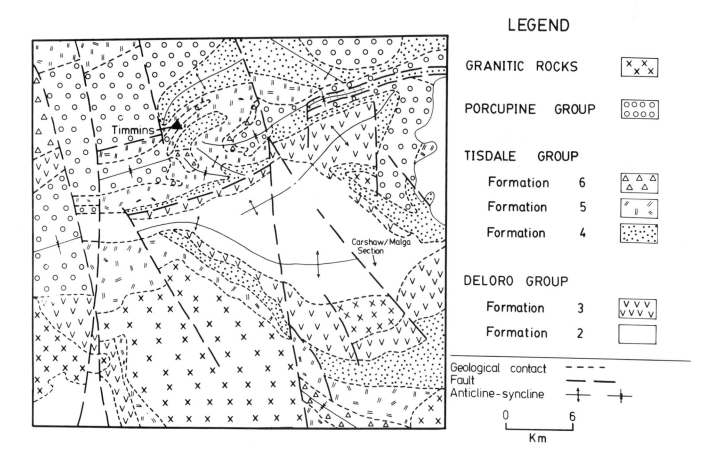

Figure 1. *Location of the Carshaw and Malga iron formation properties in the Deloro Group.*

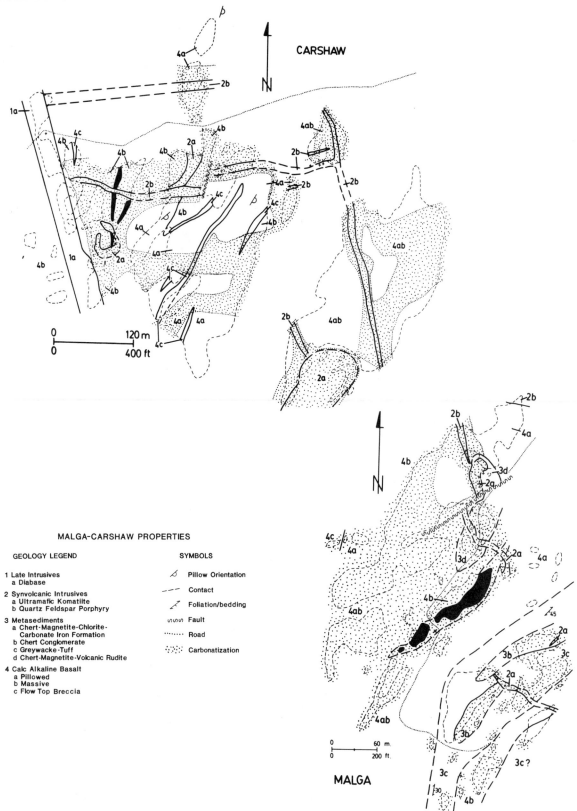

MALGA-CARSHAW PROPERTIES

GEOLOGY LEGEND

1 Late Intrusives
  a Diabase

2 Synvolcanic Intrusives
  a Ultramafic Komatiite
  b Quartz Feldspar Porphyry

3 Metasediments
  a Chert-Magnetite-Chlorite-
    Carbonate Iron Formation
  b Chert Conglomerate
  c Greywacke-Tuff
  d Chert-Magnetite-Volcanic Rudite

4 Calc Alkaline Basalt
  a Pillowed
  b Massive
  c Flow Top Breccia

SYMBOLS

  Pillow Orientation
- - - Contact
  Foliation/bedding
  Fault
······· Road
  Carbonatization

Figure 2. *Surface geological plan of the Carshaw (top left) and Malga (lower right) iron formation properties.*

INTENSE CARBONATIZATION

Much of the volcanic rock has been intensely dolomitized (see Figure 2) . In general, this type of alteration consists of at least two notable assemblages. The most intensely altered basalts consist of dolomite, quartz, and sericite with traces of relict albite and chlorite. This dolomite zone grades abruptly into a calcite, quartz, albite, relict chlorite zone which in turn grades into the least altered rocks containing chlorite, tremolite, albite, epidote and quartz.

All exposed ultramafic dikes or sills have been carbonatized and consist of dolomite, quartz, white mica, traces of chlorite and may contain magnesite. Dolomitized felsic dikes seldom contain more than 10-15 modal percent secondary dolomite, accompanied by white mica, albite, and quartz.

Where developed in basaltic flows, the dolomite alteration may occur as irregular and discordant zones cutting across stratigraphy. A second alteration morphology exists as dolomitized zones which envelop the felsic dikes; however the entire strike length of the dike need not be enveloped by dolomitized basaltic rock. Where ultramafic dikes are carbonatized, the adjacent basaltic rock is often dolomite-free.

The presence of dolomitized basaltic rock adjacent to the felsic dikes, which are interpreted as synvolcanic feeder dikes (Pyke 1981), implies that this alteration habit possibly developed in response to local hydrothermal systems initiated by the intrusion of hot igneous material. This would imply that the dike-associated dolomitization developed relatively early in the evolution of the volcanic pile, in a subvolcanic environment. Alternatively, the fracture system which localized the intrusion of the dike might also have served as a conduit for later, exotic, CO_2-rich hydrothermal fluids. That the felsic dikes themselves are moderately carbonatized is consistent with both hypotheses and could have resulted either from collapse of the hydrothermal system onto the cooling dike or by sim-

ple interaction with late hydrothermal fluids utilizing the feeder conduit.

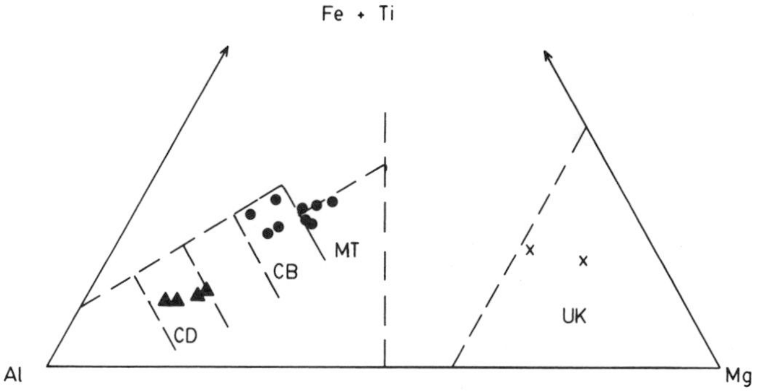

The iron formations also contain variable amounts of dolomite. Some of this carbonate is interpreted to be primary or diagenetic, while much may have been introduced during the dolomitization of the country rock. A more detailed description of the iron formation carbonate is given below.

QUARTZ VEINING

Quartz veins cut all rock types including the iron formations. Where cut by quartz veins, the iron formations are replaced by auriferous pyrite. No pyrite replacement accompanies the veins which cut igneous rock. Vein width is variable, but averages 2 cm, and vein length averages 1-2 m. The veins consist dominantly of quartz with traces of dolomite and chlorite. Textural relationships suggest that quartz is replaced by dolomite and chlorite, and that dolomite is replaced by chlorite. Chlorite also fills vugs in the quartz veins and coats quartz crystals, a textural relationship also suggesting a late paragenetic age for chlorite.

That the quartz veins cut silica-filled vesicles implies that the veining event postdated the early silica precipitation event. Similarly, that quartz veins cut all rock types, except the late diabase, whether intensely dolomitized or not, suggests that the veining postdates the intensive dolomitization event.

METAMORPHISM

All rocks except the late diabase have been metamorphosed to greenschist facies. Jolly (1978, 1980) contended that this greenschist metamorphism was imposed during the intrusion of late granitoid stocks, such as the Adams stock to the south (Pyke 1981). Fyon et al. (1981) argued that much of the carbonatization probably predated the greenschist event.

BANDED IRON FORMATION

The banded iron formation (BIF) units average 3 m in thickness and have a minimum strike length of 700 m (Ferguson et al. 1971, p. 87). They consist of chert, magnetite, chlorite and carbonate mesobands (1-5 cm thick) in the approximate volume proportion of 55:35:9:1. Most chert and magnetite mesobands also contain magnetite and chert microbands (0.1 to 1 mm) respectively which can comprise up to 50 percent by volume of the particular mesoband.

Figure 3. *Classification of samples from the Carshaw property using a cation plot (Jensen 1976). Symbols are as follows: X – ultramafic dike; ● – basalt flow, ▲ – quartz feldspar porphyry dike; UK – ultramafic komatiitic field; MT – magnesian tholeiitic basalt field; CB – calc-alkaline basalt field; CD – calc-alkaline dacite field.*

CHERT MESOBANDS

The chert mesobands consist dominantly of polygonized, recrystallized quartz grains averaging 0.04 mm in diameter. Where present, accessory magnetite occurs either as anhedral, uniformly disseminated grains ranging in diam-

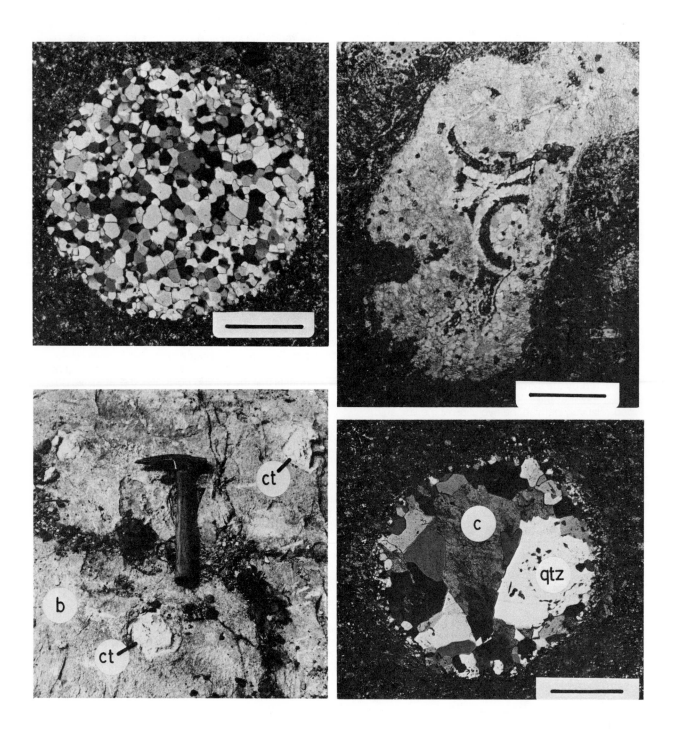

Figure 4. Photomicrographs of the vesicle-filling silica and calcite. a. Top left, polygonalized quartz filling a vesicle in basalt, bar scale is 2 mm long. b. Top right, relict colloform quartz within a vesicle in basalt, bar scale is 2 mm. c. Bottom left, large quartz-filled amygdules (ct) in carbonatized basalt (b) footwall, approximately 2 m below the Malga iron formation. d. Bottom right, vesicle in basalt filled by blocky quartz (qtz) and calcite (c), bar scale is 2 mm.

eter from 0.001 to 0.1 mm, or as microbands averaging 0.1 mm in width (Figure 5a). The microband magnetite occurs as recrystallized, subhedral to euhedral discrete grains and as "fused" grain arrays. Accessory dolomite occurs as anhedral, disseminated grains (0.15 mm), in some cases constituting up to 30 percent of an individual chert mesoband. Traces of chlorite, pyrite and pyrrhotite also occur as minor (< 5 percent) accessory phases.

MAGNETITE MESOBANDS

Magnetite mesobands consist dominantly of massive to disseminated magnetite lacking discrete grain boundaries (Figure 5b). Only on the outer edges of the mesoband does granular magnetite become apparent. Generally the magnetite mesobands contain variable , but substantial (up to 60 percent by volume), quantities of iron-rich dolomite localized in fractures or as discrete grains (Figure 5c). In dolomite-rich magnetite mesobands, a thin selvage of almost pure dolomite separates the magnetite and adjacent mesobands (Figure 5c).

In the Carshaw iron formation, graphite has been observed only once in a magnetite mesoband. This graphite occurs as very thin, wispy magnetite-graphite laminations and as elliptical forms.

Other phases in the magnetite mesobands include quartz, chlorite, pyrrhotite and pyrite. Pyrite generally occurs disseminated through the mesoband, but rarely as inclusions in recrystallized magnetite.

Some magnetite mesobands are fractured or broken and these voids have been filled by polygonized, very fine-grained (0.04 mm) quartz which is texturally identical to the annealed quartz of the adjacent chert mesoband. This variety of quartz filling is interpreted as remobilized chert which filled dessication cracks in the iron-rich mesobands.

The diagenetic history of Archean and Proterozoic iron formations is subject to uncertainty because of the degree of subsequent metamorphism. However, Dimroth (1979) suggested that the magnetite now observed in many Archean iron formations represents reduced hematite which in turn was derived by dehydration of a hydrated ferric oxide. Although the precise diagenetic pathway may remain uncertain, it is probable that the magnetite in the Carshaw and Malga iron formations is a secondary or diagenetic phase. Hematite was observed in only one loose block on surface, where a 10 cm by 4 cm hematite domain was enveloped by magnetite mesobands. It is unknown if the hematite was a precursor to the magnetite.

CHLORITE MESOBANDS

Chlorite mesobands apparently constitute only a minor proportion of the iron formation unit. They consist predominantly (> 90 percent) of clinochlore as determined by X-ray diffraction. This material occurs as a felted intergrowth and rarely shows evidence of bedding. Where present, microbands consist of carbonate, pyrite or chert.

Accessory carbonate occurs in two habits (Figure 5d). The first is microbanded carbonate averaging 0.1 mm in width. These laminations are concordant to the mesoband contacts. A second habit of carbonate is large (1-2 mm) euhedral to subhedral grains which are disseminated randomly through the chlorite mesobands. This habit of carbonate locally overgrows microband carbonate and, where present close to mesoband boundaries, the euhedral variety terminates abruptly against that boundary (Figure 5d). The habit of the large carbonate grains suggests that they are diagenetic or secondary, whereas the finer grained microband variety could be syngenetic. The microband carbonate is very rare relative to the abundance of the disseminated carbonate.

Not all chlorite mesobands contain pyrite microbands, but where present, this microbanding is striking (Figure 5e). No other mesoband variety contains such abundant and peristent pyrite microbanding. Within each microband, the pyrite has been recrystallized into euhedral cubes averaging 0.1-0.5 mm in diameter. A more complete description of this microband pyrite is included with the description of sulphide habits.

CARBONATE MESOBANDS

Carbonate mesobands consist dominantly of ferroan dolomite (> 80 percent) with accessory magnetite, chert and chlorite. Minor amounts of siderite have been detected. The carbonate mesobands show a variety of textures from granular massive bands to microbanded mesobands (Figure 5f). Magnetite is the most commonly microbanded phase.

Disseminated, euhedral to subhedral pyrite is present in some carbonate mesobands. Chlorite is also present in trace amounts either as disseminated grains or in pyrite pressure shadows. Accessory quartz (chert?) constitutes up to 10 percent of the carbonate mesobands and occurs as disseminated grains up to 0.25 mm across.

IRON FORMATION CARBONATE — PRIMARY OR SECONDARY?

Carbonate microbands in chlorite mesobands are interpreted to be syngenetic, or primary (Figure 5d). Conversely the occurrence of dolomite in cracks and fractures within magnetite mesobands, and the dolomite-rich selvage which separates these magnetite mesobands from adjacent mesobands (Figure 5c) suggest that this dolomite is secondary and possibly postdated the magnetite. Conflicting evidence is present in carbonate (ferroan dolomite) mesobands where the presence of magnetite microbands implies that both the ferroan dolomite and magnetite (or its precursor phase) exist in equilibrium, although both the carbonate and magnetite may be diagenetic phases (Figure 5f). No evidence was observed to suggest that the abundance or character of the carbonate mesobands varies along strike over a distance of 1 m. However, it is recognized that if such variations do

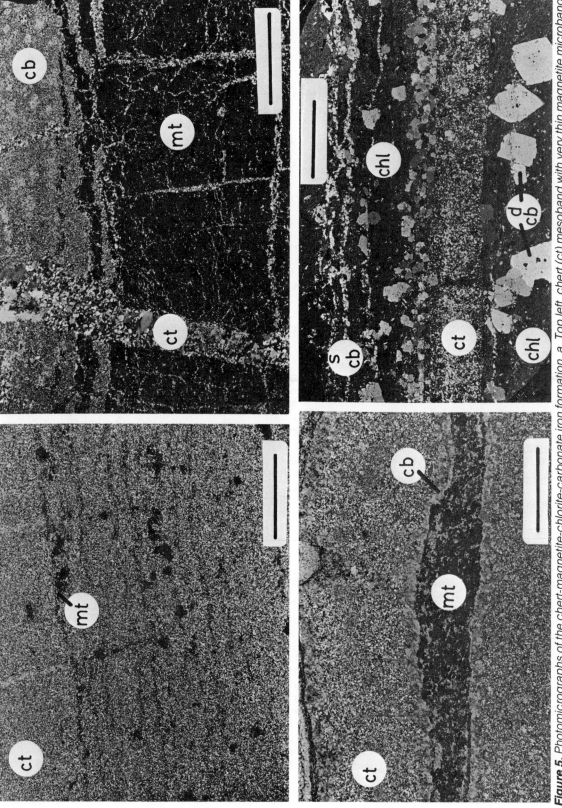

Figure 5. Photomicrographs of the chert-magnetite-chlorite-carbonate iron formation. a. Top left, chert (ct) mesoband with very thin magnetite microbands (mt) which have locally been recrystallized into coarser grains, bar scale is 2 mm. b. Top right, fractured magnetite (mt) mesoband cut by diagenetic silica veins (ct). A carbonate mesoband (cb) contains some magnetite microbands. Bar scale is 5 mm. c. Bottom left, magnetite mesoband (mt) containing abundant secondary (?) dolomite. Note concentration of dolomite (cb) selvage separating magnetite and chert (ct) mesobands. Bar scale is 5 mm. d. Bottom right, laminated or syngenetic carbonate (s-cb) and porphyroblastic (diagenetic?) carbonate (d-cb) in a chlorite mesoband (chl). A thin chert (ct) mesoband parallels the laminated carbonate. Bar scale is 2 mm.

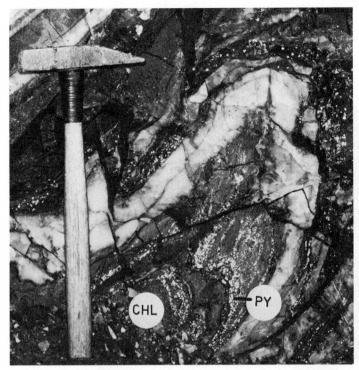

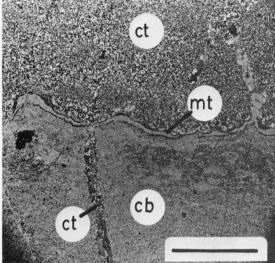

Figure 5. *continued. e. Left,stratiform (syngenetic?) pyrite (py) microbands in a chlorite mesoband (chl). f. Right, vague lamination in a carbonate mesoband (cb). Magnetite microbands (mt) lie at the contact between a chert (ct) mesoband and carbonate mesoband. A diagenetic silica vein (ct) cuts the carbonate mesoband, but appears to merge into the chert mesoband. Bar scale is 10 mm.*

occur, they probably do so over distances of tens or hundreds of metres, well beyond the available exposure (c.f. Macdonald 1982).

Hence, although much of the carbonate in the banded iron formation occurs as carbonate mesobands or accessory phases in chert and magnetite mesobands, the origin and timing of this carbonate is uncertain, as is its possible genetic relationship with the carbonatization event which affected the host igneous rocks. However, the light carbon isotope composition of the iron formation dolomite (–3 to –5.5‰ PDB) and its similarity to the ^{13}C composition of the most intensely dolomitized host igneous rocks (–3 to –4.3‰ PDB) suggest that the iron formation dolomite, excepting the rare microbanded variety in the chlorite mesobands, may have formed from the same CO_2-rich fluids which altered the host igneous rocks during that widespread intensive dolomitization event (Fyon *et al.* 1981).

SULPHIDE HABITS

QUARTZ-VEIN-ASSOCIATED REPLACEMENT PYRITE

Quartz veins which cut the iron formation are associated with pyrite replacement envelopes (Figure 6). This coarse grained pyrite (0.5 to 1 cm) preferentially replaces magnetite mesobands. The degree of magnetite replacement is virtually complete within 5 cm of the vein edge, but de-

gree of replacement decreases away from the vein contact such that secondary pyrite is sparse beyond 10 cm from the vein edge. Relict domains of magnetite mesoband material left unreplaced in the pyrite envelope are mineralogically similar to mesoband material unaffected by quartz veining. The replacement pyrite contains inclusions of native gold, chalcopyrite and pyrrhotite. These inclusions rarely exceed 0.05 mm in diameter. The thickness of the quartz veins is variable from several millimetres to 1 or 2 m, but vein widths of 2-5 cm are most common. Silicification of the adjacent iron formation also accompanies pyrite replacement (Figure 6) and is most obvious in magnetite mesobands where bleaching is pronounced.

Most of the quartz veins observed on the 125-foot level of the underground workings on the Carshaw property cut roughly orthogonally across the iron formation although a few veins trend subparallel to the iron formation bedding. Few quartz veins were observed in the ultramafic and felsic dikes which cut the iron formations, but where such veins were traced from the dikes into the adjacent iron formation, the auriferous pyrite replacement envelope was only developed in the iron formation. Similarly, for those few quartz veins hosted in the basalt country rock, no pyrite replacement envelopes were developed. Apparently, only the very iron-rich iron formation units were suitable for pyrite replacement.

Figure 6. Pyrite (PY) replacement of magnetite (MT) mesobands adjacent to a quartz vein (QV) which cuts the Carshaw iron formation. Note silicification (SI) in the pyrite replacement zones.

DISSEMINATED SULPHIDES

Disseminated throughout the iron formation are isolated grains of euhedral to subhedral pyrite and anhedral chalcopyrite and pyrrhotite. The concentration of these sulphides seldom exceeds 1 percent by volume. The proportion of pyrrhotite to pyrite is about 1:1 in the chert and carbonate mesobands, but pyrrhotite is more abundant in the magnetite mesobands. Chalcopyrite occurs only in trace amounts as isolated grains. Disseminated sulphide grain size seldom exceeds 0.1 mm. Some disseminated magnetite grains contain very small (< 0.01 mm) pyrite inclusions. Where this phenomenon is observed, invariably a coarser (0.1-1 mm) pyrite grain either abuts against or occurs within the magnetite grain array (Figure 7).

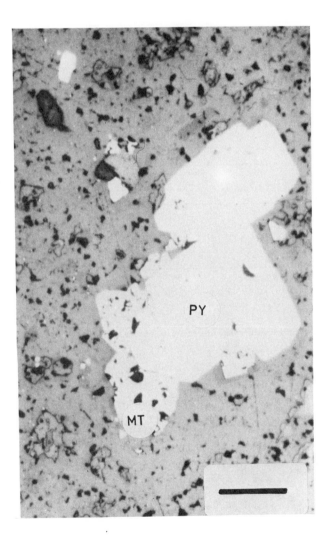

Figure 7. *Disseminated pyrite (PY) adjacent to disseminated magnetite (MT) within a chert mesoband. Bar scale is 0.1 mm.*

It is possible that the disseminated sulphides were introduced into the iron formation diagenetically. Alternatively, their presence is a manifestation of very low intensity sulphurization related to the quartz veining event. To resolve this question, it would be important to know if the distribution of disseminated sulphides in the iron formations corresponded to domains where quartz veining was intense. Unfortunately, because the present access and diamond drilling has exposed only the mineralized iron formation domain, a description of the disseminated sulphide distribution throughout the iron formation is not possible.

Regarding the pyrite-magnetite inclusion relationship, there might be a tendency to interpret this texture (Figure 7) in terms of magnetite replacement by pyrite; however, it must be acknowledged that the interpretation of sulphide-oxide textural relationships in metamorphic rocks is notoriously difficult.

In the absence of any firm evidence, we cautiously suggest that the disseminated sulphides through the exposed iron formations are secondary, related to the quartz veining and adjacent pyritization event.

SYNGENETIC PYRITE

Syngenetic pyrite occurs as recrystallized, euhedral grains (0.1 to 1 mm) which form stratiform bands in chlorite mesobands (see Figure 5e), although not all chlorite mesobands are host to pyrite microbanding. These pyrite laminations are parallel to mesoband bedding and are folded harmoniously with their host chlorite mesoband (see Figure 5e). This pyrite habit was observed in chlorite mesobands which are several metres removed from the late quartz veins and hence do not appear to represent a chlorite replacement by the vein-related pyrite. In addition, the pyrite microbands constitute only 10-20 percent by mode of the chlorite mesoband, which contrasts with the style of mesoband replacement by the vein-related pyrite. It is cautiously suggested that this pyrite is syngenetic.

GEOCHEMISTRY

Whole rock mesoband samples of iron formation and pyrite separates were analysed for gold (Au), arsenic (As), antimony (Sb), tungsten (W), carbon dioxide (CO_2) and sulphur (S) as reported by Fyon *et al.* (1981). Only the gold analyses are reproduced here (Table 1). Precision for gold, analysed by instrumental neutron activation of iron formation material, is estimated to be:

1. ± 25 percent at 1 to 50 ppm
2. ± 10 percent at < 1 ppm but > 0.005 ppm

DISSEMINATED SULPHIDES

Gold concentrations of mesoband material sampled away from obvious quartz veins range from 1 to 6000 ppb (Table 1), although the geometrical mean for the meso-

Table 1. *Gold analyses of pyrite separates and iron-formation mesobands.*

Sample Number	Description	Au (ppm)
Car-79	Pyrite separate from replacement envelope	74.
Car 132-1 -2 -3 -4 -5	Pyrite from replaced magnetite mesoband adjacent to quartz vein	60. 90. 130. 20. 45.,40.
Car-142	Pyrite from pyritized carbonate breccia- foot-wall of Carshaw BIF	5.4
Car-143	Same as 142	10.0, 6.1
Car-145	Same as 152	3.3
Car-147	Same as 142	0.6
Car-146	Pyrite separate from chlorite mesoband (possibly syngenetic pyrite)	2.1
Car-152	Pyrite separate from chlorite mesoband (possibly syngenetic pyrite)	1.1, 1.2
Whole	) Chert mesobands	9.8 ppb ± 0.81 (log transformed) r = 0.7 to 1400 ppb n = 19
Rock	) Magnetite mesobands	28.2 ppb ± 1.14 (log transformed) r = 0.9 to 5900 ppb n = 12
Analyses	) Carbonate mesobands	13.2 ppb ± 0.74 (log transformed) r = 1.6 to 660 ppb n = 10

r = range; n = number of analyses

bands is about 15 ppb (Table 1). The strong correlation between Au and S of 0.79, 0.77 and 0.73 at the 0.01 level of significance in chert, carbonate, and magnetite mesobands respectively (Fyon *et al.* 1981) implies that the disseminated replacement sulphides carry the gold. No mesoband material contained more than 2 ppm As (Fyon *et al.* 1981). No visible gold was observed in these sulphides.

VEIN-RELATED REPLACEMENT PYRITE

Abundant microscopically visible gold was observed in the pyrite that replaces magnetite mesobands adjacent to quartz veins, and therefore it is not surprising that this pyrite contains between 20 and 130 ppm gold (Table 1).

SYNGENETIC PYRITE

Only two pyrite separates from the chlorite mesobands have been analysed for gold and, hence, these data must be interpreted cautiously because they may not be representative. Both samples of pyrite separates contain about 1 to 2 ppm Au (Table 1).

DISCUSSION

The geochemical data demonstrate that the iron formation was enriched in gold primarily as a result of the quartz veining and attendant pyrite replacement of the adjacent magnetite-rich mesobands. However, the fact that the laminated pyrite in the chlorite mesobands carries some gold (about an order of magnitude or two less than the vein envelope pyrite) illustrates that a volumetrically minor component of gold was syngenetically enriched in the iron formation, bearing in mind the reservations regarding the number of samples analysed.

It was acknowledged by Fyon *et al.* (1981) that the gold hosted in the vein systems could represent redistributed, indigeneous (syngenetic or diagenetic) iron formation gold. This seems unlikely because syngenetic, microbanded, auriferous pyrite in chlorite mesobands, although recrystallized, has remained within its original depositional unit. Even if this pyrite had lost all its gold to a redistribution process, the volume of this material exposed in the iron formation is too small to account for the mass of gold hosted in the vein systems. Similarly, the disseminated sulphides, even if diagenetic or syngenetic, are not present in sufficient amounts, nor do they contain enough gold, to account for the mass of gold tied up in the quartz vein systems.

It must follow that an exotic auriferous fluid interacted with the banded iron formations along fracture systems, presumably formed by brittle deformation of the iron formation units. By virtue of their high iron content and possibly by the relative accessibility of this iron, sulphur from the exotic hydrothermal fluid was preferentially fixed in magnetite mesobands. The intimate spatial association of gold and the replacement pyrite supports gold-pyrite coprecipitation.

CONCLUSIONS

The gold mineralization of the banded iron formations is epigenetic and resulted from sulphurization of iron-rich mesobands. Sulphurization is most intense adjacent to late quartz veins where magnetite-rich mesobands are preferentially replaced by pyrite containing 20-130 ppm gold. Sulphurization is much less intense away from the quartz veins where pyrite and pyrrhotite occur as disseminated grains and as replacements after magnetite and ferroan dolomite. Mesobands carrying these disseminated sulphides contain between 0.001 and 6.0 ppm gold, but average 0.015 ppm.

Laminated pyrite of possible syngenetic origin, hosted in chlorite mesobands, contains between 1 and 2 ppm gold; however, this material contributes little to the overall gold tenor of the iron formation units due to its volumetrically small proportion.

The igneous rocks and the banded iron formation units have been subjected to the following sequence of alteration events, listed chronologically: (1) silica dumping in vesicles and amygdules; (2) intense dolomitization; and (3) quartz veining. The magnitude of the temporal difference between these events cannot be absolutely quantified; however, it is conceivable that these events are consanguineous and represent the progressive evolution of a mega-hydrothermal system. Chemical evolution of the hydrothermal system is apparent even at the event scale where a mineralogical succession (quartz replaced by dolomite replaced by chlorite) is observed in the quartz vein system. The sulphurization of the banded iron formations accompanied the quartz vein event; however, although quartz veins cut all rock types, it is only in the iron-rich banded iron formation unit that sulphurization was focused.

ACKNOWLEDGEMENTS

We extend our sincere appreciation to Mr. John Stirling, President, Gowganda Resources Limited, and to Mr. Jack Willars, Consultant, who enthusiastically provided access to the Carshaw property and to company data. This study constitutes part of a regional examination of gold deposits and rock alteration in the Timmins area and was financially supported in full by Geoscience Research Grant 49 from the Ontario Geological Survey of the Ministry of Natural Resources.

REFERENCES

Andrews, A.J., Sharpe, D.R., and Janes, D.A.
1981: A Preliminary Reconnaissance of the Weagamow-North Caribou Lake Metavolcanic-Metasedimentary Belt, Including the Opapimiskan Lake (Musselwhite) Gold Occurrence; p.203-231 in Summary of Field Work, 1981, by the Ontario Geological Survey, edited by J. Wood, O.L. White, R.B. Barlow, and A.C. Colvine, Ontario Geological Survey, Miscellaneous Paper 100, 255p.

Dimroth, E.
1979: Facies Models 16: Diagenetic Facies of Iron Formation; p.83-189 in Facies Models, edited by R.G. Walker, Geoscience Canada, Report Series 1, 211p.

Ferguson, S.A., Groen, H.A., and Haynes, R.
1971: Gold Deposits of Ontario: Part 1, Districts of Algoma, Cochrane, Kenora, Rainy River, and Thunder Bay; Ontario Division of Mines, Mineral Resource Circular 13, 315p. (Reprinted 1973).

Fleischer, R. and Routhier, P.
1973: The Consanguineous Origin of a Tourmaline-Bearing Gold Deposit, Passagem de Mariana (Brazil); Economic Geology, Vol. 68, p.11-22.

Fripp, R.E.P.
1976: Stratabound Gold Deposits in Archean Banded Iron Formation, Rhodesia; Economic Geology, Vol. 71, No. 1, p.58-75.

Fyon, J.A., Crocket, J.H., Schwarcz, H.P., Kabir, A., and Knyf, M.
1981: Trace Element and Stable Isotope Geochemistry of Auriferous Iron Formations in the Timmins Area, Grant 49; p.90-107 in Geoscience Research Grant Program, Summary of Research 1980-1981, edited by E.G. Pye, Ontario Geological Survey, Miscellaneous Paper 98, 340p.

Gordon, J.B., Lovell, H.L., de Grijs, J., and Davies, R.F.
1979: Gold Deposits of Ontario, Part 2: Part of District of Cochrane, Districts of Muskoka, Nipissing, Parry Sound, Sudbury, Timiskaming, and Counties of Southern Ontario; Ontario Geological Survey, Mineral Deposits Circular 18, 253p.

Jensen, L.S.
1976: A New Cation Plot for Classifying Subalkalic Volcanic Rocks; Ontario Division of Mines, Miscellaneous Paper 66, 22p.

Jolly, W.T.
1978: Metamorphic History of the Archean Abitibi Belt; Geological Survey of Canada, Paper 78-10, p.63-77.

1980: Development and Degradation of Archean Lavas, Abitibi Area, Canada, in Light of Major Element Geochemistry; Journal of Petrology, Vol. 21, p.323-363.

Macdonald, A.J.
1982: The MacLeod-Cockshutt and Hard Rock Mines, Geraldton: Examples of an Iron Formation Related Gold Deposit; p.188-191 in Summary of Field Work, 1982, by the Ontario Geological Survey, edited by John Wood, Owen White, R.B. Barlow, and A.C. Colvine, Ontario Geological Survey, Miscellaneous Paper 106, 235p.

Malga Porcupine Gold Mines Limited
1944: *Information Bulletin*; Malga Porcupine Gold Mines Limited, 19p.

Matheson, A.F. and Douglas, J.H.
1948: Hard Rock Mine; p.406-413 in Geology of Canadian Ore Deposits, Canadian Institute of Mining and Metallurgy, Jubilee Volume, 948p.

Nunes, P.D. and Pyke, D.R.
1980: Geochronology of the Abitibi Metavolcanic Belt, Timmins - Matachewan Area - Progress Report; p.34 - 39 in Summary of Geochronology Studies 1977-1979, edited by E.G. Pye, Ontario Geological Survey, Miscellaneous Paper 92, 45p.

Page, C.E.
1979: B-Zone Deposit: Cullaton Lake, District of Keewatin, Northwest Territories; p.323-347 in Proceedings of the Gold Workshop, Yellowknife, Northwest Territories, December 3-7, 1979, edited by R.D. Morton, 354p.

Pyke, D.R.
1981: Relationship of Gold Mineralization to Stratigraphy and Structure in Timmins and Surrounding Area; p.1-15 in Genesis of Archean, Volcanic-Hosted Gold Deposits, Symposium Held at the University of Waterloo, March 7, 1980, Ontario Geological Survey, Miscellaneous Paper 97, 175p.

Willars, J.D.
1982: Report on Gowganda Resources Incorporated Carshaw Gold Property, Timmins Area, Ontario; Unpublished Company Report, 12p.

110

Alteration, Metamorphism, and Structural Patterns Associated with Archean Gold Deposits — Preliminary Observations in the Red Lake Area

A.J. Andrews[1] and H. Wallace[2]

[1]Mineral Deposits Section, Ontario Geological Survey, Toronto
[2]Precambrian Geology Section, Ontario Geological Survey, Toronto

ABSTRACT

A district-scale study was recently initiated in the eastern section of the Red Lake volcanic-sedimentary belt, to determine the geological relationships of alteration, metamorphism and structural patterns to gold mineralization.

The regional stratigraphic and structural patterns can be modelled in terms of a large-scale antiform combined with a major limb thrust-fault, the latter sited along an ultramafic intrusive body known as the East Bay Serpentinite. The area is dominated by greenschist grade rocks which have experienced a later, regional carbonatization, resulting in pervasive introduction of calcite along various structural features. The area encompassing the past- and present-producing mines has experienced intense alteration in the form of Fe-carbonatization, silicification and sericitization. This area is also characterized by a strong component of brittle deformation in the form of intense fracturing and small-scale faulting. The position and outline of the highly altered zone has a similar configuration to that of the regional antiform.

Geological relationships observed at specific surface exposures indicate that gold mineralization has occurred late in the geological history of the area; that is, at least post-folding and post-Fe-carbonatization. The significance of carbonatization to gold mineralization may have been in preparing the rock for brittle failure, thus producing fractures to host gold-bearing quartz veins. The intense fracturing thus produced would be significant to localization of gold.

INTRODUCTION

In recent years there has been considerable effort, but little success, in utilizing alteration patterns in the search for Archean, volcanic-hosted gold deposits. An extensive evaluation of this subject, conducted by the Mineral Deposits Section of the Ontario Geological Survey in 1982, indicates that this situation is not due to lack of potential; rather it reflects a basic lack of knowledge. In particular there is a dearth of knowledge regarding the processes responsible for alteration and metamorphism in Archean volcanic-sedimentary belts and their spatial and temporal relationships to mineralization. Until such knowledge is gained, alteration/metamorphic patterns cannot be used intelligently as an exploration tool for gold deposits.

It is our opinion that the construction of such a data base requires coordinated, systematic study on a district scale. To our knowledge there are few, if any, "greenstone" belts in the world where this type of approach has been adequately developed.

During the 1982 field season we initiated such a study in the Red Lake area of northwestern Ontario. For the initial phase of this project, emphasis is being placed on the eastern section of the belt including the Townships of Balmer, Bateman, Dome and McDonough. Our strategy is to first delineate the geological characteristics of the area as a whole. On this basis, we will then focus attention on the more complex, highly altered areas associated with the mines.

The following is a progress report based primarily on initial field observations. To date, these observations are based almost exclusively on surface exposures.

GENERAL GEOLOGY

The Red Lake camp has recently been the focus of detailed (1:12 000) mapping (Pirie and Sawitzky 1977; Pirie and Grant 1978a, 1978b), regional stratigraphic and structural syntheses (Pirie 1981; Wallace 1980, 1981, 1982), geochronological studies (Thurston *et al.* 1981), and studies of individual mines and their environs (Rigg and Helmstaedt 1981; Rigg and Scherkus, this volume; MacGeehan and Hodgson 1981; Durocher, this volume). More specialized works dealing with particular aspects of gold mineralization have been conducted by Cowan and Crocket (1980), Kerrich *et al.* (1981), Mathieson and Hodgson (in preparation), and Lavigne and Crocket (this volume). With this comprehensive data base the Red Lake volcanic belt lends itself well to a coordinated, district-scale study on the metallogeny of gold.

On the basis of observations by Pirie and Wallace (references cited above), regional geological patterns in the study area have been well characterized. The most significant of these are illustrated in Figure 1 and summarized as follows:

1. Most of the study area is underlain by a thick accumulation of tholeiitic to komatiitic, mafic to ultramafic volcanic rocks. This package is overlain to the south and northwest by a sequence of calc-alkaline vol-

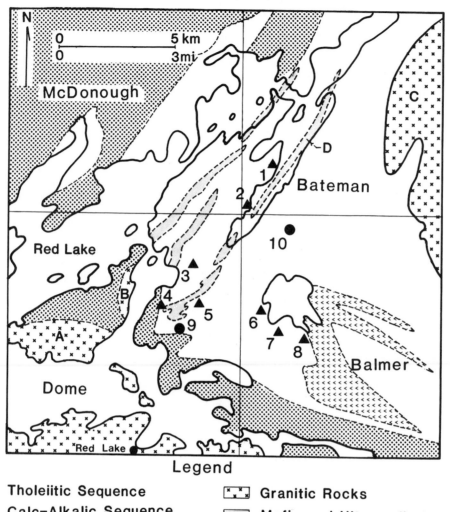

Legend

☐ **Tholeiitic Sequence**   ☒ **Granitic Rocks**

▨ **Calc-Alkalic Sequence**   ▧ **Mafic and Ultramafic Intrusives**

                                   ⬚ **Clastic and Chemical Sediments**

1. McFinley mine
2. Abino mine
3. McMarmac mine
4. Cochenour mine
5. Marcus mine
6. H. G. Young mine
7. Campbell mine
8. Dickenson mine

9. Rahill Property
10. Redcon Property

A. Dome Stock
B. McKenzie Stock
C. Eastern Granitic Batholith
D. East Bay Serpentinite

Figure 1. *Simplified, regional geology of the Red Lake study area. Triangles 1-6 are past producing mines; 7 and 8 are present producers.*

canic rocks which characteristically includes a significant component of pyroclastic rocks and volcanogenic sedimentary rocks.

2. The predominantly tholeiitic sequence includes a wedge-shaped accumulation of clastic and chemical sedimentary rocks to the southeast and a series of stratiform, mafic to ultramafic intrusions in the northwest.

3. The volcanic assemblage as a whole is bounded on the east by a large, granitic (granodiorite-trondjhemite-diorite) batholith and on the west by an intravolcanic (granodiorite) intrusion known as the Dome Stock.

4. Past- and present-producing mines in the area occur within and near the stratigraphic top of the tholeiitic sequence. A few-past producers located within the Dome Stock and related McKenzie stocks represent the only exceptions.

5. The area defined by past- and present-producing mines (volcanic-hosted) and other known mineralization is underlain by an extensive zone of highly altered rock, which also appears to be contained within and near the stratigraphic top of the tholeiitic sequence (see Figure 4).

VOLCANIC STRATIGRAPHY

Figure 2 is a summary compilation of all information presently available concerning the volcanic stratigraphy and regional structural elements of the study area. This interpretation is based on data gathered from Ontario Geological Survey preliminary maps (1:12 000) referred to above, airborne electromagnetic data (1:20 000 preliminary maps) (OGS 1978), previous geological work as documented in the Ontario Geological Survey assessment files, and recent observations by the present authors. The pattern resulting from this compilation reveals a number of interesting stratigraphic and structural features and these are briefly outlined as follows.

1. Lithological contacts (where observed) and foliations within the volcanic pile adjacent to the eastern granitic batholith generally parallel the boundary of this large intrusive body and dip in a west to southwesterly direction. In Balmer Township and the southern part of Bateman Township, dips range, for the most part, between 50 and 70°SW. This fabric would be consistent with a west to southwesterly dipping volcanic-granite contact.

2. In the northwestern part of the study area the volcanic stratigraphy generally strikes at about 060 degrees and dips to the northwest. In the southeastern part of the area the strike is about 120 degrees with dips and facing directions to the southwest.

3. Marked stratigraphic discordances have been recognized in areas **A** and **B** (Figure 2a). The former appears to coincide with the exact location of a large ultramafic intrusive body referred to locally as the East Bay Serpentinite (see Figure 1).

4. Complex minor folding and distortion of bedding characterize a relatively large area located to the immediate south and southeast of the Cochenour Mine.

PRELIMINARY STRUCTURAL MODEL

In the past, two main theories have been proposed to explain the regional pattern of structure and stratigraphy of the area. One theory, alluded to in much of the old literature and most recently discussed by Ferguson *et al.* (1972), invokes the generation of a major northeast-trending structural break in the general vicinity of the East Bay Serpentinite. Point (3) above lends some credence to this suggestion. The other theory, recently proposed by Pirie (1981), invokes the presence of a regional antiform, with the hinge zone located in the vicinity of the Cochenour Mine and the axial trace trending northeasterly. Points (2) and (4) above support this suggestion. The orientation of this fold with respect to the position and outline of the eastern granitic body may suggest a genetic relationship.

Based on our present compilation of data we are exploring a model which involves a combination of these two theories, the basis of which is simply illustrated in Figure 3. This model involves the establishment of a major antiform, as suggested above, but combined with this is the generation of a major limb thrust-fault as illustrated in Figure 3b and 3c. The development of limb thrust-faulting during folding has been described in detail by Ramsay (1974, Figure 8b). Such faulting is due to the presence of unit(s) of anomalous thickness and/or competency in a layered sequence, which cannot accomodate the same degree of shortening attained in the surrounding rocks. As diagrammatically illustrated in Figure 3 these units tend to break near their hinge and override the material on the opposite limb. Applied to the Red Lake study area (Figure 3d), this model satisfactorily complies with all the observations listed above, in particular, the stratigraphic discordances noted in point (3). The apparent discordancy in area **B** (see Figure 2a) would actually represent part of the hinge zone of the major antiform (Figure 3d). The East Bay Serpentinite would be the anomalous unit along which the limb thrust has developed (arrow on Figure 3b and d). Well developed shear zones are known to occur along the length of this intrusive body.

Foliation trends in the region generally parallel the gross stratigraphic trends as illustrated in Figure 2. However, a notable exception to this occurs in the form of a prominent fabric trending 120 degrees, best developed in the east and west central parts of Balmer and Dome Townships respectively (see Figure 2b). This fabric, which manifests as both fracture cleavage and penetrative foliation, is approximately parallel to volcanic stratigraphy in the eastern half of this area. Proceeding west into Dome Township, however, it persists across the East Bay Serpentinite and is observed to cross-cut the volcanic stratigraphy on the west limb of the proposed antiform. The generation of this fabric, therefore, would appear to postdate regional folding and limb thrust-faulting. We are considering the possibility that this late stage de-

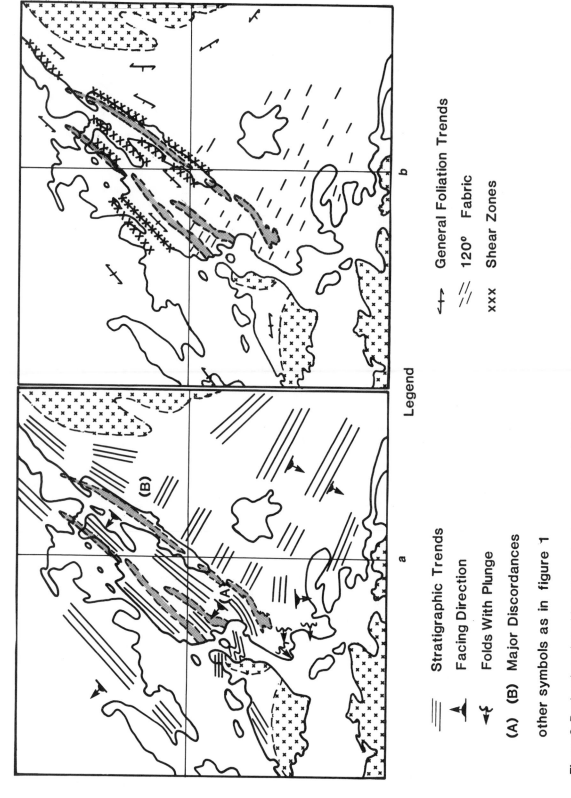

Legend

General Foliation Trends

/// 120° Fabric

xxx Shear Zones

Stratigraphic Trends

Facing Direction

Folds With Plunge

(A) (B) Major Discordances

other symbols as in figure 1

Figure 2. Regional stratigraphic and structural patterns compiled from presently available data (see text). For nomenclature, see Figure 1.

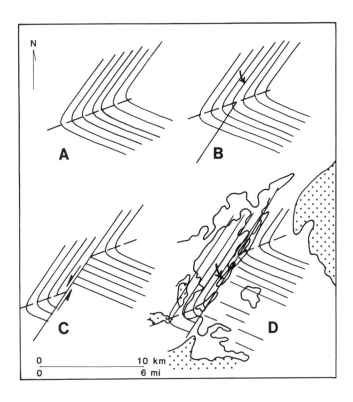

Figure 3. *The development of folding accompanied by limb-thrust faulting (a to c) and the application of this model to the study area (compare d to Figure 2a). The arrow in 3b indicates a unit of anomalous thickness and/or competency in the sequence which is represented by the East Bay Serpentinite in 3d. In this model, stratigraphic discordances **A** and **B** on Figure 2a, represent the plane of the thrust fault and the hinge zone of the fold, respectively.*

formation is related to the intrusion of the Dome Stock, although at this time more evidence is needed to test this hypothesis.

In summary, our preliminary interpretation of the major stratigraphic and structural elements of the region would suggest that: (1) the East Bay Serpentinite and spatially related mafic and ultramafic intrusions in the northwest part of the region were emplaced relatively early in the history of the area, probably predating the emplacement of the eastern granitic body; (2) the volcanic-sedimentary sequence is disposed in a regional antiform, the configuration of which is sympathetic to the general outline of the eastern granitic body; (3) the East Bay Serpentinite on the northwest limb of the antiform was the site for development of limb thrust-faulting in a left sinistral sense; and (4) a prominent fabric, trending 120 degrees and best developed in the south-central part of the region, was the result of deformation that postdated the regional folding and possibly was related to the intrusion of the Dome Stock.

This model represents only one of a number of possible structural solutions for the area and will be subject to significant modification and expansion as the study evolves. Detailed structural analysis to commence during the 1983 field season will serve to test the validity of this and alternative structural models.

METAMORPHISM AND ALTERATION

Perhaps the most striking feature of the study area is the existence of a large, triangular zone of highly altered rocks (HAZ) which was originally recognized and defined by Pirie (1981). This zone is superimposed upon a background of mainly greenschist grade metavolcanics in the surrounding region and appears to encompass all the past- and present-producing (volcanic hosted) mines in this part of the belt (Figure 4). While its nature, origin, and significance to gold mineralization are not well known, it can be stated that the HAZ is characterized by a highly complex pattern of alteration and deformation which is clearly distinct from the surrounding country rocks. In order to highlight these differences, we describe the surrounding country rocks.

115

BACKGROUND PATTERNS

The majority of rocks outside the HAZ are of greenschist grade, consisting of fibrous amphibole, chlorite, carbonate, occasional epidote and biotite, and rare garnet. Biotite often appears to be characteristic of mafic to intermediate, tuffaceous units. Ultramafic extrusive rocks tend to be actinolite-rich, while ultramafic intrusive rocks, such as the East Bay Serpentinite, are usually serpentinized to varying degrees. The processes responsible for these alteration types are being determined on the basis of field, petrographic and geochemical data.

Amphibolite grade metamorphic rocks constitute a relatively wide aureole (up to 2 km in width) adjacent to the granite batholith in Bateman and Balmer Townships (Figure 4). The extent of contact metamorphic effects beyond the amphibolite grade boundary is not yet known; however, in Bateman Township biotite appears to become increasingly more abundant toward the amphibolite zone. The amphibolite grade rocks consist predominantly of hornblende, plagioclase and quartz with subordinate amounts of epidote and garnet. The surface extent of the aureole may be used to support the suggestion made previously that the eastern granitic body may actually dip in a southwesterly direction beneath the volcanic carapace, towards the location of the mines. It is interesting in this respect that amphibolite grade metamorphic assemblages have been observed on the lower levels of the Campbell and Dickenson mines (D.M. Rigg, Corporation Falconbridge Copper Limited, personal communication; Mathieson and Hodgson, in preparation).

Calcite is a persistent and pervasive secondary phase occurring in all volcanic rocks outside the HAZ (2-30 volume percent), giving evidence of a regional carbonatization event. This mineral occurs primarily within structural features such as microfractures, veins, and along foliation planes, which appear related to the regional deformation. As such this carbonatization does not appear to reflect early, synvolcanic seawater systems,

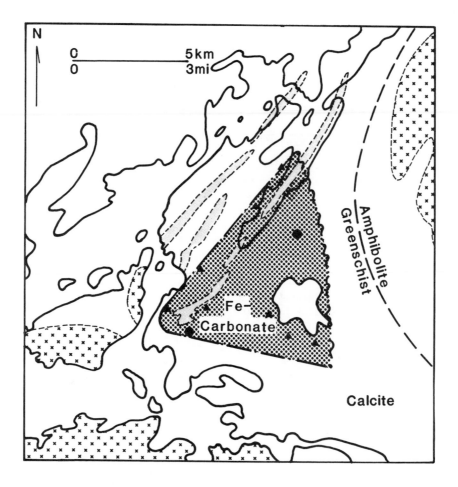

Figure 4. *Simplified alteration and metamorphic patterns. The heavy stippled area represents the highly altered zone (HAZ). All other areas (blank) exhibit regional greenschist to amphibolite grade assemblages, as indicated. Fe-carbonate (mainly dolomite) predominates within the HAZ whereas calcite occurs in all the surrounding regions. All other symbols as on Figure 1.*

but more likely represents a later stage, syn-to post-regional-deformation event.

Deformation in these rocks is predominantly ductile. Predictably, intense deformation occurs in an area approximately 1 km in width adjacent to the eastern granitic body. This manifests as pillow flattening, boudinage and the development of penetrative foliation. Beyond this area of intense, pervasive deformation, the structural style is characterized by the occurrence of relatively large areas with little or no significant deformation, interrupted by discrete shear zones. A well developed system of shear zones occurs in the northwest section of the study area as illustrated in Figure 2b. Individual shear zones are somewhat restricted in width (< 15 m), but extend up to kilometres in length. They parallel stratigraphy, preferentially occurring between units of contrasting competency (such as basalt adjacent to massive gabbro or serpentinite). Many of these shear zones are characterized by intense Fe-carbonatization (ferroan dolomite) in the form of massive veins and intense stringer systems. Calcite represents the dominant carbonate in the surrounding, less deformed, volcanic rocks. The location of these shear zones appears to be related to the presence of stratiform, mafic to ultramafic intrusions within the volcanic sequence just as the major limb thrust-fault discussed above appears to be related to the East Bay Serpentinite.

HIGHLY ALTERED ZONE

ALTERATION TYPES

The rocks of the HAZ exhibit at least three distinct alteration types: silicification, sericitization and carbonatization. Silicification, which is rather erratic in its distribution, is the least common of the three alteration types and results in significant bleaching and hardening of the rock. In specific zones, silicification has occurred via pervasive addition of SiO_2 to the rock and the generation of numerous quartz veins. Sericitization appears largely, though not exclusively, lithologically controlled. It occurs, for the most part, in felsic rock types; however, certain parts of pillow basalt units also appear sericitized. Ultramafic bodies which extend from the surrounding country rocks into the HAZ exhibit important changes in alteration across this boundary. In the former, they are moderately to highly serpentinized. In the latter, the serpentine alteration is often accompanied by extensively carbonatized and talcose (± fuchsite) shear zones that occur within and along the contacts of the intrusive body.

The HAZ is most characterized by intense, relatively pervasive iron-carbonatization (ferroan dolomite ± ankerite) occurring as intense stringer systems, massive carbonate veins (centimetres to metres in width) and pervasive carbonate addition to the massive rock. The dominant mineral assemblage observed in highly carbonatized basalts consists of plagioclase and dolomite with variable, but usually subordinate, amounts of chlorite and quartz. Pervasive carbonatization appears to coincide with intense fracturing and small scale faulting of the altered rock.

At the time of writing a limited number of chemical analyses of basalts from the HAZ were available and these are listed on Table 1. Preliminary interpretation of these data is summarized as follows:

1. Silicified and carbonatized rocks appear to form two discrete groups. As such, these two alteration processes may have acted separately and selectively.
2. The silicified basalts have experienced no significant addition of CO_2, but strong depletions in CaO, Na_2O and to a lesser extent MgO have occurred.
3. The carbonatized basalts exhibit close to normal abundances of SiO_2, Na_2O and MgO and only slight to moderate depletions of CaO. It is presumed that during alteration of mafic minerals, FeO, MgO and CaO were simply transferred to carbonate minerals (ferroan dolomite ± calcite).
4. Significant additions of K_2O appear evident in both groups.
5. Large additions of As have occurred in both groups; however, the values are highly variable and show no systematic correlation with other components.

STRUCTURE

In terms of structure, the HAZ is characterized by three prominent features:

1. The general shape of the HAZ is sympathetic to the configuration of the proposed regional antiform (see Figure 4 and 3d). As such it resembles, at least in form, a large scale saddle reef structure. The potential significance of this observation must await further study.
2. Volcanic rocks within the HAZ characteristically exhibit a strong component of brittle failure which manifests as intense fracturing and small scale faulting. This style of deformation is most clearly evident in pillow basalt units. Individual pillows, while well preserved in their general outline, are typically segmented to varying degrees by numerous fractures and small scale offsets. As mentioned above, intense fracturing and small scale faulting appear to coincide with areas of pervasive carbonatization. We are exploring the possibility that addition of large amounts of dolomite to basalt, combined with the destruction of ferromagnesium minerals, has rendered the rock more competent and therefore amenable to brittle failure. As previously described, plagioclase and dolomite are dominant components of these altered basalts. These minerals are inherently very strong and exhibit extensive fields of brittle failure.
3. Massive carbonate veins present in the HAZ typically show evidence of deformation in the form of internal brecciation, boudinage and folding. The late stage 120-degree fabric prominent in this area (described above), is observed to be axial planar to the folded, massive carbonate veins (Figure 5). As such this fabric would be considered as a post-carbonatization event.

Table 1. *Partial chemical analyses of silicified and carbonatized basalts from the Highly Altered Zone (HAZ) in the Red Lake area. Analyses by Geoscience Laboratories, Ontario Geological Survey, Toronto. Major elements given in weight percent, As in parts per million.*

Sample No.	SiO_2	MgO	CaO	Na_2O	K_2O	CO_2	As
Silicified basalt							
1	57.5	4.28	0.98	0.46	3.09	1.49	240
2	57.5	4.18	1.25	0.73	1.39	0.94	500
3	60.9	2.19	1.10	0.59	1.12	0.26	990
4	56.8	4.05	1.82	1.02	1.18	1.39	480
5	63.9	2.50	0.49	0.51	0.13	0.10	1000
Carbonatized Basalts							
6	44.7	7.33	8.69	2.29	0.08	7.28	110
7	48.3	5.98	6.37	1.94	2.67	10.00	1300
8	49.7	6.14	7.62	2.99	1.31	11.6	440
9	49.6	4.46	4.84	1.30	1.36	7.23	540
10	47.6	4.88	5.67	1.49	0.76	4.61	100

GOLD MINERALIZATION

Interesting spatial and temporal relationships are observed between the distribution of known gold mines, gold mineralization observed on surface exposures, and specific geological features of the area as discussed above.

SPATIAL RELATIONSHIPS

Known gold deposits in the area exhibit a pattern which is coincident with the proposed, regional antiform; that is,

the Cochenour, McMarmac, Abino and McFinley Mines form a linear array on the northwest limb, and the Cochenour, Marcus, H.G. Young, Campbell and Dickenson Mines form a linear trend in the southwest limb (see Figure 1). The location of the Cochenour Mine, which is coincident with the hinge area of the antiform, forms the intersection of these two arrays. The northwest array is closely associated with a northeast-trending system of massive, Fe-carbonate veins and shear zones as illustrated in Figure 2b (Fe-carbonate veins and carbonate alteration zones have been documented as important hosts to gold mineralization on the McMarmac, Abino and McFinley properties). This system, in turn, exhibits a close

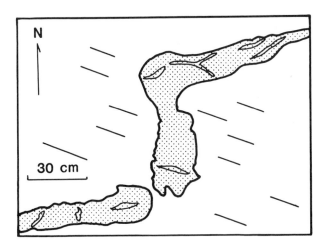

Figure 5. *Relationship between folded, Fe-carbonate veins (stipled) and the 120° fabric (oblique lines) observed in the HAZ, a deformation possibly related to the intrusion of the Dome Stock. The irregular lens shapes represent undeformed, gold-bearing, quartz ± tourmaline veins.*

spatial association with the East Bay Serpentinite. As cited above, evidence suggests that this sill-like intrusive body has been the focus of major northeast-trending fault movement.

The geology of the rocks underlying the southwest array is complex, poorly exposed and, as yet, not well understood. It is therfore unclear as to how the distribution of these mines relates to the underlying geology. An interesting feature to be investigated, in this regard, is a prominent aeromagnetic linear (a possible major fault structure) which occurs to the immediate north of the Campbell and Dickenson Mines (OGS 1978). The strike projection of this feature includes the H.G. Young, Marcus and Cochenour Mines.

TEMPORAL RELATIONSHIPS

Detailed studies of well exposed outcrops on the Redcon, Rahill and Marcus properties (see Figure 1) provide some tentative indications as to the timing of gold mineralization relative to other geological features observed at these particular locations. At the Redcon property (Figure 6) a large, stripped outcrop consists of a sequence of massive and pillowed basalts, cross-cut by a system of Fe-carbonate veins. A preliminary structural analysis has revealed a history of events which is briefly outlined as follows:

1. patchy silicification and polygonal fracturing;
2. main shearing; patches of remnant polygonal fracturing (1) are observed in these zones;
3. cross-faulting; these faults transpose parts of the shear zones generated in (2);

4. Fe-carbonate veining; not affected by the cross-faulting (3);
5. mafic dike intrusion; this dike cross-cuts the main carbonate veins (4);
6. oblique faulting; which transposes both the mafic dike (5) and offshoots of the carbonate vein (4);
7. gold-bearing quartz veining; these veins are undeformed and cross-cut both the mafic dike (5) and the massive carbonate vein (4); as such they are the latest features discerned.

These geological relationships strongly suggest that gold mineralization occurred late in the structural history of the area.

Similar relationships have been observed at the Marcus and Rahill properties. That is, late stage, relatively undeformed, often gold-bearing quartz ± tourmaline vein systems are hosted by and/or cross-cut deformed, Fe-carbonate veins. As noted earlier and illustrated diagrammatically in Figure 5, the deformation of these carbonate veins appears related to the generation of a penetrative fabric established subsequent to regional folding. As such, the available evidence would suggest that at least one gold mineralizing event occurred late in the alteration-structural history of the area, that is, at least postdating regional folding and carbonatization.

SUMMARY

Based on initial studies conducted in Balmer, Bateman, Dome and McDonough Townships of the Red Lake volcanic belt, observations have been discussed concerning the nature and history of structure, metamorphism, alteration and gold mineralization. These are diagrammatically illustrated in Figure 7 and are briefly summarized below.

1. Regional stratigraphic and structural patterns are tentatively modelled in terms of regional folding (antiform) combined with limb thrust-faulting. In this model the East Bay Serpentinite (and possibly other mafic and ultramafic intrusions) located on the northwest limb of the fold was the site of the limb thrust-faulting.

2. A regional carbonatization event has resulted in pervasive generation of calcite in the study area as a whole. This event appears to have been syn- or post-regional-deformation and probably postdates the establishment of greenschist grade alteration (metamorphism?) in these rocks.

3. A large area of highly altered rock (HAZ) which encompasses all the past- and present-producing mines (volcanic-hosted) is characterized by Fe-carbonatization, silicification and sericitization. The relative timing between regional carbonatization (point 2 above) and Fe-carbonatization in the HAZ is not yet known.

4. A penetrative fabric (trending 120 degrees), best developed in the south-central part of the study area, appears to be a post-regional-folding event, possibly related to the intrusion of the Dome Stock. This event

also seems to have been responsible for deformation of massive, Fe-carbonate veins in the HAZ.

5. Geological relationships observed at specific surface exposures within the HAZ indicate that a gold mineralization event occurred late in the geological history of the area. The mineralization occurs in relatively undeformed quartz ± tourmaline veins which cross-cut the deformed Fe-carbonate veins described in point (4). This mineralization would therefore postdate regional folding and Fe-carbonatization.

6. The significance of carbonatization to gold mineralization may have been in preparing the rock for brittle failure (i.e., the generation of fractures to host gold-bearing quartz veins). Increase in competency of basalt may be achieved during carbonatization through the replacement of ferromagnesian minerals by dolomite.

7. The distribution of past- and present-producing mines and the configuration of the HAZ which contains them are sympathetic to the position and outline of the regional antiform. On the northwest limb of the antiform, faulting along the East Bay Serpentinite may have exerted significant structural control on gold mineralization in this area.

As indicated in Figure 7 there is still much uncertainty regarding the relative timing of certain major geological events and their significance to gold mineralization. While we have identified one, late stage, gold mineralizing event, there is still much to learn about the total history of gold mineralization in the region as a whole. Continuing field, petrographic and geochemical investigations will serve to refine our understanding in this regard.

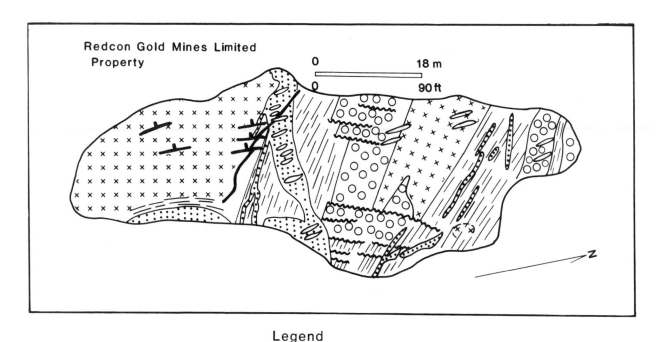

Legend

◯◯ Pillowed Units		::: Fe-Carbonate Veins	
× × Polygonal Fracturing		/ Mafic Dike	
/// Main Shear Zones		✓ Oblique Faults	
∿∿ Cross Faults		⬭ Au Bearing Quartz Veins	

Figure 6. Simplified geology of the Redcon Gold Mines Limited property, northwest Balmer Township (Figure 1). The generation of gold-bearing, quartz veins represents the last discernible event, culminating a relatively complex structural history (see text).

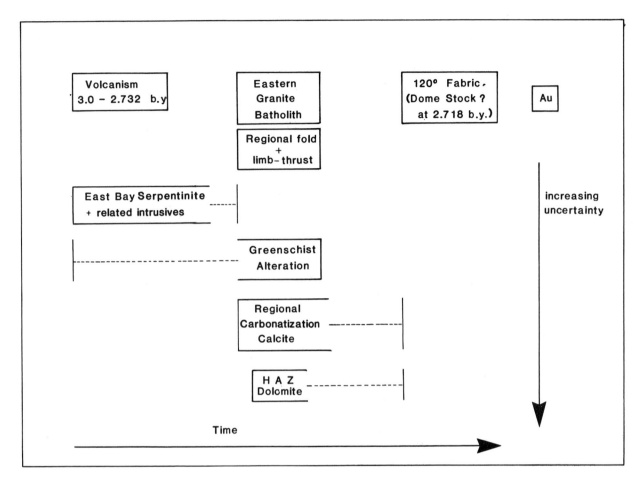

Figure 7. Major geological events and suggested temporal relationships. The vertical axis and horizontally extended boxes indicate degrees of uncertainty involved at this stage of the study. As discussed in the text, good evidence exists for late-stage, gold mineralization as indicated; however, this does not necessarily represent the only mineralizing event. Radiometric ages were determined on zircons (U-Pb) by F. Corfu (Department of Geology, Royal Ontario Museum).

REFERENCES

Cowan, P. and Crocket, J.H.
1980: The Gold Content of Interflow Metasedimentary Rocks From the Red Lake Area, Ontario - A Preliminary Evaluation; Current Research, Part B, Geological Survey of Canada, Paper 80-1B, p.129-133.

Ferguson, S.A., Jarvis, W.L., Hutton, D.A., Watt, A., Delaney, J.F., Jeffries, J.D., Riley, R.A. and Grant, F.S.
1972: Some Papers on the Geology of the Red Lake Area, District of Kenora, Patricia Portion; Ontario Division of Mines, Open File Report 5078, 106p.

Kerrich, R.W., Fryer, B.J., Milner, K.J., and Pierce, M.G.
1981: The Geochemistry of Gold-Bearing Chemical Sediments, Dickenson Mine, Red Lake, Ontario: A Reconnaissance Study; Canadian Journal of Earth Sciences, Volume 18, p.624-637.

MacGeehan, P.J. and Hodgson, C.J.
1981: The Relationship of Gold Mineralization to Volcanic and Alteration Features in the Area of the Campbell Red Lake and Dickenson Mines, Red Lake Area, Northwestern Ontario; p.94-110 in Genesis of Archean, Volcanic-Hosted Gold Deposits, Symposium Held at the University of Waterloo, March 7, 1980, Ontario Geological Survey, Miscellaneous Paper 97, 175p.

Mathieson, N.A. and Hodgson, C. J.
in preparation: Alteration, Mineralization and Metamorphism in the Area of the East South 'C' Ore Zone, Dickenson Mine, Red Lake, Northwestern Ontario.

OGS
1978: Airborne Electromagnetic Survey, Total Magnetic Intensity Survey, Red Lake Area; Ontario Geological Survey, Preliminary Maps P.1571-1574, 1579, 1581, Scale 1:20 000. Survey by Questor Surveys Limited.

Pirie, J.
1981: Regional Geological Setting of Gold Deposits in the Red Lake Area, Northwestern Ontario; p.71-93 in Genesis of Archean, Volcanic-Hosted Gold Deposits, Symposium Held at the University of Waterloo, March 7, 1980, Ontario Geological Survey, Miscellaneous Paper 97, 175p.

Pirie, J. and Grant, A.
1978a: Balmer Township Area, District of Kenora (Patricia Portion); Ontario Geological Survey, Preliminary Map P.1976A, scale 1:12 000 or 1 inch to 1000 feet, Geological Series, Geology 1977.
1978b: Bateman Township, District of Kenora (Patricia Portion); Ontario Geological Survey, Preliminary Map P. 1569, scale 1:12 000.

Pirie, J. and Sawitzky, E.
1977: McDonough Township, District of Kenora (Patricia Portion); Ontario Geological Survey, Preliminary Map P. 1240, scale 1:12 000.

Ramsey, J.G.
1974: Development of Chevron Folds; Geological Society of America Bulletin, Vol. 85, p.1741-1754.

Rigg, D.M. and Helmstaedt, H.
1981: Relations Between Structures and Gold Mineralization in Campbell Red Lake and Dickenson Mines, Red Lake Area; p.111-127 in Genesis of Archean, Volcanic-Hosted Gold Deposits, Symposium Held at the University of Waterloo, March 7, 1980, Ontario Geological Survey, Miscellaneous Paper 97, 175p.

Thurston, P.C., Wallace, H. and Corfu, F.
1981: Tentative Stratigraphic Correlation of the Birch-Uchi and Red Lake Belts (abstract); in Geoscience Research Seminar, December 9-10, 1981, Abstracts, Ontario Geological Survey, 15p.

Wallace, H.
1980: Red Lake Synoptic Project, District of Kenora; p.10-12 in Summary of Field Work, 1980, by the Ontario Geological Survey, Edited by V.G. Milne, O.L. White, R.B. Barlow, J.A. Robertson, and A.C. Colvine, Ontario Geological Survey, Miscellaneous Paper 96, 201p.
1981: Red Lake Synoptic Project, District of Kenora; p.12-14 in Summary of Field Work, 1981, by the Ontario Geological Survey, edited by John Wood, O.L. White, R.B. Barlow, and A.C. Colvine, Ontario Geological Survey, Miscellaneous Paper 100, 255p.
1982: Red Lake Synoptic Project, District of Kenora; p.5-7 in Summary of Field Work, 1982, by the Ontario Geological Survey, edited by John Wood, Owen L. White, R.B. Barlow, and A.C. Colvine, Ontario Geological Survey, Miscellaneous Paper 106, 235p.

The Nature of Hydrothermal Alteration Associated with the Madsen and Starratt-Olsen Gold Deposits, Red Lake Area

M.E. Durocher

Resident Geologist, Ontario Ministry of Natural Resources, Red Lake

ABSTRACT

Mapping and sampling of the Madsen and Starratt-Olsen Mines area, situated in Baird and Heyson Townships, was initiated in 1981. The Red Lake metavolcanic-metasedimentary belt had previously been divided into a lower tholeiitic-komatiitic and an upper calc-alkalic sequence. On the basis of results obtained from analysis of 164 samples, the boundary between the two sequences was shifted 1-2 km to the south. As a result, the Howey and Hasaga Mines, previously thought to belong to the lower calc-alkalic sequence, are now included in the upper tholeiitic-komatiitic sequence. It also became apparent that the felsic rocks of the calc-alkalic sequence are significantly more potassic than the underlying tholeiitic rocks.

En echelon, stratabound ore zones are hosted by heterogeneous, highly altered tuff units, occurring in the lower parts of the tholeiitic-komatiitic sequence. The main host (Austin tuff), is a highly deformed unit which may represent a structural break. Analyses of 147 surface samples indicate an extensive alteration halo (9 km along strike), centred on, and extending above and below, the tuff units. It consists of significant depletion in Na_2O, low CO_2, and addition of K_2O. Anomalous gold values show direct correlation with As and Sb, suggesting that these elements can be used as indicators of proximity to ore zones.

INTRODUCTION

The Early Precambrian Red Lake "greenstone" belt is located in the western part of the Uchi Subprovince of the Superior Province. The volcanic stratigraphy in the Red Lake belt has been divided into two major sequences by Pirie (1981) (Figure 1). The lower sequence is composed of dominantly mafic to ultramafic metavolcanics with subordinate amounts of felsic metavolcanics and metasediments. This lower tholeiitic to komatiitic sequence is overlain by three geographically distinct calc-alkalic sequences, which comprise dominantly felsic and intermediate metavolcanics with minor amounts of interlayered mafic metavolcanics and metasediments (Pirie 1981).

The study area including the Madsen and Starratt-Olsen Mines is located in Baird and Heyson Townships, in the southwest part of the Red Lake greenstone belt.

PREVIOUS WORK

The study area was mapped in detail by Horwood (1940). Ferguson (1965, 1968) mapped portions of Baird and Heyson Townships. During 1979, J. Pirie mapped Heyson Township in detail. Wallace (in preparation) carried out detailed mapping of the Baird Township in 1983. During 1981 and 1982 the author carried out detailed mapping in the vicinity of the Madsen and Starratt-Olsen former gold producers (Durocher and van Haaften 1982).

GENERAL GEOLOGY OF THE MADSEN – STARRATT-OLSEN AREA

The general geology of the Madsen – Starratt-Olsen area is shown in Figure 2. The rocks in this area can be grouped into two major sequences: a lower tholeiitic to komatiitic sequence and an upper calc-alkalic sequence (Pirie 1980; Wallace 1981; Durocher and van Haaften 1982). The two sequences are part of the southeast-facing southern limb of a large fold or domal structure centred to the north of the study area (Wallace 1981). The strike and dip of the rock units varies systematically across the study area, defining a large open S-shaped flexure. In the vicinity of the Starratt-Olsen Mine to the southwest, the units strike 055 to 60° and dip 70° southeast. In the central part of the area, close to the Madsen Mine, the strike is 030°, and the dip is 65° southeast. One kilometre northeast of the Madsen Mine the strike is 045° and the dip is 70 to 75° southeast. Foliation generally strikes 045 to 060° and dips 70 to 75° southeast.

THOLEIITIC-KOMATIITIC SEQUENCE

On the basis of new chemical data obtained from analysis of 164 surface and underground samples (Figures 3,4,5,6) the tholeiitic-komatiitic sequence in the study area can be divided into upper and lower parts. The lower part is composed dominantly of tholeiitic basalt, with subordinate amounts of intercalated peridotitic komatiite and basaltic komatiite flows (Figure 3). The tholeiitic basalts are generally pillowed. Massive medium grained flows are uncommon, and variolitic flows are rare. The basaltic komatiites occur either as pillowed flows or as pillow breccia beds. Mineralogically they are composed almost entirely of actinolite with minor amounts of plagioclase. The peridotitic komatiites were only observed in rubbly flow-top breccia beds. Individual fragments within these breccia beds exhibit relict spinifex textures. Mineralogically they are composed of talc-serpentine-magnetite assemblages.

The lower part of the sequence also contains several altered tuff units. Of these, the Austin tuff located at the top of the lower part of the sequence, is particularly significant as it is host to almost all of the mined gold in this area. These altered tuff units are lithologically and chemically (Figure 4) very heterogeneous. They comprise interlayered sequences of hydrothermally altered mafic flows and intermediate to felsic pyroclastic rocks. The tuff units are characterized by aluminous mineral assem-

blages. They contain variable proportions of muscovite, biotite, cordierite, staurolite, and garnet.

The upper part of the lower (tholeiitic-komatiitic) sequence comprises dominantly felsic to intermediate volcanic rocks with minor amounts of interspersed mafic volcanic rocks (Figure 5). The felsic and intermediate volcanic rocks are characterized by rhyolitic tuff and tuff-breccia, and spherulitic flows of dacitic composition, respectively. The mafic volcanic rocks typically occur in thin units consisting of interlayered pillowed and massive flows and minor pillow breccia. Compositionally, these rocks are high-iron tholeiitic basalts. Variolitic lavas of tholeiitic andesite composition were observed in a few localities.

Rocks in the upper part of the sequence were previously thought to be part of the calc-alkalic sequence (Pirie 1980, 1981; Wallace 1981; Pirie *et al.* 1982; Durocher and van Haaften 1982). Recognition of their tholeiitic affinity has resulted in the boundary between the tholeiitic-komatiitic and calc-alkalic sequence being shifted south by 1-2 km. The present work and work to the northeast of the study area by Wallace (1983, personal com-

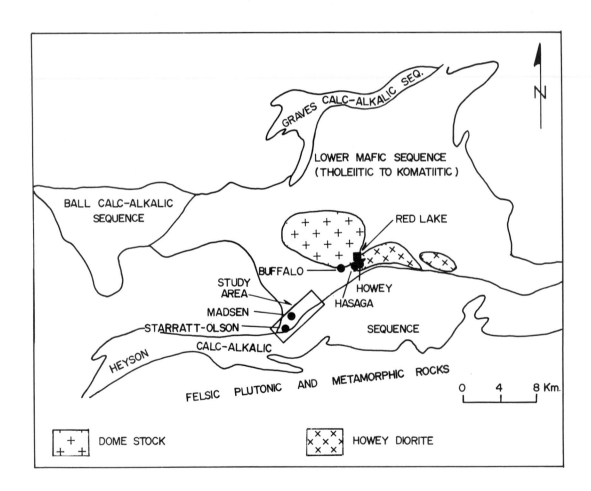

Figure 1. *Major volcanic sequences in the Red Lake area (modified after Pirie 1981).*

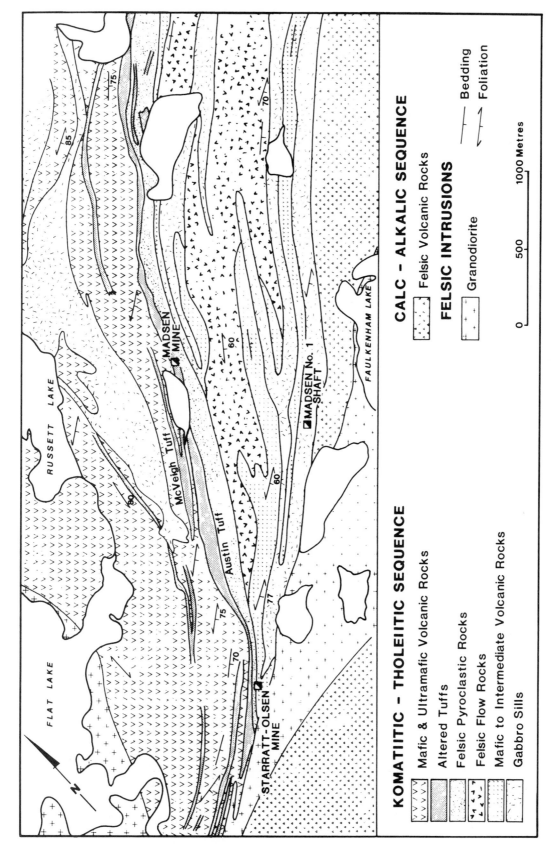

Figure 2. General geology of the Madsen and Starrat-Olsen area (modified after Horwood 1940 and Ferguson 1965).

125

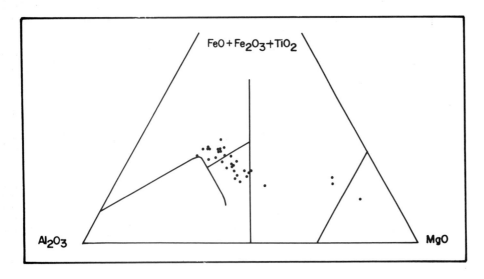

Figure 3. *Cation plot of 33 samples from the lower part of the lower tholeiitic-komatiitic sequence.*

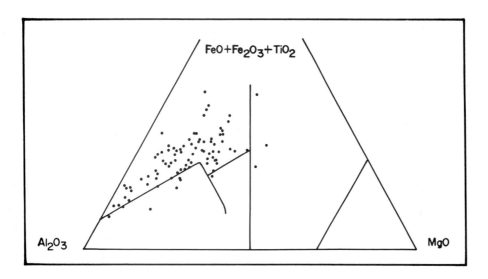

Figure 4. *Cation plot of 85 samples from the altered tuff units of the lower part of the lower tholeiitic-komatiitic sequence.*

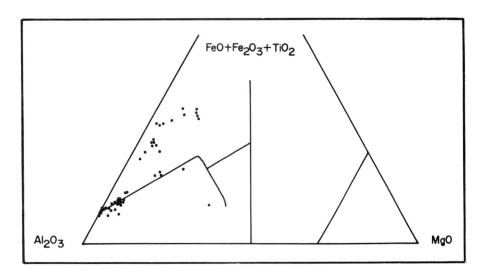

Figure 5. *Cation plot of 46 samples from the upper part of the lower tholeiitic-komatiitic sequence.*

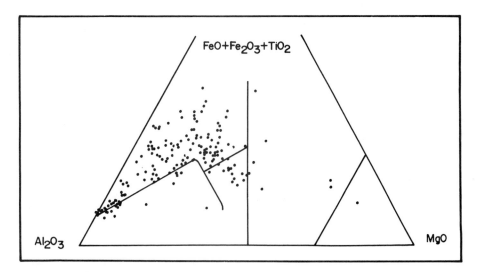

Figure 6. *Cation plot of 164 samples from all rock types.*

munication) suggests that the boundary between the two sequences should be modified as shown in Figure 1. This boundary modification is significant in that the Howey and Hasaga former gold producers are now considered to be located in the upper part of the tholeiitic-komatiitic sequence rather than in the lower part of the calc-alkalic sequence.

Gabbro sills and dikes are present in both the upper and lower parts of the sequence. Some of the sills appear to be slightly differentiated with mafic gabbro or feldspathic pyroxenite lower zones and quartz gabbro upper zones. Compositionally, these sills are very similar to the tholeiitic basalts.

CALC-ALKALIC SEQUENCE

Only the lower part of the calc-alkalic sequence is exposed in the study area. It comprises rhyolitic flows, tuffs and breccias. To the east of the study area these felsic volcanic rocks interdigitate vertically and laterally with dacitic, andesitic and basaltic rocks (Pirie 1980). On the basis of chemical data received to date, and work carried out by Wallace (1983, personal communication) the felsic volcanic rocks in the lower part of the Heyson calc-alkalic sequence appear to be significantly more potassic than the underlying felsic rocks of the tholeiitic suite.

The youngest rocks in the area are the granodiorites of the Faulkenham Lake Stock, and the Killala Baird Batholith. Granodiorite dikes have been found to cut across orebodies in the Madsen Mine (Horwood 1940).

Preliminary results of petrographic studies indicate that the volcanic and mafic intrusive rocks in the area have been subjected to amphibolite facies regional metamorphism, and apparently were subsequently subjected to contact metamorphism associated with intrusion of the Faulkenham Lake Stock and the Killala Baird Batholith.

ORE DEPOSITS

To date, all gold production in the area has come from two mines: the Madsen Mine, and the Starratt-Olsen Mine (see Figure 2). The Madsen Mine was in production from 1938 to 1976, and produced 2,416,609 ounces of gold and 417,567 ounces of silver from ore with an average grade of 0.292 ounces Au per ton and 0.05 ounces Ag per ton. The Starratt-Olsen Mine operated from 1948 to 1956 and produced 163,990 ounces of gold, and 27,432 ounces of silver from ore with an average grade of 0.180 ounces Au per ton and 0.03 ounces Ag per ton.

The ore zones at the Madsen Mine are situated in the Austin tuff (Horwood 1940). In the vicinity of the Starratt-Olsen Mine the Austin tuff bifurcates into several small subparallel units. The Starratt-Olsen ore zones are situated in the most northerly of these tuff units (Ferguson 1965). Ore zones in both mines are stratabound within these tuff units and occur where they exhibit significant increase in apparent thickness.

Ore zones at the Madsen Mine comprise several en echelon orebodies (Figure 7), consisting of lenses of sheared sulphide-bearing tuff (Horwood 1940). These ore zones are parallel to bedding and oblique to foliation. Individual orebodies within ore zones are oblique to bedding and parallel to foliation (Figure 7). The ore zones rake at 45-48° northeast (Figure 8), whereas the orebodies within these zones do not rake. Ore zones at the Starratt-Olsen Mine are very similar to those at the Madsen Mine, but do not rake (Figure 8).

The ore zones at both mines contain variable quantities of pyrite, pyrrhotite, arsenopyrite, sphalerite, chalcopyrite, magnetite, and gold. Scheelite and molybdenite are rare. Finely disseminated pyrite is by far the most abundant sulphide mineral (Horwood 1940). Most of the gold occurs in the native state as minute (4-5 micrometres) inclusions in silicate minerals, and to a lesser extent as coatings on sulphide minerals (Ferguson 1965).

HYDROTHERMAL ALTERATION

Field observations and preliminary petrographic and geochemical studies of 147 surface samples collected from all rock types (analysed by the Geoscience Laboratories of the Ontario Geological Survey) indicate that there is an extensive hydrothermal halo associated with the Madsen and Starratt-Olsen gold deposits. The alteration halo extends along strike for at least 9 km, and is not confined to the Austin tuff but extends up to 600 m into the underlying rocks and up to 200 m into the overlying rocks. The most intense hydrothermal alteration is centred on the Austin and McVeigh tuffs. The location of the samples and the distribution of selected major and minor oxides, and trace elements in the vicinity of these deposits is illustrated in Figures 9-20.

NA$_2$O

The distribution pattern (Figure 10) of Na$_2$O in rocks in the vicinity of these deposits is indicative of intense Na$_2$O depletion in the altered tuff units, and somewhat less intense Na$_2$O depletion in the adjacent rocks. Mineralogically the intense Na$_2$O depletion is indicated by the presence of andalusite, cordierite, staurolite, almandine garnet, biotite and muscovite in these rocks.

K$_2$O

The distribution pattern (Figure 11) of K$_2$O is indicative of potassic metasomatism. The most intense zone of potassic metasomatism is centred on the Austin and McVeigh tuffs, and on the overlying felsic pyroclastic rocks. The underlying tholeiitic basalts and gabbro sill have been metasomatized to a lesser degree. The spherulitic dacitic flows, and mafic flows of the upper part of the tholeiitic-komatiitic sequence appear to have been largely unaffected by the potassic metasomatism. Mineralogically the potassic metasomatism is indicated by the presence of abundant biotite and muscovite in these rocks.

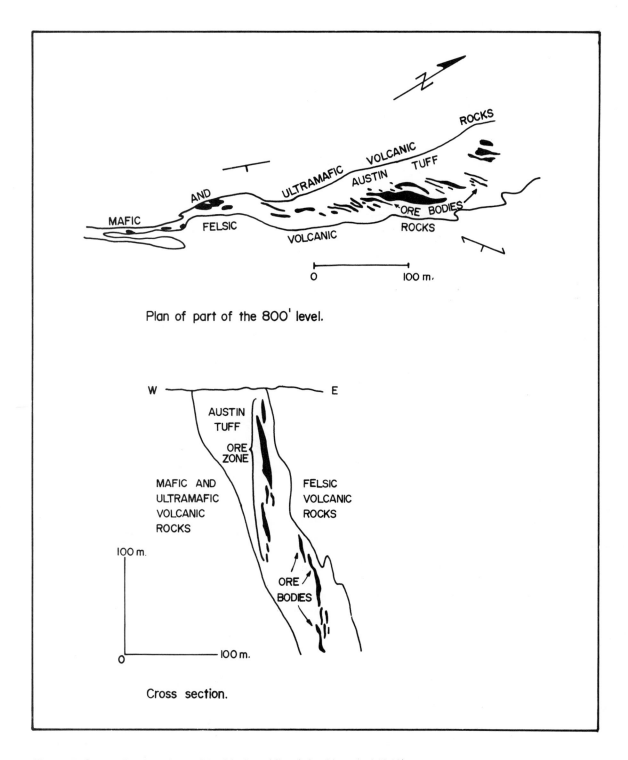

Plan of part of the 800' level.

Cross section.

Figure 7. Generalized geology of the Madsen Mine (after Horwood 1940).

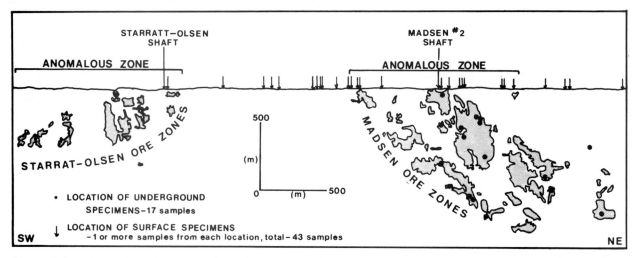

Figure 8. *Longitudinal section, in the plane of the Austin tuff, showing the distribution of the Madsen and Starratt-Olsen ore zones.*

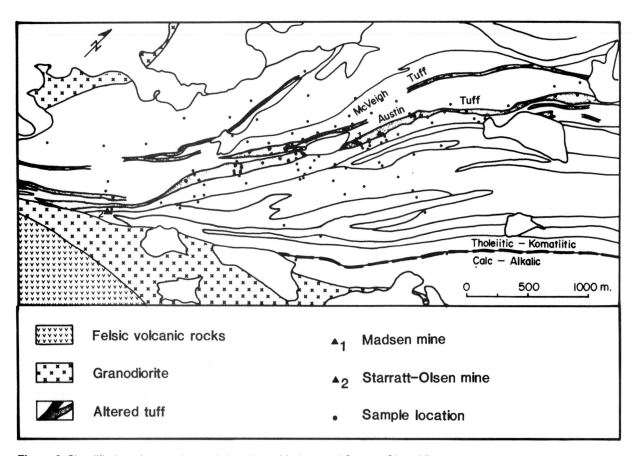

Figure 9. *Simplified geology and sample locations, Madsen and Starratt-Olsen Mines area.*

CO₂

The distribution pattern (Figure 12) of CO_2 is similar to that of Na_2O in that, there is a CO_2 'low' centred on the Austin and McVeigh tuffs in the vicinity of the Madsen and Starratt-Olsen Mines. The mafic rocks situated immediately below the McVeigh tuff have high CO_2 contents. The CO_2 'high' correlates well with the occurrence of many small quartz-carbonate veins in these rocks.

GOLD

All specimens were analysed for gold content by graphite furnace atomic absorption spectroscopy, and by optical emission spectroscopy (Geoscience Laboratories, Ontario Geological Survey). Results from the two methods are comparable, and presented in Figure 13. In the case of a significant discrepancy in results from the two methods the lower of the two values was utilized. There is a pronounced gold anomaly immediately above the Madsen ore zones (compare Figures 8 and 13). This anomaly is centred on the Austin tuff and to a lesser extent on the

McVeigh tuff. It extends for less than 50 m into the adjacent rocks. There is probably a similar anomaly associated with the Starratt-Olsen ore zones. There are several smaller anomalies in the Austin tuff to the northeast of the Madsen Mine, and between the Madsen and Starratt-Olsen Mines.

ARSENIC

The distribution pattern for arsenic (Figure 14) resembles that of gold (Figure 13). There is a well defined arsenic anomaly directly above the Madsen ore zones. It is centred on the Austin and McVeigh tuffs and does not extend for more than a few metres into the adjacent rocks. There are several smaller anomalies elsewhere in the Austin and McVeigh tuffs and in the rocks immediately adjacent to these tuff units. Geochemical data received to date suggest that there may also be a significant arsenic anomaly associated with the Starratt-Olsen ore zones. These arsenic anomalies correlate with the presence of arsenopyrite in these rocks.

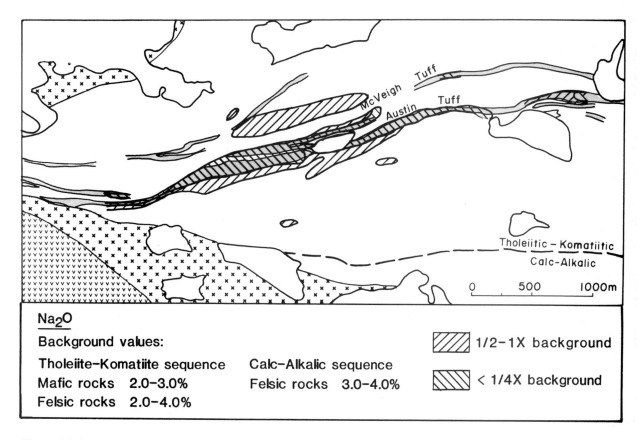

Figure 10. Distribution pattern of Na₂O in rocks of the Madsen and Starratt-Olsen Mines area.

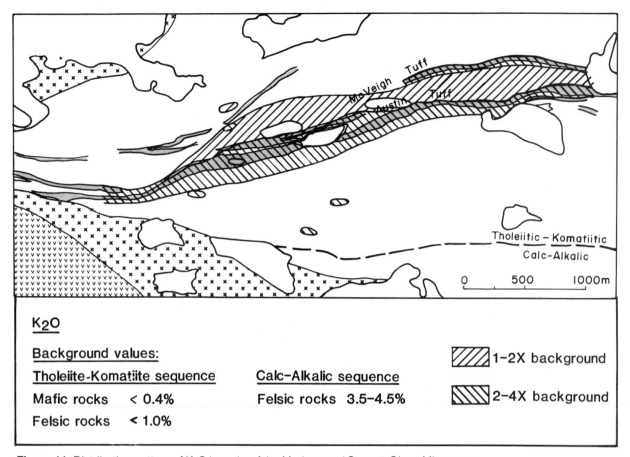

K₂O

Background values:

Tholeiite-Komatiite sequence

Calc-Alkalic sequence

Mafic rocks   < 0.4%

Felsic rocks   3.5–4.5%

Felsic rocks   < 1.0%

░░░ 1–2X background

▓▓▓ 2–4X background

Figure 11. *Distribution pattern of K₂O in rocks of the Madsen and Starratt-Olsen Mines area.*

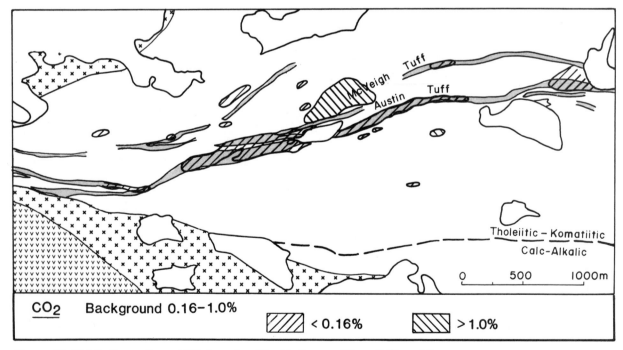

CO₂   Background 0.16–1.0%   ░░░ < 0.16%   ▓▓▓ > 1.0%

Figure 12. *Distribution pattern of CO₂ in rocks of the Madsen and Starratt-Olsen Mines area.*

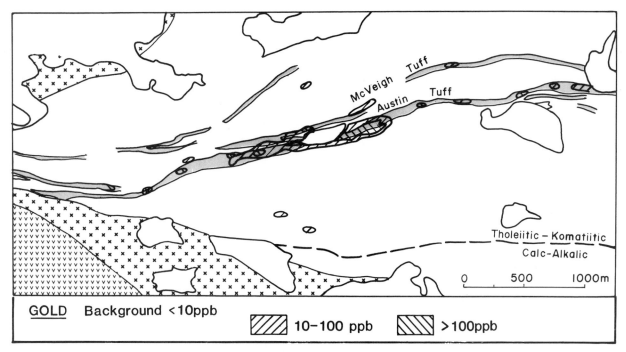

Figure 13. *Distribution pattern of Au in rocks of the Madsen and Starratt-Olsen Mines area.*

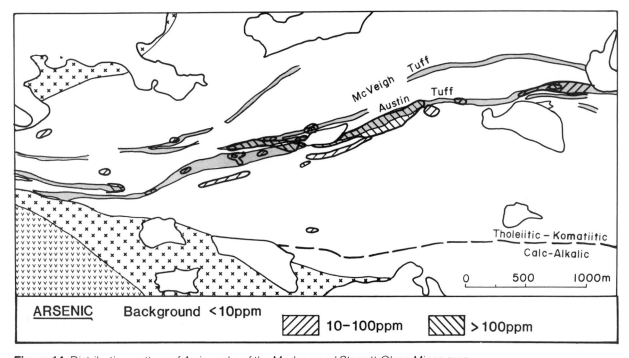

Figure 14. *Distribution pattern of As in rocks of the Madsen and Starratt-Olsen Mines area.*

SULPHUR

Sulphur forms a well defined anomaly (Figure 15) situated directly above the Madsen ore zones. Like the gold and arsenic anomalies, the sulphur anomaly is centred on the Austin and McVeigh tuffs and extends for only a few tens of metres into the adjacent rocks. Available data suggests that there is probably a similar anomaly over the Starratt-Olsen ore zones. The sulphur anomaly corresponds to significant amounts of sulphide minerals in the these rocks.

ANTIMONY

Unlike gold, arsenic and sulphur, antimony is found in higher than background amounts over a large area (Figure 16). The highest concentrations of antimony are located in or immediately adjacent to the altered tuff units. There is a pronounced anomaly over the Madsen ore zones located to the northeast of the Madsen shaft. There also appears to be a significant antimony anomaly associated with the Starratt-Olsen ore zones. Anomalous values of antimony are more widespread in the mafic rocks which underlie the Austin tuff than in the felsic pyroclastic rocks which overlie this unit. The presence of stibnite in these rocks is responsible for these anomalies.

BORON

The gross distribution of boron (Figure 17) is similar to the distribution patterns of antimony, and K_2O (Figures 11, 16). High concentrations of boron form a well defined anomaly which is centred on the Austin and McVeigh tuffs. Somewhat lower concentrations of boron extend into the underlying mafic rocks for up to 500 m and into the overlying felsic pyroclastic rocks for up to 200 m. On the basis of available chemical data, the altered tuff units in the vicinity of the Starratt-Olsen Mine appear to contain lower concentrations of boron than farther to the northeast. The high concentration of boron is indicative of tourmaline in these rocks.

LITHIUM

Slightly higher than background concentrations of lithium occur over a fairly large area (Figure 18). The highest concentrations of lithium form small anomalies directly above the southwest and northeast extremities of the Madsen ore zones, and the northeast extremity of the Starratt-Olsen ore zones (see Figure 8). As with antimony and boron (Figures 16 and 17) higher than background values of lithium are more widespread in the mafic rocks which underlie the altered tuff units than in the overlying felsic pyroclastic rocks.

COPPER AND ZINC

The copper and zinc contents of these rocks vary consid-

erably and it is not possible to establish background values with any degree of confidence. Areas in which rocks contain greater than 100 ppm copper or zinc are shown in Figures 19 and 20 respectively. In the case of copper, high values occur in the Austin tuff directly above the southwestern half of the Madsen ore zones, in the McVeigh tuff, and in the mafic volcanic rocks which immediately underlie the McVeigh tuff. High values also occur in the altered tuff directly above the northeast extremity of the Starratt-Olsen ore zone, and in the Austin tuff in the northeast part of the study area.

In the case of zinc, high values occur in parts of the McVeigh tuff, and in the underlying mafic rocks. They also occur in the Austin tuff directly above the southwest extremity and northeast extremity of the Madsen and Starratt-Olsen ore zones respectively. Midway between the ore zones of the two mines high zinc values are present in a long narrow zone in the Austin tuff. Northeast of the Madsen shaft the Austin tuff contains low values of zinc. The felsic pyroclastic rocks which overlie the Austin tuff contain only low value of zinc, whereas the intermediate and mafic flows higher up in the stratigraphy contain high values of zinc.

OTHER ELEMENTS

All of the specimens were also analysed for the following rare elements: Bi, Hg, U, Th, Pb, Be, Mo, W, Sn, Pt-Pd group. None of these elements are present in higher than background concentrations in the vicinity of these two deposits.

GEOCHEMICAL GUIDELINES FOR EXPLORATION IN THE AUSTIN TUFF

Forty-three specimens from surface exposures of the Austin tuff were collected and analysed for major oxides and trace elements. Similarly, seventeen specimens of the Austin tuff collected underground by former resident geologists of the Ministry of Natural Resources were analysed for major oxides and trace elements. The purpose of this study was to determine if there are any correlations between gold mineralization and geochemical anomalies within the ore horizon. Further analysis of the data is in progress and preliminary results are summarized graphically in Figures 21, 22, and 23. The locations of these specimens are shown in Figure 8.

Ore grade material is characterized by > 3400 ppb Au, > 4 ppm Sb, > 50 ppm As, and > 1 weight percent S. Background specimens are characterized by < 100 ppb Au, < 2 ppm Sb, < 50 ppm As, and < 1 weight percent S. Anomalous specimens have intermediate values of Au, Sb, and As. It is not possible to distinguish between background and anomalous specimens utilizing sulphur content. There is also a significant amount of overlap in As and Sb contents between anomalous and ore grade specimens.

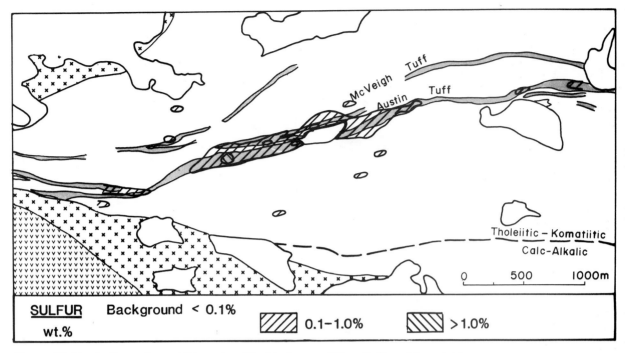

Figure 15. *Distribution pattern of S in rocks of the Madsen and Starratt-Olsen Mines area.*

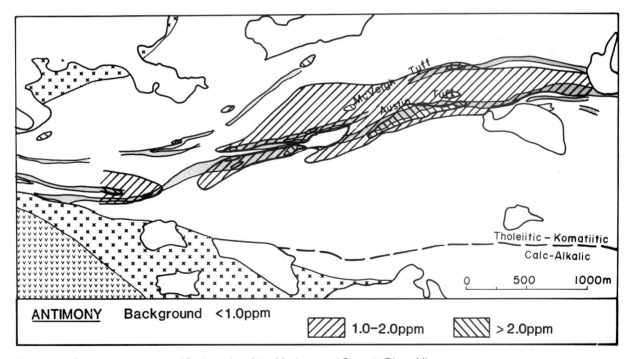

Figure 16. *Distribution pattern of Sb in rocks of the Madsen and Starratt-Olsen Mines area.*

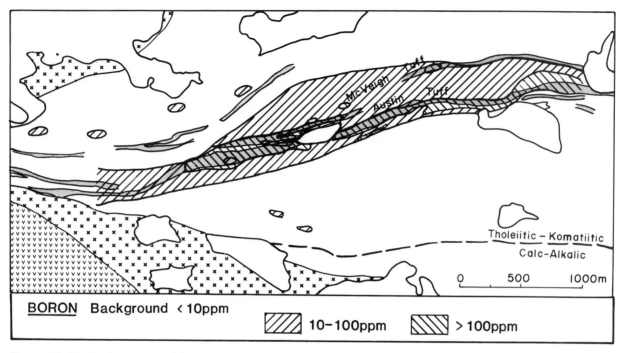

Figure 17. *Distribution pattern of B in rocks of the Madsen and Starratt-Olsen Mines area.*

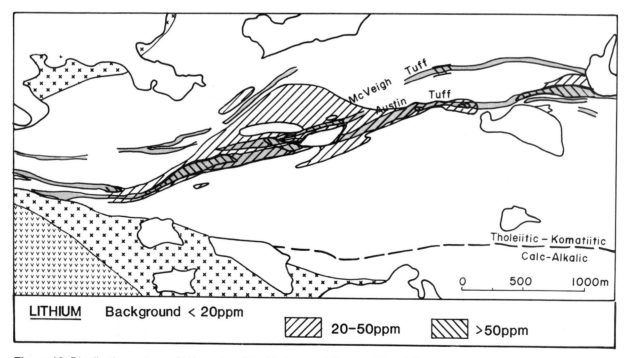

Figure 18. *Distribution pattern of Li in rocks of the Madsen and Starratt-Olsen Mines area.*

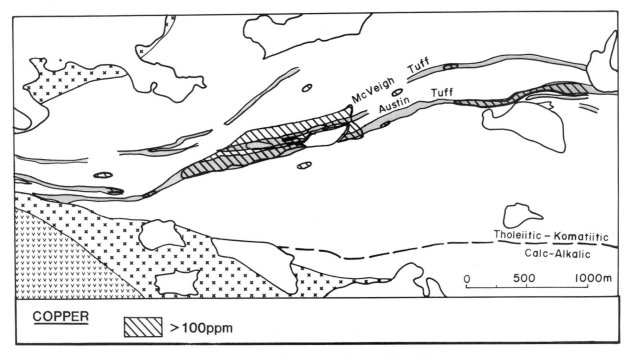

Figure 19. *Distribution pattern of Cu in rocks of the Madsen and Starratt-Olsen Mines area.*

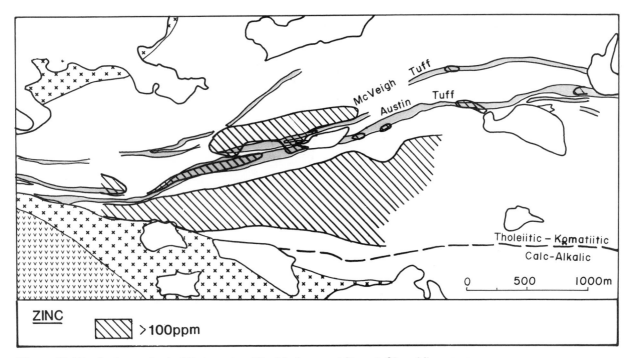

Figure 20. *Distribution pattern of Zn in rocks of the Madsen and Starratt-Olsen Mines area.*

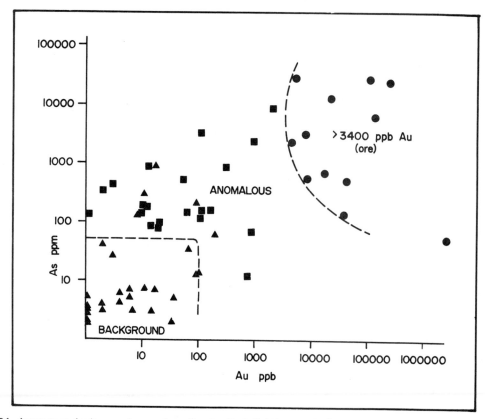

Figure 21. *Au versus As in specimens from the Austin tuff (60 samples). ● = ore grade (> 3400 ppb Au); ■ = underground sample collected close to orebody or surface sample from directly above orebody or ore zone; ▲ = surface sample not located directly above orebody or ore zone.*

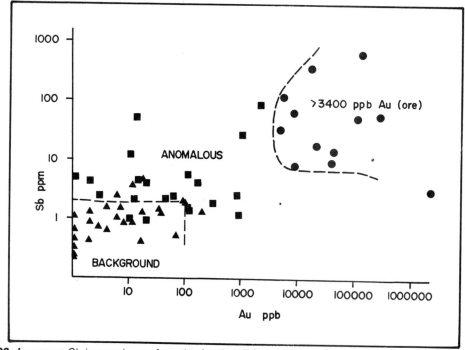

Figure 22. *Au versus Sb in specimens from the Austin tuff (60 samples). Symbols as for Figure 21.*

Due to the many problems associated with sampling and analysing for gold it is suggested that specimens of the Austin tuff assayed for gold, should also be analysed for As, Sb, and S. Specimens containing > 50 ppm As, > 4 ppm Sb, and > 1 weight percent S and low gold values should be re-assayed.

The distribution patterns of Au, As and Sb (Figures 13, 14, 16) indicate the presence of several small spot anomalies within the Austin tuff. Furthermore, these Au, As, and Sb anomalies are not always superimposed on each other.

The significance of these anomalies can be evaluated by using multi-element geochemical screens. Specimens located adjacent to or directly above orebodies or ore zones are all characterized by one of three types of anomalies. These are:

1. high Au (> 100 ppb), high As (> 50 ppm), high Sb (> 2 ppm)

2. high Au (> 100 ppb), high As (> 50 ppm), low Sb (<2 ppm)

3. low Au (< 100 ppb), high As (> 50 ppm), high Sb (> 2 ppm).

Use of these multi-element screens eliminates most of the spurious small spot anomalies. Those that remain can be assessed by analysing several specimens from the same outcrop. If most of the specimens from a given outcrop are not anomalous the anomaly is not indicative of the presence of ore nearby.

DISCUSSION

This work has highlighted several geological features which are associated with the gold mineralization in this area.

1. The gold mineralization is stratabound within a well defined volcanic stratigraphic succession with a strike length of at least 9 km. Gold showings are largely restricted to the more felsic tuff units and to date, economic concentrations have been found mainly within the thicker Austin tuff.

2. The gold mineralization consistently lies within a zone of highly altered rocks. The alteration zone is elongate northeasterly and is centred on the Austin tuff and to a lesser degree on the McVeigh tuff. It affects both, the underlying mafic volcanic rocks, and the overlying felsic pyroclastic rocks. The alteration zone is more widespread in the underlying mafic rocks, and is characterized by intense Na_2O depletion, and addition of substantial amounts of K_2O. Au, As, Sb, S, B, Li, and Cu are also present in anomalous amounts. The highly altered rocks are also characterized by low CO_2 contents. Au, As, S, and Sb form well defined anomalies directly above the ore zones. K_2O, B, Li, and also Sb form much broader anomalies which extend into the underlying rocks. Horwood (1940) observed that there are mineralogical differences between some of the ore zones. The location of the different trace element anomalies with respect to the ore zones is probably a reflection of zonation within and between ore zones.

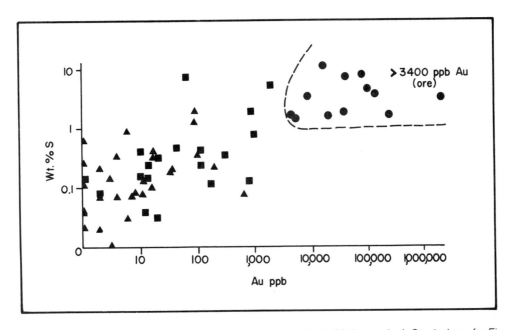

Figure 23. *Au versus S (weight percent) in specimens from the Austin Tuff (60 samples). Symbols as for Figure 21.*

3. The main gold host, the Austin tuff, lies consistently along the contact zone between two lithologically dissimilar rock sequences. Rocks of the Austin tuff are highly deformed, and the ore is structurally controlled. The Austin tuff may represent a significant structural break. The Howey and Hasaga former producers are located 12 km to the northeast along the strike extension of this postulated structural break.

4. Ore-grade material in the Austin tuff is characterized by > 3400 ppb Au, > 50 ppm As, > 4 ppm Sb, and > 1 weight percent S. Background rocks are characterized by < 100 ppb Au, < 50 ppm As, and < 2 ppm Sb. Multielement Au, As, and Sb anomalies can be used as indicators of close proximity to ore.

ACKNOWLEDGEMENTS

The author thanks S. van Haaften and K. Peden for their assistance during the field work and Henry Wallce for comments and for information provided during the preparation of this paper. C.D. Van Leeuwen provided assistance in the plotting of the initial data.

REFERENCES

Durocher, M.E., and van Haaften, S.
1982: Geology of the Madsen Gold Area, Red Lake; p.185-187, in Summary of Field Work, 1982 by the Ontario Geological Survey, edited by John Wood, Owen L . White, R.B. Barlow, and A.C. Colvine, Ontario Geological Survey, Miscellaneous Paper 106, 235p.

Ferguson, S.A.
1965: Geology of the Eastern Part of Baird Township, District of Kenora; Ontario Department of Mines, Geological Report 39, 47p. Accompanied by Map 2207, scale 1 inch to 1000 feet.
1968: Geology of Northern Part of Heyson Township, District of Kenora; Ontario Department of Mines, Geological Report 56, 54p. Accompanied by Map 2125, scale 1 inch to 1000 feet.

Horwood, H.C.
1940: Geology and Mineral Deposits of the Red Lake Area; Ontario Department of Mines, Annual Report, Volume 42, Part 2, p.174-189.

Jensen, L.S.
1976: A New Cation Plot for Classifying Subalkalic Volcanic Rocks; Ontario Division of Mines, MP66, 22p.

Pirie, J.
1980: Regional Geological Setting of Gold Mineralization in the Red Lake Area, Northwestern Ontario; p.303-358, in Genesis of Archean, Volcanic-Hosted Gold Deposits, edited by R.G. Roberts, Symposium held at the University of Waterloo, Ontario Geological Survey, Open File Report 5293, 387p.
1981: Regional Setting of Gold Deposits in the Red Lake Area, Northwestern Ontario; p.71-93 in Genesis of Archean Volcanic-Hosted Gold Deposits, Symposium held at the University of Waterloo, March 7, 1980, Ontario Geological Survey, Miscellaneous Paper 97, 175p.

Pirie, J., Durocher, M.E., and Wallace, H.
1982: Volcanic Stratigraphy, Alteration and Gold Deposits of the Red Lake Area, Northwestern Ontario. Geological Association of Canada, Field Trip No. 8 Guidebook.

Wallace, H.
1981: Red Lake Synoptic Project, District of Kenora; p.12-14, in Summary of Field Work, 1981, by the Ontario Geological Survey, edited by John Wood, O.L. White, R.B. Barlow, and A.C. Colvine, Ontario Geological Survey, Miscellaneous Paper 100, 255p.
in preparation: Geology of Baird Township; Ontario Geological Survey, Preliminary Map, Scale 1 inch to ¼ mile or 1:15,480.

Geology of the East South C Ore Zone, Dickenson Mine, Red Lake

M.J. Lavigne and J.H. Crocket
Department of Geology, McMaster University, Hamilton

ABSTRACT

The geology, whole rock chemistry and sulphur isotope compositions of the East South C ore zone in the Dickenson Mine at Red Lake, northwestern Ontario, were studied to test the hypothesis that the ore zone represents exhalative gold mineralization. The study has shown that:

1. The ore zone is largely cataclastic, cross-cuts sulphide facies banded iron formation and other stratigraphic horizons and is restricted to a shear zone of fissile mafic volcanic rocks.
2. Mineralization occurred largely after cleavage had developed and is superimposed on a medium grade metamorphic assemblage.
3. Sulphur isotope data support a dual source of sulphur.

The observations and data are interpreted to indicate that the mineralizing system intersected the sulphide facies banded iron formation, which acted as an impermeable barrier to eastward flowing mineralizing solutions. Sulphur from the iron formation mixed with the ore solutions. Other components of the mineralized veins, including gold, were released from the volcanic pile during metamorphism.

INTRODUCTION

The concept of exhalative gold mineralization in the Archean could provide exploration geologists with a potentially useful tool. It is necessary, however, that this concept be proven before it can be applied. This project was undertaken with the aim of determining the origin of East South C (ESC) ore zone at the Dickenson Mine, Red Lake. This ore zone has been considered by Kusmirski and Crocket (1980) and Kerrich *et al.* (1981) to have been deposited syngenetically with the enclosing volcanic and sedimentary rocks.

In this study, geological data, whole rock chemical compositions and sulphur isotopes of the ESC were compared with those of sulphide facies banded iron formation (SFBIF) and a variety of epigenetic mineralization in both the Dickenson Mine and the Campbell Red Lake Mine. This paper includes a geological description of the ESC and SFBIF followed by brief summaries of whole rock chemical compositions and sulphur isotopic data. Descriptions of the regional geology can be found in Pirie (1981) and descriptions of the geological environment surrounding the mines and of the vein mineralization can be found in MacGeehan and Hodgson (1982).

MINE STRUCTURES

There are two major structural fabrics at the Dickenson and Campbell Red Lake Mines. The dominant strike defined by major lithological contacts on the 15th level at the Campbell Red Lake Mine and in the northeast and southwest portions of the Dickenson Mine is east (Figure 1). Bedding in the sedimentary rocks in the area shown at the top of Figure 1 trends both east and north, parallel to the sedimentary rock-serpentinite contact. This contact, exposed on the 23rd level, is conformable and faces south (Figure 2). The SFBIF, which is approximately 400 feet southwest of the sedimentary rock-serpentinite contact, also strikes east (Figure 3). SFBIF examined in the ESC ore zone on the 26th and 27th levels also strikes east.

Superimposed on the trend defined by the primary lithologic contacts is a fabric which strikes northwest. On Figure 1, this trend is defined by the strikes of most of the ore zones and of those lithologic contacts in the vicinity of the D and ESC ore zones. The fabric is parallel to the well developed foliation. In detail, the northwest-trending fabric is defined by well developed foliation in the mafic volcanic rocks, carbonate veinlets, narrow zones of silicification and bleaching, pillow elongation, fault gouge, sulphide streaks, and a strong schistosity in the ultramafic rocks. These features are particularly well developed in a narrow elongate zone of highly fissile rock at the Dickenson Mine. The northeastern boundary of this zone is outlined by the open circles on Figure 1. The southwestern boundary is not as well defined and lies in the vicinity of the A-SC-ESC ore zones. Mathieson and Hodgson (in press) have interpreted these as fault boundaries. Within this zone pillows have been flattened, often beyond recognition, and the mafic volcanic rocks are strongly foliated and locally contain up to 50 percent carbonate veinlets parallel to foliation. Fault gouge and slickensides are common. Pre-deformation veinlets which were oriented oblique to the foliation have been variably transposed parallel to foliation. These features suggest that the fissile zone is a shear zone.

The amount of movement along the fault traces can

141

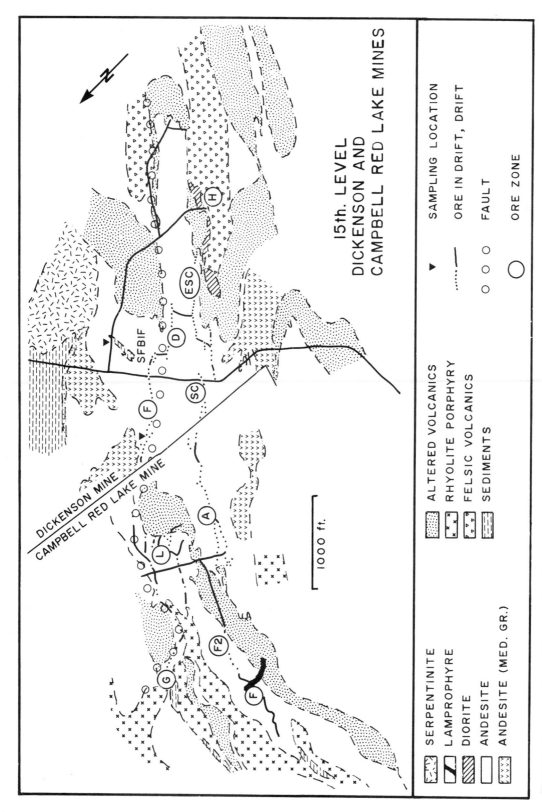

Figure 1. Geology of the 15th level at the Campbell Red Lake and Dickenson Mines.

15th. LEVEL
DICKENSON AND
CAMPBELL RED LAKE MINES

▼ SAMPLING LOCATION

ORE IN DRIFT, DRIFT

○○○ FAULT

○ ORE ZONE

SERPENTINITE

LAMPROPHYRE

DIORITE

ANDESITE

ANDESITE (MED. GR.)

ALTERED VOLCANICS

RHYOLITE PORPHYRY

FELSIC VOLCANICS

SEDIMENTS

DICKENSON MINE

CAMPBELL RED LAKE MINE

1000 ft.

SFBIF

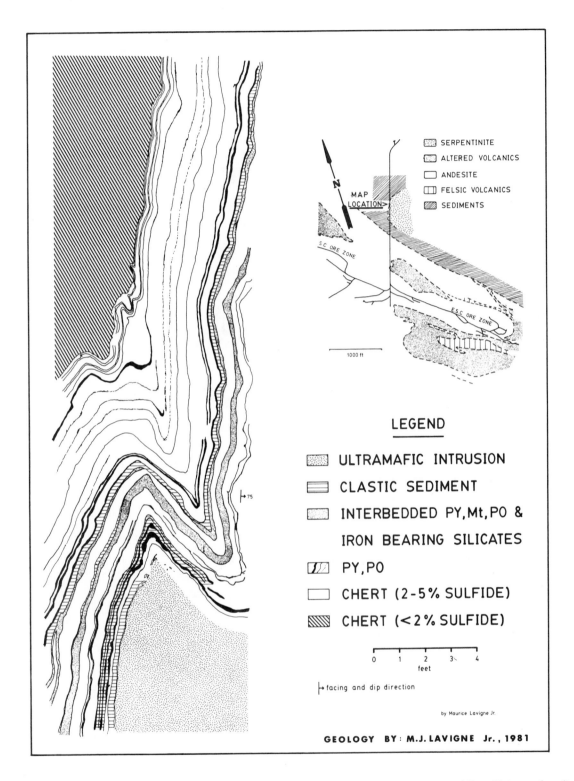

Figure 2. *Detailed geology of sediment-associated iron formation, 23rd Level, Dickenson Mine. Note conformity of iron formation-intrusion? contact.*

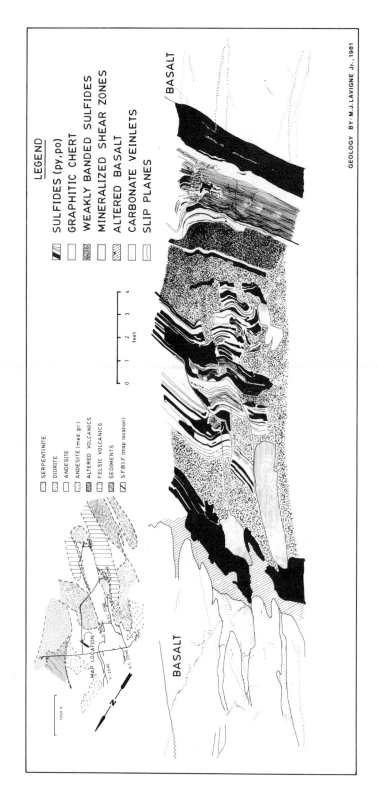

Figure 3. *Detailed geology of graphitic sulphide facies banded iron formation, 15th Level, Dickenson Mine.*

be interpreted from the mine-scale geology. Blocks of altered rock on the northeast side of the fault delineated on Figure 1 become aligned with blocks of altered rock on the southwest side of the fault if the 2000 feet of left-lateral movement is reversed. In doing so, the SFBIF on the north side of the fault becomes aligned with the SFBIF at the southeast end of the ESC.

Thus, mine-scale reconstruction and small-scale evidence of slip strongly support the contention that the fissile zone is a fault zone and that major lithologic contacts near this zone are fault contacts. Therefore the lithologic contacts in the fissile zone at the Dickenson Mine do not define primary bedding attitudes. Subsequent interpretations of parallelism of the ESC ore zone to lithologic contacts cannot be used as evidence to indicate that the ore zone is stratabound.

HOST ROCK

The host rock to the ESC ore zone, as it is for most ores at the Campbell Red Lake and Dickenson Mines, is mafic volcanic. Within the fissile zone the mafic volcanic rocks have highly variable characteristics due to both deformation and metasomatism. In areas of low strain two varieties have been observed. One is essentially unaltered, as found outside the fissile zone; the other is bleached. This latter type is a light brownish orange colour, and, where pillowed, has garnet-chlorite-biotite-magnetite pillow selvages. Where sheared, the altered pillowed flows yield a well banded rock of interlayered biotite-chlorite-garnet-magnetite and siliceous aphanitic light brownish orange bands. The siliceous bands consist of quartz and muscovite and very few mafic minerals. Based on its simple mineralogy, it appears to be depleted in Fe, Ca and Mg.

The most common form of the mafic volcanic rocks in the fissile zone is a strongly foliated rock with banding on a millimetre to centimetre scale. The dark bands are mafic and garnetiferous while the green bands are siliceous. These siliceous bands have a marked reduction in grain size and ferromagnesian content in comparison to the dark bands. Pre-deformation carbonate veinlets which were oblique to foliation are transposed parallel to foliation by slip along the green bands. Since this banded rock is the most common rock type in the fissile zone and represents shearing, the fissile zone must be interpreted to be a shear zone. It is common to find up to 50 percent carbonate veinlets parallel to the foliation within the fissile zone. Such intense carbonate veining, in conjunction with bleaching and shearing, has made mapping and establishing stratigraphy in the fissile zone a difficult task. It proved impossible to establish the detailed stratigraphy needed to determine whether or not the ESC is conformable.

MINE-SCALE FEATURES OF THE ESC

The ESC ore zone is restricted to the mafic volcanic rocks within the fissile zone at the Dickenson Mine (Figures 1, 4). It extends from the 15th to the 30th level, the deepest level at the mine and is, therefore, 2500 feet in the vertical dimension. The maximum lateral continuity is approximately 2000 feet. The ore zone is parallel to the dominant foliation and is planar on a mine scale. The ESC zone is the on-strike extension of the F-A-SC vein system (see Figure 1). Where the ore zone intersects altered rock, it terminates. This is clearly demonstrated in a cross-section (Figure 5), which shows that the roughly planar ESC terminates against a highly folded unit of altered rock. The fold closure defined by the altered rock plunges to the southeast, and the foliation is axial planar to the fold. This feature is common in vein mineralization; Figure 1 shows that the A, F2 and L zones at the Campbell Red Lake Mine all terminate against altered rock.

The ESC zone, as will be described in detail in the next section, is characterized by a wide variety of types of mineralization. One feature of the ESC which cannot be deduced from mine plans, but only by walking out the ESC on several levels, is that the eastern half of the ESC is sulphide-rich, banded mineralization while the western half is sulphide-poor quartz and quartz-carbonate veins. The sulphide-rich portion is clearly coincident with the occurrence of a sulphide facies banded iron formation (SFBIF). The vertical extent of this iron formation is from the 17th to the 30th level, an interval in which there is almost perfect superposition of the SFBIF and the sulphide rich portion of the ESC.

SULPHIDE FACIES BANDED IRON FORMATION (SFBIF)

Three distinct types of SFBIF occur at the Dickenson Mine: (1) graphitic, mafic volcanic-hosted; (2) tuffaceous, carbonaceous, felsic volcanic-hosted; and (3) a mixed sulphide-oxide-silicate facies type with sedimentary affiliations. Of these three, the graphitic type is the most important, due to its close spatial association with the ESC ore zone. Description of the graphitic type is based on the exposure on the 15th level (see Figure 3), since it is undeformed in comparison with those exposed in the vicinity of the ESC. As previously interpreted, this exposure is the same SFBIF as the one in the ESC, but has been dislocated due to faulting.

The graphitic SFBIF is roughly 3000 feet in the vertical dimension, has a maximum lateral continuity of 400 feet and an average thickness of roughly 10 feet. It therefore appears that this volumetrically insignificant SFBIF was deposited in a linear trough, underlain and overlain by mafic volcanic flows.

In detail, the graphitic SFBIF is a monotonous repetition of pyrite interbedded with black graphitic siliceous bands and a few clean chert bands (Figure 3). The basalt on the north side has some well developed pillows while the basalt on the south side is massive. Foliation is perpendicular to bedding and is defined by dislocation planes within the SFBIF, carbonate veinlets and bleached mineralized zones in the basalt. Pre-deformation veinlets are ptygmatically folded. Bleached mineralized zones in the basalt are restricted to the north side of the SFBIF.

These are narrow zones parallel to foliation; however, juxtaposed against the SFBIF is a narrow zone which also has been bleached and mineralized. It appears therefore that the SFBIF acted as an impermeable barrier to solutions circulating along cleavage in the basalt. The basalt on the south side is unaltered and it therefore appears that the solutions flowed eastward. It is unlikely that the SFBIF escaped alteration by the solutions.

The siliceous bands in the SFBIF are a mixture of colourless, low birefringent phyllosilicates with minor cherty quartz and quartz clasts. In most bands the mineralogy is masked by dense ultra-fine-grained (invisible) graphite. A few siliceous bands have disseminated sphalerite. The sulphide bands are dominated by pyrite and lesser pyrrhotite. Secondary arsenopyrite replaces the primary sulphides in a few samples examined. The arsenopyrite streaks cross-cut bedding.

ESC-SFBIF SPATIAL ASSOCIATION

Examination of mine plans revealed several locations in the ESC where SFBIF is exposed in the drifts. Three such locations, on the 21st, 26th and 27th levels were examined.

Figure 6 is a section of the 21-12102E drift where SFBIF was examined. To be noted on the figure is the position of the replacement silicification mineralization and the 21-12102 stope. At this location the SFBIF is highly deformed and primary bedding orientation cannot be deduced (Figure 7). The least deformed portion of the SFBIF is juxtaposed against the siliceous replacement mineralization. Here bedding is perpendicular to foliation. Sulphides have been extensively remobilized to streaks parallel to foliation. It should be noted that the replacement mineralization is juxtaposed on the north side and not the south side of the SFBIF.

On the 26th level, SFBIF is well exposed and preserved (Figure 8). Diamond-drill hole data have permitted a confident orientation to be determined for the SFBIF, which strikes east and dips south. It has been folded and therefore a portion strikes north. Foliation is axial planar to the fold.

There are two types of mineralization exposed near

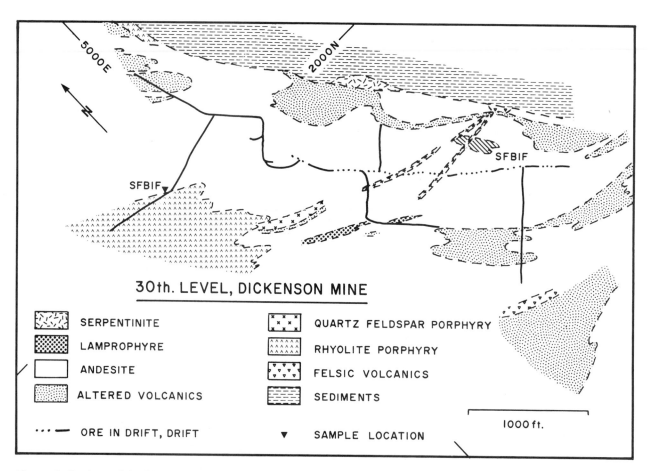

Figure 4. *Geology of the 30th level, Dickenson Mine.*

146

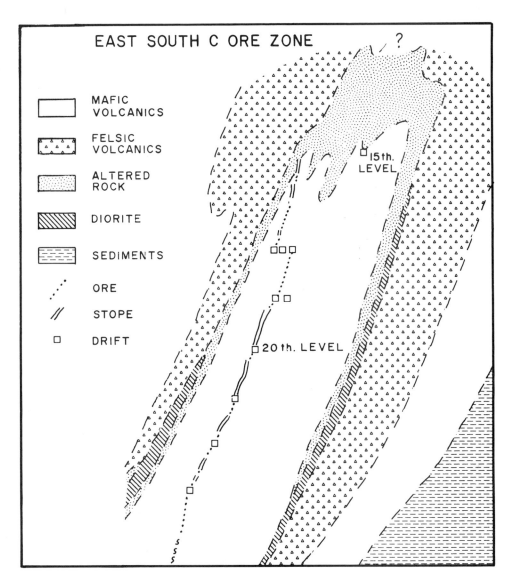

Figure 5. *Section, looking west, of the East South C ore zone.*

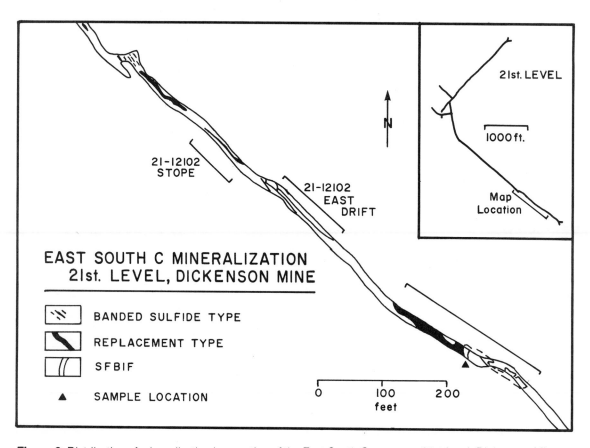

Figure 6. *Distribution of mineralization in a portion of the East South C ore zone, 21st level, Dickenson Mine.*

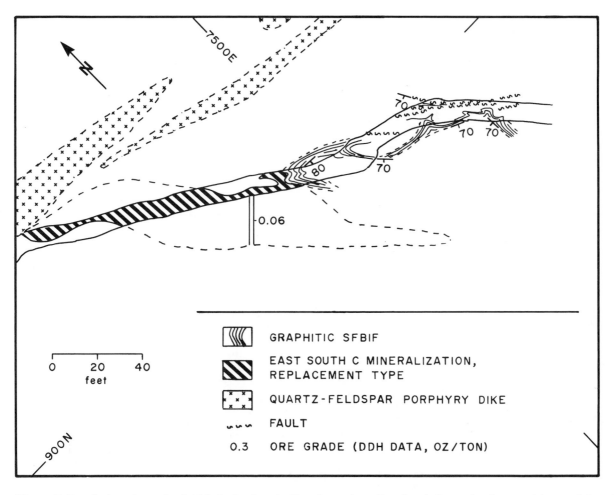

Figure 7. *Detailed geology of sulphide facies banded iron formation - East South C ore showing spatial association, 21st level, Dickenson Mine.*

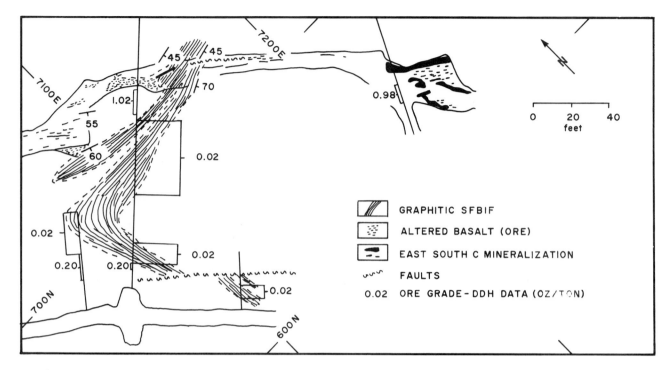

Figure 8. *Spatial association of East South C ore with sulphide facies banded iron formation, 26th level, Dickenson Mine.*

the SFBIF. To the southeast, there is some typical banded sulphide mineralization (Figure 8). On the north side and juxtaposed against the SFBIF is sulphide-poor mineralization unlike all other types of mineralization seen by the author at the mine (Figure 9). It is difficult to distinguish the mineralized basalt from wallrock basalt as no obvious visible alteration is apparent. The mineralized mafic volcanic rock displays slight bleaching and fewer carbonate veinlets than normally found in the basalt. A tongue of this ore crosscuts the SFBIF. Assays of diamond-drill hole core show that this ore has about 1 ounce gold per ton and that the basalt on the entire north side of the SFBIF is enriched in gold, while the SFBIF itself has a gold content reported as trace. The basalt on the south side of the SFBIF is also unmineralized.

SFBIF on the 27th level also strikes east (Figure 10). There is abundant banded sulphide mineralization and a pod of silification replacement mineralization to the Southeast of the SFBIF. Figure 11 is a detailed map of the SFBIF. The exposure of the SFBIF in the drift has been severely deformed by a cross-cutting carbonate vein. On the north side of the SFBIF, as exposed on the south wall of the drift the carbonate vein appears to be conformable. On the back, however, the carbonate vein clearly transects the SFBIF so that on the north wall, the carbonate vein is now on the south side of the SFBIF. This vein is not auriferous.

DETAILED DESCRIPTION OF ESC ORE ZONE

Sections of the ESC zone were examined on the 21st, 24th, 26th, 27th and 30th levels at the Dickenson Mine.

On the 21st level, a portion of the ESC was examined in the 21-12102 stope (Figure 6). The ore zone is a linear, foliation-parallel shear zone in pillowed amygdaloidal basalt. The ore lens is approximately 80 feet long and has a maximum width of 7 feet, and is fairly uniform in character along its entire length. Figure 12 is a detailed map of a representative section of ore. Pre-deformation, foliation-oblique, carbonate veinlets, common in the wallrock, are ptygmatically folded, transposed parallel to the foliation and assimilated into the ore zone. In the ore zone, where areas of low strain are coincidental with pillows, selvages are preserved. This feature is common throughout the ore lens, as are pillow selvages that terminate against the ore-wallrock contact.

Mineralogically the zone is simple. The areas of low strain consist of quartz, biotite and carbonate with minor muscovite, while zones of high strain have an increased proportion of muscovite and a decrease in grain size. The ore zone is approximately 5 percent sulphides with roughly equal proportions of pyrite, pyrrhotite and arsenopyrite and 0.5 percent magnetite. These minerals occur as disseminations, streaks and blebs.

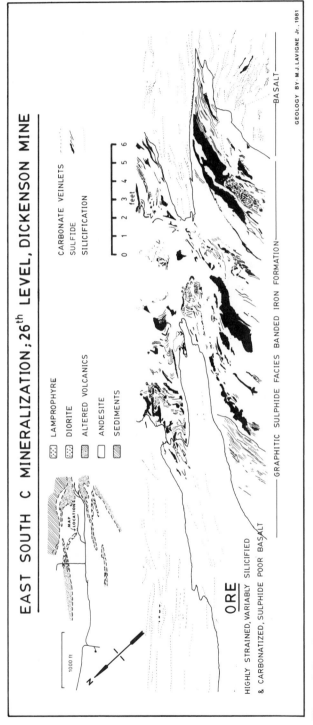

Figure 9. *Detailed geology of sulphide facies banded iron formation and associated East South C ore, 26th level, Dickenson Mine.*

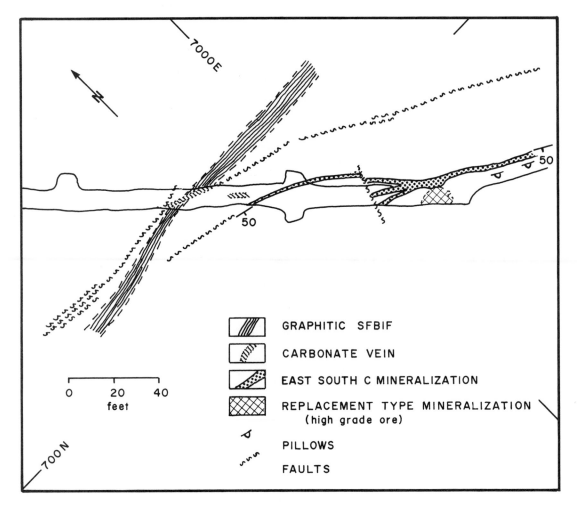

Figure 10. Spatial association of East South C mineralization and sulphide facies banded iron formation, 27th level, Dickenson Mine.

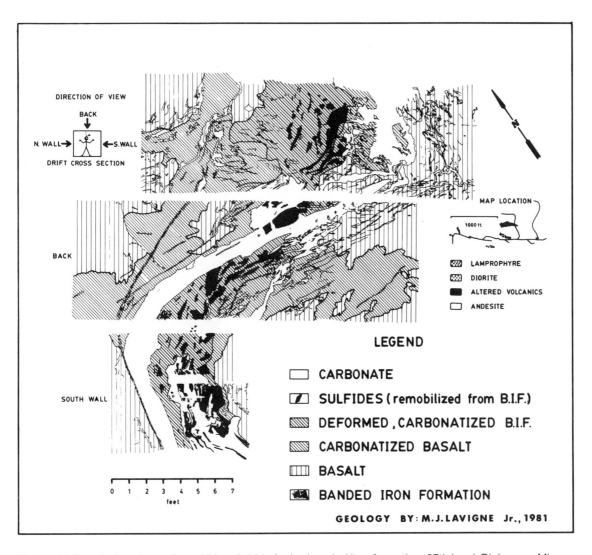

Figure 11. *Detailed geology of graphitic sulphide facies banded iron formation, 27th level, Dickenson Mine.*

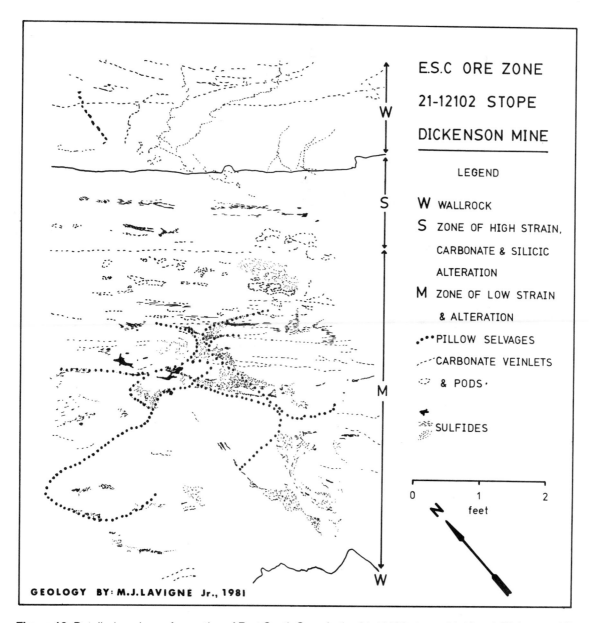

Figure 12. Detailed geology of a section of East South C ore in the 21-12102 stope, 21st level, Dickenson Mine. Note pillows preserved in ore.

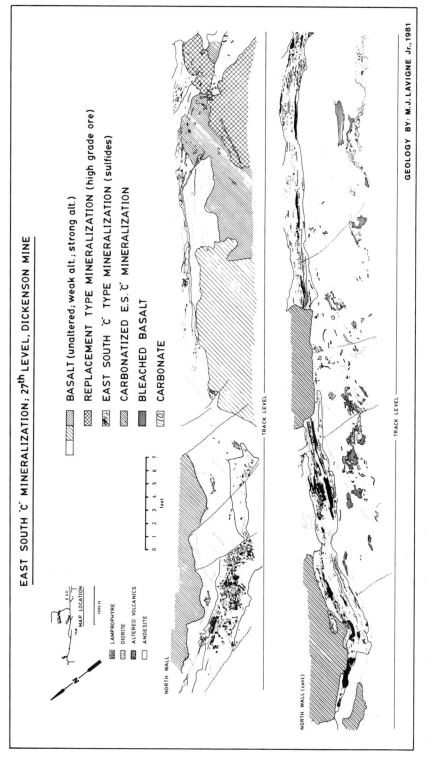

Figure 13. *Detailed geology of the East South C, 27th level, Dickenson Mine.*

The ESC ore zone on the 24th level has been described by both Rigg (1980) and Mathieson and Hodgson (in press) and it suffices to say here that there are two types of mineralization on this level. One is a siliceous high grade pod, steel grey in colour due to a high percentage of arsenopyrite. The irregular pod, roughly 20 feet thick, is found almost exclusively on the north side of a foliation-oblique quartz-carbonate vein. The other type of mineralization is a fragmental banded sulphide unit. Where this type occurs, the sulphides clearly impregnate wallrock basalt.

Figure 13 is a detailed map of the ESC on the 27th level. Although the mineralization appears to be typical ESC banded sulphides, it is not ore. The most westerly sulphide-rich unit has abundant sulphide streaks parallel to foliation. It also has a fragmental appearance due to an abundance of zones with contorted, folded, banded sulphides. This pod is interpreted as SFBIF which has been transposed parallel to foliation. The pod is fault-bounded and, on its southeast side, is translated southwards (see Figure 10) where it continues eastward. It reappears on the wall of the drift just above the replacement type mineralization. Some of the sulphide bands at this location are tentatively interpreted as contorted bedding. The siliceous replacement type mineralization has disseminated pyrite and arsenopyrite and abundant visible gold. The pod is unfoliated, is carbonate rich and has an alteration halo. To the east of the pod, the banded sulphides have been carbonatized. This carbonatized basalt is non-auriferous and is considered to be temporally distinct from the replacement mineralization. The banded sulphide body continues eastward and is gradually depleted in carbonate. At the face, pillow selvages in the wallrock can be traced into the mineralization where the amount of strain is low, but the selvages are assimilated in areas of high strain. The basalt has been bleached to a light brown colour.

The ESC ore zone was examined in several locations on the 30th level, located on Figure 14. Sections across the ore at Δ3053 and Δ3058 (sample locations) are described in Tables 1 and 2 respectively. To be noted again, is the close proximity of SFBIF to ore.

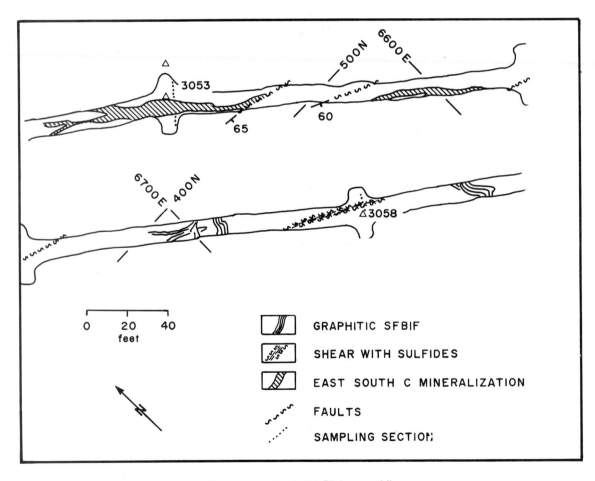

Figure 14. *Geology of the East South C ore zone, 30th level, Dickenson Mine.*

Table 1. *Description of section across the East South C ore zone at Δ3053, 30th Level, Dickenson Mine*

0.0-0.6 feet: wall rock; garnetiferous mafic volcanic

0.6-1.9 feet: carbonate breccia with wall rock fragments; 1% py, asp

1.9-3.3 feet: wallrock, garnetiferous mafic volcanic, ML-80-615

3.3-5.0 feet: ore; foliated mafic volcanic; mm to cm banding defined by strongly foliated quartz-biotite and biotite-carbonate, separated by bands of hornblende; biotite bands often become siliceous laterally and grade into quartz veins; has few carbonate veinlets contain chlorite and asp infillings; po, the only sulphide, occurs as streaks parallel to foliation replacing both the biotite and hornblende rich bands; minor magnetite; ML-80-615, 617

5.0-6.4 feet: ore; foliated brown siliceous zone of quartz and biotite with few hornblende and plagioclase bands; boudinaged carbonate veinlets are abundant; 5% po, 1% mt and variable py in stringers parallel to foliation; ML80-618.

6.4-6.8 feet: wallrock; mafic volcanic with hornblende, quartz and radiating clusters of actinolite; locally altered to biotite in shears, garnet has been fragmented and transposed into foliation ML-80-619.

6.8-8.3 feet: ore; strongly foliated bleached zone with banding defined by quartz-biotite and quartz-muscovite; has few plagioclase porphyroblasts, 5 diss. py and 1% po; mt occurs as needles in silicate; ML-80-620.

8.3-10.4 feet: wallrock; mafic volcanic with few amygdules; weak foliation defined by quartz-biotite and chlorite-plagioclase; garnet has been fragmented and transposed into foliation; minor diss. py; ML-80-621.

10.4-12.0 feet: ore; strongly foliated and veined zone; banding defined by variable quartz, biotite, and carbonate; carbonate veinlets are boudinaged; 3% po, 1% py., 0.5% asp, and trace mt; asp occurs as bands of diss. rhombs, producing distinctive aphanitic steel grey bands; ML-80-622, 623

12.0-19.0 feet: no exposure

19.0-22.0 feet: ore; foliated and fragmented; banding defined by quartz-biotite and quartz-hornblende-plagioclase; py, po, asp and mt are disseminated ; ML-80-866, 867, 868.

22.0-22.2 feet: ore; steel grey asp rich; carbonate, quartz, muscovite; also has diss. py, po, and mt; ML-80-869

22.2-24.2 feet: ore; strongly foliated zone; banding defined by quartz-muscovite, muscovite-biotite, and quartz-biotite-carbonate; has abundant cherty quartz fragments with interstitial sulphides; py. and asp are the dominant sulphides with trace po and mt; ML-80-870, 871

24.2-25.2 feet: ore; banded sulphide zone; silicate banding defined by quartz-muscovite and quartz-biotite-garnet-plagioclase-spinel; garnet porphyroblasts have preserved an earlier foliation defined by mt inclusions, sulphides were also overgrown; garnet is highly corroded, fragmented and transposed into the foliation; andalusite, spinel, and plagioclase porphyroblasts have also overgrown sulphides; pargasite (tentatively identified) is spatially associated with sulphides; 14% py, 5% po, and trace asp and mt; sulphides define an earlier banding which is folded about the foliation; ML-80872, 873

25.2- :wallrock; banded mafic volcanic

Table 2. *Description of section across the East South C ore zone at Δ3058, 30th level, Dickenson Mine.*

0.0: wallrock; mafic volcanic

0.0-0.4 feet: ore; strongly foliated quartz-muscovite-biotite schist; staurolite, garnet, andalusite and plagiocase porphyroblasts are abundant; minor hornblende is intergrown with sulphide and mt; dumortierite occurs in trace amounts; po and mt are intergrown with sulphide and mt; dumortierite occurs in trace amounts; po and mt are intergrown with minor py; asp occurs as distinct bands of diss. rhombs replacing po and mt, and intergrown with mt as larger single crystals; ML-80-603

0.4-1.0 feet: wallrock, mafic volcanic

1.0-2.0 feet: ore; bleached foliated zone of muscovite, andalusite, quartz and trace dumortierite; the foliation defined by muscovite is kinked; py occurs as stringers; ML-80-605

2.0-4.4 feet: wallrock, mafic volcanic with weak alteration to andalusite and few sulphide stringers; ML-80-606, 607, 608

4.4-6.0 feet: ore; bleached foliated zone; banding defined by quartz-muscovite and biotite-garnet; garnet and andalusite are porphyroblastic and often appear to have been shattered and dispersed; andalusite is spatially associated with sulphides; py occurs as interfolded stringers; ML-80-609, 610

6.0-7.0 feet: ore; strongly foliated bleached zone of quartz, biotite and andalusite, with some phyllonitic zones spatially associated with pyrite; py occurs as a massive band with minor po, asp, and mt; py, po and asp also occur as stringers, asp replacing po and py; ML-80-611, 612

SUMMARY OF ESC GEOLOGICAL CHARACTERISTICS

1. The type of mineralization is highly variable. It may occur as banded sulphide, fragmental banded sulphide, siliceous arsenopyrite bodies, silicification replacement mineralization, bleached shear zones and mineralized weakly altered basalt.

2. The entire ore zone is restricted to a zone of highly fissile mafic volcanic rocks interpreted to be a shear zone.

3. The ore is commonly concentrated on the north side of impermeable bodies such as altered rock, SFBIF and quartz-carbonate veins.

4. The ore zone is parallel to foliation and cross-cuts stratigraphy and cross-cuts SFBIF.

5. Sulphide-rich ores are spatially associated with SFBIF.

6. The ore zones impregnate and alter basalt. Primary features such as pillows are preserved in the ore.

7. The ore assemblage replaces an earlier medium grade metamorphic assemblage. The latter locally preserves an earlier sulphide assemblage.

8. The ore zone is largely cataclastic.

SUMMARY OF GEOCHEMICAL DATA

1. The SFBIF has a primary gold content which is less than 50 ppb and is often enriched to ore grade.

2. ESC mineralization is characterized by an enrichment in K, Fe, S, Zn, Au, As and W and depletion in Ca and Mg with respect to wallrock.

3. Sub-ore-grade banded sulphides in the ESC do not have the above alteration except for Fe and S enrichment.

4. The whole rock chemical compositions of the ESC reflect a basaltic composition, but a few samples approach the composition of SFBIF.

5. The ESC ore zone has a $\delta^{34}S_{py}$ of 0 to +8‰. Vein mineralization at the Dickenson and Campbell Red Lake Mines has $\delta^{34}S_{py}$ and $\delta^{34}S_{po}$ of +4‰ to +8‰. SFBIF associated with the ESC has $\delta^{34}S_{py}$ of –5.5‰ to +4.4‰. Sub-ore-grade banded sulphides have a $\delta^{34}S_{py}$ of +4‰.

CONCLUSIONS

1. The majority of ESC mineralization occurred during and after cleavage development and is superimposed on an earlier medium grade metamorphic assemblage. Mineralization is therefore late in the tectonic-metamorphic history of the volcanic pile.

2. The proximity of the SFBIF to the ESC is largely coincidental in that the F-A-SC-ESC mineralizing system happened to intersect it, and sulphide from the SFBIF mixed with the ore fluids. The SFBIF did have a role in producing mineralization. It behaved as an impermeable barrier to eastward flowing mineralizing solutions and the mix of sulphide from the SFBIF with the ore solutions probably induced precipitation.

3. Consideration of $\delta^{34}S_{fluid}$ supports a dual source of sulphur for the ESC.

4. It is geologically reasonable to consider that the source of sulphide in the sub-ore-grade banded sulphides, which impregnate basalt near the SFBIF on the 27th level, was the SFBIF. Thus, during remobilization the $\delta^{34}S$ increased by 4‰ to 5‰. This mechanism is considered to be responsible for producing the high $\delta^{34}S$ values found in the veins. Therefore, the sulphide found in the veins was released from the volcanic pile during metamorphism along with all other vein components, including gold.

ACKNOWLEDGEMENTS

We would like to thank the Dickenson and Campbell Red Lake mine staffs for their support, helpful suggestions and access to the underground. Financial assistance was provided by Energy, Mines and Resources Canada, Research Agreement 213-4-80.

REFERENCES

Kerrich, R., Fryer, B.J., Milner, K.J., and Peirce, M.G.
1981: The geochemistry of gold bearing chemical sediments, Dickenson Mine, Red Lake, Ontario: A reconnaissance study; Canadian Journal of Earth Sciences, Volume 18, p.624-637.

Kusmirski, R.T.M., and Crocket, J.H.
1980: Metallogeny of the gold deposits in the Dickenson Mine, Red Lake, Northwestern Ontario - A preliminary report; p.135-144, in Current Research, Part B, Geological Survey of Canada, Paper 80-1B.

MacGeehan, P.J. and Hodgson, C.J.
1982: Environments of gold mineralization in the Campbell Red Lake and Dickenson Mines, Red Lake District, Ontario; p.184-210, in Geology of Canadian Gold Deposits, CIMM Special Volume 24.

Mathieson, N.A., and Hodgson, C.J.
in press: Alteration, Mineralization, and Metamorphism in the Area of the East South 'C' Ore Zone, Dickenson Mine, Red Lake, Northwestern Ontario.

Pirie, J.
1981: Regional Geological Setting of Gold Deposits in the Red Lake Area, Northwestern Ontario; p.71-93 in Genesis of Archean, Volcanic Hosted Gold Deposits, Symposium Held at University of Waterloo, March 7, 1980, Ontario Geological Survey, Miscellaneous Paper 97, 175 p.

Rigg, D.
1980: Relationship between Structure and Gold Mineralization in Campbell Red Lake District, Ontario; Unpublished M.Sc. thesis, Queens University, Kingston, 153 p.

Geology of the Wilmar Mine, Red Lake Area

D.M. Rigg[1] and E.W. Scherkus[2]

[1]Corporation Falconbridge Copper, Thunder Bay

[2]Wilanour Resources Limited, Cochenour

ABSTRACT

The Wilmar property, located 6 km north of Red Lake, has been the focus recently of considerable surface and underground geological, geochemical and geophysical exploration. The dominant geological feature of this property is a large, easterly to north-northeasterly trending, canoe-shaped wedge of highly altered, mafic volcanic rocks, bounded to the north and south by two, laterally continuous, ultramafic dikes. Within this zone, auriferous mineralization occurs in a variety of rock types and structural settings that can be described in terms of three major types.

1. Low-grade but widespread gold mineralization occurs in association with a structurally controlled hydrothermal conduit, focused along the contact of the northern ultramafic dike. Ponding of hydrothermal fluids beneath an impermeable, felsic, volcanic cap may have contributed to the low-grade, widespread nature of this mineralization.

2. Localized, high grade mineralization occurs in association with patches of intense silicification, which has caused replacement of the host rock and the generation of numerous quartz veins. This type of mineralization is best developed within the core of the hydrothermal conduit described in (1).

3. Late stage, cross-cutting quartz ± tourmaline ± carbonate veins occur in a variety of competent rock types, and contain sporadic, generally non-economic gold mineralization.

INTRODUCTION

Over the last four years Wilanour Resources Limited has undertaken a major reassessment and exploration program on the Wilmar, Consolidated Marcus, Cochenour Willans and Annco properties, formerly controlled and operated by Cochenour Willans Gold Mines Limited.

Surface exploration has focused primarily on the Wilmar and Consolidated Marcus properties with extensive compilation work, line cutting, geophysics, geological mapping and over 50,800 feet of diamond drilling. In 1980 the decision to conduct underground exploration and development work was made and dewatering of the old workings began. Subsequently the company switched emphasis toward an extensive underground exploration program. In June 1982 Wilanour Resources Limited went into interim receivership. Little exploration and no mining has been undertaken since then; however, maintenance on the property and underground has continued.

LOCATION

The 69 claims (2,643 acres) of the mine property operated by Wilanour Resources Limited lie in Dome and Balmer Townships, northwestern Ontario (Figure 1). The Wilmar property, the focus of this paper, consists of 15 claims (679 acres) in east-central Dome Township, 6 km north of Red Lake, in the immediate vicinity of the Red Lake Airport (Figure 2).

MINE HISTORY

DEVELOPMENT AND PRODUCTION

The original 14 claims of the Cochenour Willans Mine were staked in 1925 by W.M. Cochenour and associates. After several surface and underground exploration programs Cochenour Willans Gold Mines Limited was incorporated in 1936 with production commencing in 1939. Between 1945 and 1965 the main 3 compartment shaft of the Cochenour Willans Mine was periodically deepened from 325 feet to 2600 feet, its current depth.

The 15 claims of the Wilmar property were explored between the time of the initial staking and 1959 by Martin McNeeley Mines Limited. Exploration focused on the Rahill Zone and a quartz porphyry dike (the Windsock porphyry) (Figure 3). However, this exploration was unsuccessful. In 1959 an agreement was reached with Cochenour Willans Gold Mines Limited to explore the underground potential of the property. A major 5000-foot exploration drive was developed during 1959 and 1960 from the Cochenour Willans main shaft, 1300 level. (All levels are given in depth in feet below mine collar.) Exploration drilling from this drive was successful in identifying a new type of ore structure, the Wilmar East Breccia Zone. Subsequently an internal shaft and several new levels were developed from the 1300 Wilmar level, and the internal shaft was completed to the 2050 level in 1964.

Production from the Wilmar property began in 1967 with the Cochenour-Annco ore near exhaustion to the

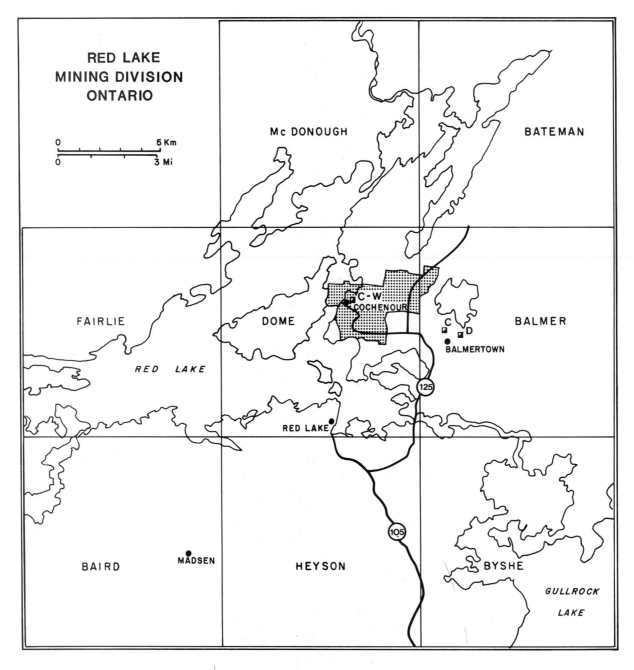

Figure 1. *Location of the property operated by Wilanour Resources Limited. C-W = Cochenour Willans Mine; C = Campbell Mine; D = Dickenson Mine.*

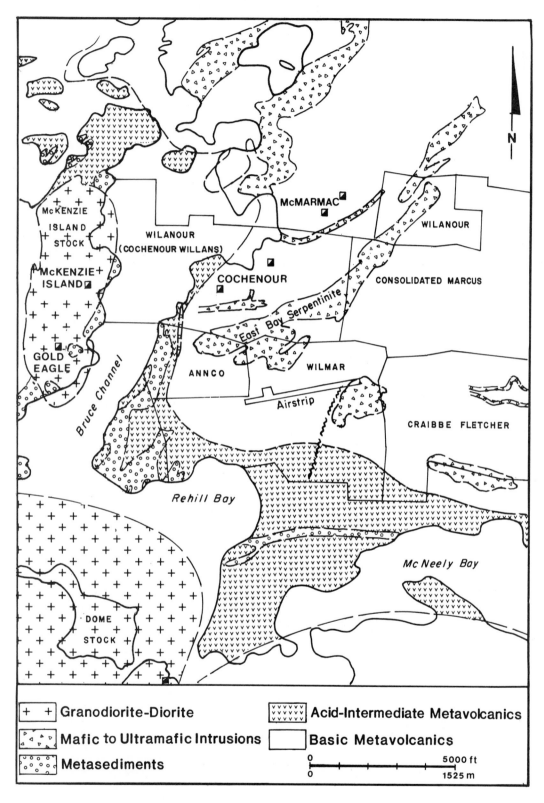

Figure 2. Simplified geology of the Wilanour Resoures Limited properties.

2200 level. At this time Wilmar ore was considered vital to the continuity of the mine with 28 percent of the mill feed coming from this property in 1967 and 63 percent in 1968. The mine continued to operate until 1971 when the Cochenour Willans Mine was allowed to flood to the 1450 level and all production stopped. Minor production and extensive drilling was continued on the Wilmar East Breccia Zone and a low grade orebody known as the Granodiorite or Wilmar West Zone. Due to high operating costs and decreasing gold prices from 1973 to 1975, the mine was finally forced to close.

A total of 1,131,000 ounces of gold were recovered from over 2 million tons of ore from 1939 to 1975 at the Cochenour Willans Mine. The Wilmar Mine contributed approximately 200,000 tons.

RECENT WORK

In November of 1978, Camflo Mines Limited contracted the consulting firm of I.M. Watson and Associates Limited of Vancouver to evaluate the Red Lake holdings of Cochenour Willans Gold Mine Limited. On the basis of this evaluation it was recommended that a detailed exploration and evaluation of the Cochenour holdings be undertaken with specific interest to be paid to the Wilmar East (Breccia) and Wilmar West (Granodiorite) Zones (Figure 3). It was concluded that these zones offered the best exploration potential and according to previous company reports offered known drill-indicated reserves. On June 18, 1979, Cochenour Willans Gold Mines Limited was renamed Wilanour Resources Limited with Camflo Mines Limited holding a 23.3 percent interest in the company. This interest was subsequently increased to 54.2 percent. In 1981 a substantial change in economic climate forced curtailment of all exploration and development on the property. In June 1982 Wilanour Resources Limited went into interim receivership. Maintenance on the property has continued such that underground exploration and development could be rapidly re-started.

REGIONAL GEOLOGY[1]

The Wilmar property is underlain by a mafic volcanic complex which is part of the Lower Tholeiitic-Komatiitic sequence of Pirie (1981). This is bounded to the south by a felsic volcanic-sedimentary sequence, possibly part of the Upper Heyson calc-alkaline sequence (Pirie 1981) (see Figure 2). The mafic volcanic complex is composed of metamorphosed tholeiitic basalt, andesite, minor felsic volcanic rocks and intraformational iron formation. The southern, south-facing felsic volcanic-sedimentary sequence is composed of felsic to intermediate tuff, lapillistone and breccia with large volumes of bedded exhalative chert, chert breccia, cherty iron formation and clastic metasediments.

---

[1]Geological information was derived in part from unpublished company reports. These are listed in the selected references.

The major structural and lithological trends of the Wilmar property (Figure 3) strike east to northeast, a continuation of trends near the Campbell Red Lake Mine, located 4 km to the east. However, they are strongly oblique to structural and lithological trends to the north and west, along the shore of Bruce Channel (Figure 2) (also Figure 2, Andrews and Wallace, this volume). The rapid change in orientation of these trends suggests a major anticlinal fold axis which strikes approximately east to northeast across the Wilmar and Annco properties respectively and plunges southwest along the peninsula between Rahill Bay and Bruce Channel. The regional cleavage appears to strike roughly east throughout the area and is, in part, oblique to the interpreted fold axis. The major strike change could also be attributed to a major northeast-striking fault within the Annco property. A third alternative is a major, domal sequence of mafic volcanic rocks (the main mafic complex) overlain to the west and south by encroaching, onlapping sequences of felsic volcanic rocks and sedimentary rocks. Detailed structural analysis is required to test the validity of these alternative models.

Throughout the region there are several major intrusive bodies of variable composition. The Dome Stock lies approximately 1.5 km to the southwest of the property and consists of an orbicular, differentiated, granodiorite mass, somewhat similar to the elongate, differentiated dioritic McKenzie Island Stock 0.8 km to the northwest of the property (see Figure 2). A small granodioritic dike, named the Wilmar West Granodiorite Zone, is located on the west central part of Wilmar property (see Figure 3). This dike may be related to a quartz-porphyry plug on the Rahill Bay – Bruce Channel peninsula, the McKenzie Island Stock or the main Dome Stock. Insufficient work has been conducted to outline these relationships.

Major ultramafic intrusive bodies also occur. The East Bay Serpentinite, which strikes southwest across Bateman Township, terminates in Dome Township on the Annco property, crosscutting the more northwesterly parts of the Wilmar property (see Figure 2). This body has a central core of relatively unaltered peridotite with a 'skin' of talc-carbonate rocks of variable thickness. Several ultramafic dikes strike approximately east through the central portion of the Wilanour property. They have great lateral continuity and appear to merge at depth into a large ultramafic stock identified in the mine workings. These intrusive rocks may be related to the East Bay Serpentinite and/or an orbicular mafic intrusion which occurs on the Wilmar-Craibbe Fletcher property boundary to the east (see Figure 2, 3).

Gold mineralization is common throughout the area and occurs in several different environments. The main mafic volcanic sequence hosts the ores of the past-producing Abino, McMarmac, Cochenour Willans, Annco, Wilmar and H.G. Young Mines and the currently producing Campbell Red Lake and Dickenson Mines to the east (see Andrews and Wallace, Figure 1, this volume). The McKenzie Island Stock and the Dome Stock host the ores of the McKenzie Island, Gold Eagle and Gold Shore Mines. The ore environments of these mines are very varied and the deposits may be classified as mafic volcanic-

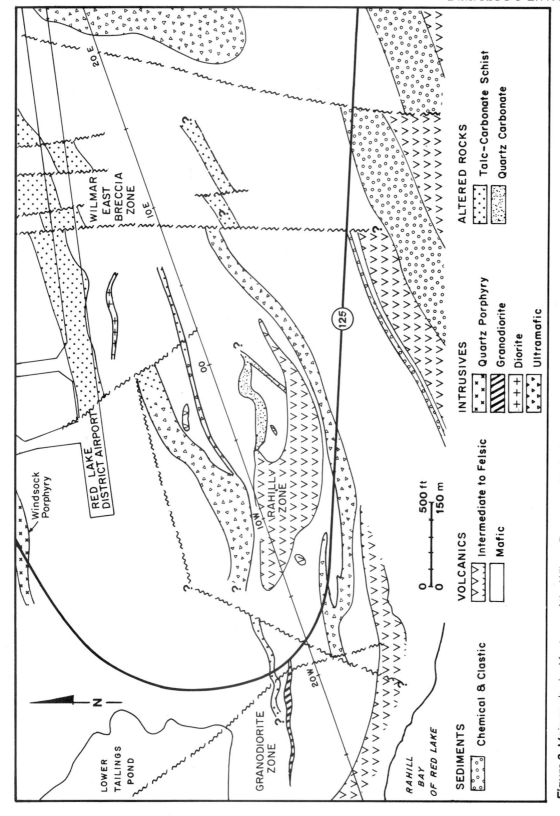

Figure 3. *Main geological features of the Wilmar Resources Limited property, as deduced from surface outcrops, diamond drilling and underground workings.*

hosted, felsic intrusive-hosted and stratabound (Pirie 1981). The Wilmar ore zones can be classified as mafic volcanic-hosted and felsic intrusive-hosted deposits. It is the proximity and close association of the mafic volcanic-hosted (Wilmar East) and the felsic intrusive-hosted (Wilmar West) deposits with the area of major structural changes which results in numerous interpretive and compilation problems within the Wilmar property and mine property as a whole.

DETAILED MINE GEOLOGY

MAIN MAFIC VOLCANIC COMPLEX

VOLCANIC AND SEDIMENTARY ROCKS

Mafic Volcanic Rocks. The complex is composed mainly of pillowed to massive, mafic volcanic flows. The basalts are usually medium-green (chloritic) with fine to medium grained, equigranular texture. The basalts are often amygdaloidal or variolitic with localized layers of pillow-breccia. Hydrothermal alteration is developed to varying degrees with carbonatization, silicification and epidotization common. The rocks are moderately to strongly foliated and contain 1-2 percent finely disseminated, euhedral pyrite or rare magnetite crystals, and 5-30 percent transposed, quartz-carbonate (dolomite/ankerite) stringers.

Felsic Volcanic Rocks. Felsic volcanic rocks occur mainly in the west-central Rahill Zone (Figure 3). They are medium to fine grained with a waxy, translucent, yellow colour and a vitreous lustre. Reddish, hematitic tinges or greenish epidote stains are developed adjacent to basalt contacts and sericitic alteration is common throughout. Carbonatization and silicification are locally well developed.

The origin of these felsic rocks is somewhat controversial; however, contact relationships suggest that they are extrusive.

Sedimentary Rocks. Intraformational chemical metasediments occur throughout the mafic volcanic rocks. They are usually very thin, moderately to strongly folded and laterally restricted. They are thin to medium bedded with inter-digitating beds of graphitic chert (±carbonate ±magnetite ±pyrite/pyrrhotite) and are therefore readily delineated by geophysics (VLF electromagnetic and magnetometer). The cherts are usually highly fractured, replaced to varying degrees by carbonate, and cross-cut by veins infilled with locally remobilzed quartz, pyrrhotite and pyrite.

Cherty, mafic tuffs were recently identified in the immediate vicinity of one of the Wilmar East breccia zones. The limited diamond drill program which identified them was insufficient to detail their extent or overall importance.

INTRUSIVE ROCKS

A very large variety of intrusive bodies are to be found throughout the area. They vary in size, shape, composition and age, and present a very complex intrusive history which has yet to be unravelled. A brief description of these rocks is herein presented and the most important bodies are described in more detail in later sections.

Mafic to Ultramafic Intrusions. (1) Two gabbro-diorite plugs, one on the Wilmar-Craibbe Fletcher property boundary (Figure 2) and the other on the southeast part of the Wilmar property, appear to be differentiated, with diorite cores and gabbroic shells. The rock is medium to coarse grained, generally massive with a weak foliation and locally contains magnetite. Strong, pervasive carbonatization is widespread. Although contact relationships with adjacent metabasalts are unclear and appear to be locally gradational, on a larger scale they are clearly cross-cutting. (2) Several gabbro-serpentinite bodies occur within the main volcanic complex, as steeply dipping dikes which trend east across the central part of the property, parallel to the main structural trend (see Figure 3). At depth they appear to coalesce into a major elongate stock several hundred metres wide and up to 1300 m long (Figure 4). These bodies rarely outcrop on surface and due to strong lateral variations in hydrothermal alteration, which obliterates their geophysical expression, they are extremely difficult to identify. The fresh rocks are dark grey-green, massive and uniformly magnetic. They are moderately to highly foliated and contain varying quantities of chlorite, talc and carbonate. The exact composition depends on the nature of hydrothermal alteration. (3) Numerous, laterally extensive lamprophyre dikes occur. They are usually 1 or 2 m wide, commonly focused along major contact areas and cross-cut all other dikes. They are medium grained, dark brown and commonly contain 5 to 10 percent mafic phenocrysts. The dikes very rarely contain quartz ± tourmaline veins, which in most cases are barren.

Intermediate to Felsic Intrusions. These dikes postdate the ultramafic intrusions and range in composition from quartz (feldspar) porphyry to diorite. (1) The quartz porphyry dikes contain medium grained, quartz phenocrysts which are often cut by hairline, carbonate-filled fractures. These are set in a fine grained, brownish, glassy matrix which is often weakly to moderately foliated. The dikes are commonly deformed and rarely contain mineralized quartz-tourmaline tension fractures. They predate lamprophyre and diorite dikes. (2) A large granodiorite dike located on the western part of the Wilmar property (see Figure 3) forms a potentially large tonnage/low grade ore zone. It is cut by diorite and lamprophyre dikes. (3) The diorite dikes vary considerably and may themselves be of several generations. They are moderately chloritic, massive, fine to medium grained bodies with locally well developed chilled margins up to several inches wide. Their colour varies greatly from black to olive green to light grey, the latter related to moderate to strong carbonatization and slight silicification. They usually contain 1-2 percent disseminated pyrite or magnetite and 1-5 percent quartz-carbonate filled fractures. Locally the dioritic dikes appear variolitic and porphyroblastic.

SOUTHERN FELSIC VOLCANIC – SEDIMENTARY SEQUENCE

This sequence occurs in a synclinal belt on the southern portion of the Wilmar property (see Figures 2 and 3). The

sequence is composed of large volumes of felsic volcaniclastic rocks, clastic metasediments and metasedimentary exhalites. Because this sequence lies to the south of the mine workings and is distal to the present areas of interest it will not be further described.

HYDROTHERMAL ALTERATION

Within the main mafic volcanic sequence hydrothermal alteration is widespread and varies considerably in de-

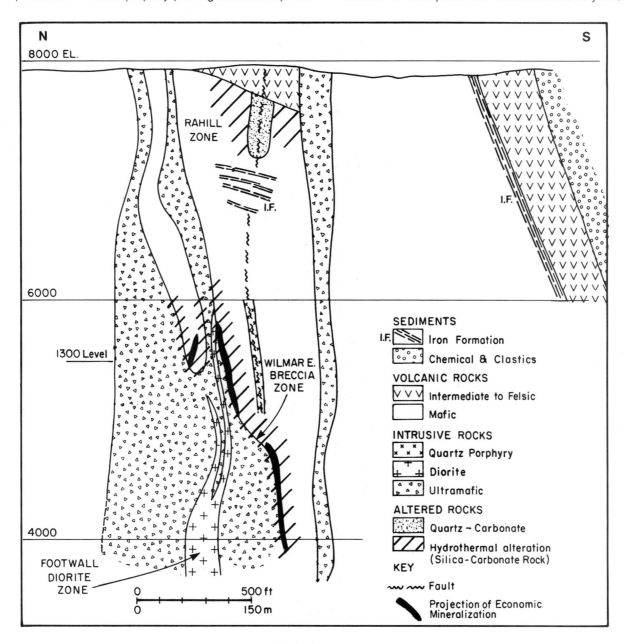

Figure 4. *Cross-section through the Wilmar Resources Limited property as deduced from surface outcrops, diamond drilling and underground workings.*

gree and style. This alteration appears to have occurred in several stages, from synvolcanic, seafloor spilitization to late stage, syn- or post-metamorphic alteration. Detailed work is necessary before the alteration history of the area can be fully documented.

Chloritization, carbonatization, silicification, sericitization and epidotization are all common within the Wilmar and adjacent properties and often disguise the primary nature of the rocks. In this respect it has been necessary to adopt descriptive terms to identify two apparently different SiO_2-CO_2 rich rock types discussed below: silica-carbonate (SC) and quartz-carbonate (QC).

The strongest megascopic alteration of the mafic volcanic and ultramafic rocks is moderate to strong carbonatization (ankerite/dolomite) and weak to strong silicification. Within this alteration, chlorite, epidote, talc and/or fuchsite may be common. Variations in intensity and character of alteration of the mafic volcanic rock have led to the use of numerous mine terms. An understandable misinterpretation of their primary mafic nature is common in earlier works, where they had been identified as andesitic to rhyolitic in composition.

Detailed mapping and core logging has shown that alteration halos or zones are very difficult to identify due to their strong lateral and vertical variations. In general, the contact areas of ultamafic intrusive bodies are the focus of most intense alteration. This contact alteration varies from centimetres to metres in width, the latter being more common.

Alteration along the contacts of the ultramafic rocks is highly variable but generally involves the development of an enclosing envelope of talc-carbonate-chlorite schist, which is non-magnetic in the areas of the strongest alteration. These envelopes grade into the less altered, coarser grained, ultramafic cores and often overprint the ultramafic contacts and adjacent volcanic rocks. The volcanic rocks are chlorite-talc rich and moderately to strongly carbonatized, silicified and sericitized, producing contact "zones" (up to 7 m wide) in which there are no sharp, identifiable ultramafic contacts. It has become obvious from mapping, geophysical work and surface drilling that a major alteration halo occurs around the Wilmar East Breccia Zone and increases in intensity towards the east. A marked increase in the degree of faulting, quartz-carbonate veining and the strength of deformation of these veins also occurs within the Wilmar East alteration halo and suggests that this zone was a structurally controlled hydrothermal conduit. It would appear that solutions permeated upwards along the contact-controlled conduits, causing the ore-bearing solutions to mineralize selected areas within the alteration halo.

Wilanour initiated a geochemical study to distinguish between mineralized and non-mineralized alteration zones which megascopically appear identical. This geochemical study may be extremely rewarding since the major alteration zones are readily identified by geophysics on the Wilmar and adjacent properties.

QUARTZ CARBONATE (QC) – SILICA CARBONATE (SC) ROCKS

Due to the varying character and strength of carbonatization and silicification these terms have been adopted to identify two rock "types" which may in fact be end members of a complete series grading from mafic volcanic or ultramafic rocks to QC or SC.

Typical QC is composed of crystalline, fine to medium grained, equigranular, milky to grey quartz and white dolomitic to ankeritic carbonate. The rock is usually cross-cut by 5-30 percent quartz or quartz-carbonate filled fractures or veins and may contain up to 5 percent sulphides as disseminations or stringers. Since QC components are similar to vein material (veins are generally 1 to 30 cm wide) and usually exhibit sharp contacts with adjacent rocks, it is thought to have originated as open space fillings. The major development of this material occurs within the Rahill Zone. Drill intersections to the north of Wilmar East structures suggest that similar bodies may exist elsewhere on the property.

In contrast to QC, typical silica carbonate (SC) is a very fine grained, light grey, amorphous looking, SiO_2-CO_2-rich rock, with 1-50 percent wisps, threads, seams and patches of chloritic or talcose material. The SC is massive to weakly foliated with the branching wisps and threads poorly defining the foliation. A very characteristic appearance is imparted by a combination of 1-5 percent irregular, branching, black to earthy brown tourmaline threads, 1-2 percent fine grained QC stringers and fine grained, disseminated sulphides (pyrite, 1-3 percent ± pyrrhotite, 1-4 percent). Fuchsite is developed to varying degrees within the amorphous looking SC (within the threads, seams, wisps and patches) giving the rock an irregular pale green to bright green colour. Textural variations within the SC occur over very short distances; angular breccias, swirled irregular masses and diffuse patches are relatively common. SC commonly grades into carbonatized and silicified ultramafic, and rarely, mafic volcanic rocks. Although recognizable, these rocks contain from 10-50 percent irregular patches of alteration very similar to the SC. This gradation strongly suggests that SC originated from a primary rock which has undergone replacement during SiO_2-CO_2 flooding. SC frequently occurs in intimate association with talc-carbonate schists (altered ultramafic rocks) along the most strongly altered and deformed contact zones of ultramafic intrusions.

The similarities between SC and QC are obvious and their development appears to depend on the fracturing and alteration style of the original rock types.

STRUCTURAL GEOLOGY

The mafic volcanic sequence and the southern felsic sequence have been interpreted as a paired anticlinal belt with the mafic volcanic anticline striking east and plunging towards the southwest. The banded iron formation and interflow sedimentary rocks show strong folding with fold axes paralleling the southwesterly trend. The obliteration of many primary features and contacts due to strong flattening and a penetrative foliation makes fold delineation extremely difficult. Foliation, however, may be observed crosscutting some contacts at high angles. Several drill intersections under the Rahill Zone suggest that intraformational metasediments are subhorizontal to slightly south dipping (see Figure 4). This bedding attitude appears to be subparallel to the mafic-felsic volcanic contact in the area and is in strong contrast to the near vertical attitude of the sedimentary and intermediate to felsic volcanic rocks to the south.

In the central Wilmar area structural trends are generally east to east-northeast with a subvertical (north) to vertical dip. These trends manifest as a strong, penetrative foliation in the mafic volcanic rocks and two subparallel fracture cleavages in the massive felsic volcanic rocks. Two ultramafic dikes in this area strike approximately east and dip steeply (see Figure 4). It is clear that these dikes cross-cut stratigraphy at a high angle but parallel the structural fabric through the area. The ultramafic dikes define the most important feature of the property and appear to form the limits of various types of mineralization. The northern ultramafic dike, lying to the south of the airport runway, and a southern serpentinite dike adjacent to Highway 125, confine a canoe-shaped wedge of volcanic rocks (see Figures 3 and 4). This wedge strikes approximately east-northeast and has a lateral extent of up to 1300 m. The confining dikes appear to converge at a depth of 700 m (2000 feet) or more. The southern serpentinite dike dips very steeply northwards and is a relatively regular feature, on average 30 m wide. It is only slightly to moderately altered and rarely offset by faulting. Recent drill information indicates that this dike feathers out on its eastern end. At a depth of about 700 m this feather zone plunges westward in the vicinity of the Wilmar East Breccia Zone. It does not appear to merge with the northern, ultramafic dike (Figure 5). In this area, the ultramafic rocks of the feather zone are strongly altered to silica carbonate (SC) and talc-carbonate schist.

The northern dike, up to 70 m in width, is much more complex. This dike dips 45 to 60° south with common rolls and undulations, possibly related to folding and faulting. A marked increase in the number of north-trending faults occurs eastward along this body and may correlate with the eastward increase in the degree of alteration (see Figure 3). This northern dike originates from a major ultramafic stock identifiable in the underground workings (see Figure 4). The stock is up to 200 m wide and extends for about 1000 m along strike. Near the 1300 level, the stock appears to feather out and its upward continuation is represented by two ultramafic dikes, the southern of which forms the northerly limit of the canoe-shaped volcanic wedge.

The canoe-shaped wedge of volcanic rocks is transected by several major structural breaks which strike between northeast and northwest. They are steeply dipping and broadly correlate with northwesterly striking faults on the Cochenour property. Three major breaks have been identified and cause major east to west correlation problems. The western break occurs between the

Granodiorite and Rahill Zones, the central break between the Rahill and Wilmar East Zones and the eastern break between the Wilmar East Zone and the stock on the Wilmar-Craibbe Fletcher property boundary (see Figure 3). As illustrated, the western break has been interpreted as two major faults. The northwest-trending fault has been correlated with dextral movement which offsets the East Bay Serpentinite near its termination on the Annco property (see Figure 2). Similarly the eastern break has been correlated with a northerly trending fault (sinistral?) which offsets the southern contact of the East Bay Serpentinite on the Marcus property. A zone of talc-carbonate alteration carrying highly anomalous (ppb) gold values (very similar to the Wilmar East Zone) occurs along the East Bay Serpentinite in this area of the Marcus property. Alteration and mineralization on the Annco property is also closely associated with a northerly trending fault.

Several other major fault orientations have been identified by previous workers. The most obvious of these are east-trending, vertical faults, also interpreted as channelways for the intrusion of quartz porphyry dikes (see Figure 4).

The relationship between faulting and mineralization has not been thoroughly studied or documented; however, it may prove to be of vital importance in future exploration programs and in the formulation of a genetic model for gold emplacement within and adjacent to the Wilmar property.

MINERALIZATION OF THE WILMAR PROPERTY

Gold mineralization occurs in four major zones within the Wilmar property. From east to west these are:

1. Wilmar East Breccia Zone;
2. Wilmar East Footwall Diorite Zone;
3. Central Wilmar Rahill Zone;
4. Wilmar West Granodiorite Zone.

These are illustrated on Figures 3, 4 and 5.

Several other small areas of mineralization, similar to the above zones have been encountered.

WILMAR EAST BRECCIA ZONE

Mineralization and alteration within this zone are focused along the southern contact of the altered ultramafic stock which defines the northern contact of the canoe-shaped wedge (see Figures 3 and 4). The zone of alteration extends for more than 30 m to the north and south of the contact. It has a strike length of up to 370 m and has been outlined as plunging to the southwest, from surface to the 2050 level. Very little information is available below the 2050 level. Sheet and pipe-like ore structures are restricted to this alteration zone. The ore zones strike east-northeast and dip 50 to 70° south (see Figure 4). They range in width from 1 to 30 m with a plunge length varying from 100 to more than 200 m (Figures 5 and 6). Correlation of these stoped out zones is difficult, and several in-

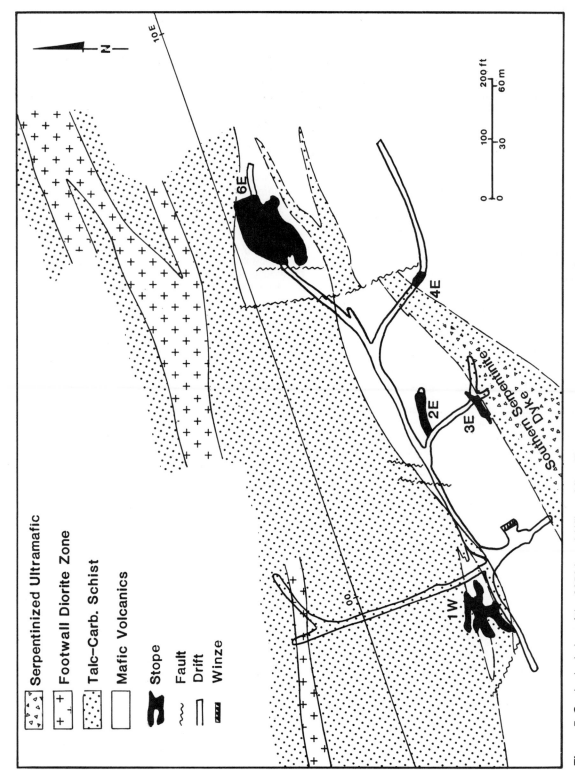

Figure 5. *Geological plan of the 2050 Level, Wilmar Mine. The southern, serpentinized, ultramafic dike and the northern, highly altered (talc-carbonate) dike remain as two distinct bodies.*

terpretations are possible. One such interpretation is shown diagramatically in Figure 6. While a major subvertical rake defines the eastern and western limits of the ore bodies as a group, the rake of individual ore zones exhibits a wide range and is generally much more shallow (25 to 30° in the 1E to 4E stope areas and 45 to 70° in the 5E to 6E areas). In cross-section the ultramafic contact is noticeably irregular with two major convex rolls identifiable between the 1300 and 2050 levels (see Figure 4). In this view, mineralization appears to be focused within the altered volcanic rocks immediately adjacent to the ultramafic contact along the steeper parts of the roll. With depth the mineralization cross-cuts the contact and penetrates the ultramafic stock for some distance. This crosscutting occurs where the contact rolls towards the south. Undoubtedly, faulting and folding have played a significant part in producing this pattern of mineralization. However, understanding the nature of structural control will require more detailed study.

Alteration within the mafic volcanic rocks is characterized by patches, lenses and major zones of moderate to strong sericitization, carbonatization and variable silicification. The alteration imparts a characteristic colour banding to the rocks, represented by light brown, light green to light grey wisps and bands (0.5 to 1.0 cm in width). Within the alteration zone dramatic variations occur in the content of milky, white to grey quartz-carbonate veining. They are usually about 0.5 to 8 cm wide, rarely up to 30 cm, and are commonly folded, boudinaged or brecciated. The veins form 2- 25 percent of the rock, with the highest volume spatially associated with most strongly altered areas adjacent to the contact. Within less altered, mafic volcanic rocks, dark chloritic seams potentially mark two pressure solution cleavages. The cleavages are nearly parallel and are thus difficult to separate during mapping.

Ultramafic rocks in the alteration zone are usually altered to incompetent talc-carbonate or talc-chlorite-carbonate schists and contain up to 25 percent strongly folded and deformed quartz-carbonate (dolomite) veins. Silica-carbonate rock (SC) is well developed along contact areas and as layers, breccias and patches within rocks on either side of the contact.

The mafic-ultramafic contact is extremely difficult to identify from drill core due to the intensity of alteration and deformation and the occurrence of late dikes in the vicinity. The contact is somewhat easier to identify in the underground workings. In this respect it is understandable why earlier workers relied more on exploration and development drives to outline structure and mineralized areas.

The free milling ores of the Wilmar East Zone are characterized by the presence of telluride minerals: hessite (Ag_2Te), petzite ($Ag,Au)_2Te$) and minor calaverite ($Ag,AuTe_2$). Native gold and silver are also relatively

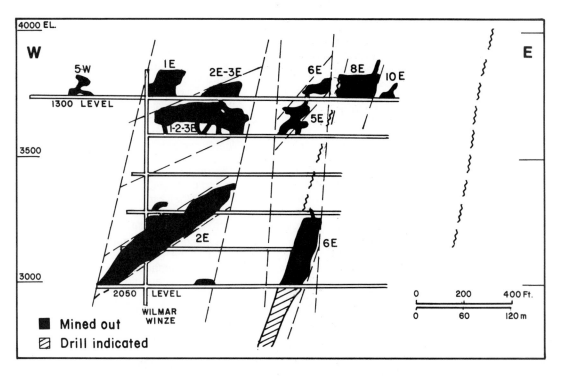

Figure 6. *Orientation of stopes in the Wilmar East Breccia Zone. Although individual stopes have variable, but generally shallow rakes, the ore bodies as a group define relatively steeply raking units.*

common with Au:Ag ratios varying between 1:10 to 1:12. Several distinct types of mineralization occur within the zone; however, they have been poorly documented during previous work. The authors have identified at least three major stages of mineralization from recent work in the area of 2050-6E stope (see Figure 6) and on other levels. The earliest stage appears to coincide with the widespread alteration and is associated with disseminated pyrite, minor chalcopyrite and pyrrhotite. This low grade, background mineralization (0.01-0.06 ounces Au per ton) occurs in weakly to moderately altered and silicified areas and in silica-carbonate (SC) rock. It is widespread within the mafic volcanic rocks and overprints the ultramafic contacts for distances up to 15 m. Minor, very fine grained disseminated tellurides and native gold occur.

High grade gold mineralization occurs in areas of very strong, pervasive (light grey to light green) silicification which overprints the background mineralization. The silicified zones commonly exhibit a poorly-preserved remnant fabric which is often breccia-like in appearance. This mineralization consists of 1-2 percent sulphides and fine to medium grained, disseminated gold with associated epidote and fuschsite spots. Within these areas numerous quartz ± tourmaline ± carbonate veinlets occur. These veins may carry considerable amounts of potentially remobilized, medium grained, native gold with no sulphides. Very late, barren sphalerite veinlets are rarely observed.

Three further types of auriferous mineralization have been previously described but not studied in detail. (1) "Talc ore" consists of platy gold which has been smeared along talc or chlorite slip planes, probably in those areas where mineralization cross-cuts the ultramafic rocks. (2) So-called "vein agglomerate ore" consists of gold-telluride mineralization within strongly silicified vein-like bodies. These bodies are usually up to 1 m wide and several metres in length. The "veins" contain numerous ghostly, replaced, breccia fragments. (3) "Quartz-carbonate breccia ore" consists of gold mineralization within large bodies of SiO_2-CO_2-rich rock, possibly similar to the quartz-carbonate bodies observed in the Rahill Zone (see below). The latter three ore types are probably morphological variations belonging to the three mineralization stages described above.

WILMAR EAST FOOTWALL DIORITE ZONE

The Footwall Diorite Zone lies approximately 30 to 70 m to the north of the main Wilmar East Breccia Zone within the ultramafic stock and below the 1300 foot level (see Figure 4). This zone has been a recommended exploration target since the underground discovery of the Wilmar East Breccia Zone, but relatively little diamond drilling and no drifting has been undertaken. During the initial compilation work, the potential of this zone was better identified and it should be a major target in future Wilmar East underground exploration programs.

The Footwall Diorite Zone consists of a number of interfingering dikes which appear to coalesce with increasing depth around the 2050 level (see Figures 4 and 6).

They are subparallel to the Wilmar East Breccia Zone, striking east-northeast for a distance of up to 500 m and dipping 50 to 70° south. In the upper levels, the dike zone has poor lateral continuity and is 3 to 15 m wide. On the 2050 level the dike zone is laterally extensive with a width of 15 to to 30 m. The continuity of the zone from the 1300 level to surface is extremely difficult to delineate; however, it is suggested that the dikes refract where they cross-cut the ultramafic-volcanic contact. In the volcanic rocks they dip at 30 to 50° south.

The diorite is medium to fine grained, equigranular, chloritic (greenish brown to greenish black) with rare occurrences of feldspar phenocrysts or light brown coloured flecks (mafic phenocrysts?). The dikes contain 1 to 5 percent disseminated pyrite with slight to moderate carbonatization and silicification. Silicification may be related to cross-cutting grey to white quartz veins which contain minor carbonate, pyrite, pyrrhotite and chalcopyrite. Mineralization occurs as specks of native gold and tellurides within the veins. No information is available on Au:Ag ratios. Similarly, the nature and origin of the veining within the dikes is not known.

CENTRAL WILMAR RAHILL ZONE

The Rahill Zone occurs at or near surface and occupies that part of the volcanic canoe-shaped wedge between the western and central structural breaks (see Figures 3 and 4). It is thus located approximately on strike of, and between, the Wilmar East and Wilmar West (Granodiorite) mineralization zones. The Rahill Zone is characterized by extremely complex geology. It is difficult, if not impossible, to extrapolate lithological contacts, alteration zones and mineralized intersections between drill holes only 17 m apart and trenches 30 to 60 m apart. This very strong vertical and lateral variability is due in part to the occurrence of very large, highly irregular QC bodies and in part to the very strong variations in carbonatization and silicification. The latter variations appear to be closely related to primary textures; however alteration commonly cross-cuts volcanic contacts, making the lower contact of the felsic volcanic cap (see Figure 4) difficult to identify in some areas. The most obvious feature of this zone is a large, east-trending body of QC, up to 17 m wide on surface and 70 m in depth. It cross-cuts the mafic volcanic stratigraphy and plunges southwest beneath the felsic volcanic cap (see Figures 3 and 4).

Trenching, surface sampling and over 21,000 feet of drilling completed in the immediate area of the Rahill Zone over the last four decades have uncovered many mineralized areas but, to date, no economic concentrations of gold.

Two types of mineralization have been identified within this zone.

DISSEMINATED MINERALIZATION

Low grade mineralization occurs within the QC and highly altered mafic volcanic rocks. This irregular, patchy mineralization may be associated with disseminated (1-5 percent) fine grained pyrite, persistant throughout the area. To the west of the Rahill Zone, thin SC units associated with moderately altered ultramafic dikes are occasionally mineralized. The SC units and the mineralization cannot be correlated with any certainty.

QUARTZ-TOURMALINE (QT) VEINS

These occur within the competent QC bodies and within a later, cross-cutting, porphyritic, diorite dike. The veins are 1 to 5 cm wide and are spaced irregularly, about 1 to 3 m apart. They strike approximately north and dip 10 to 50° to the east, parallel to a regionally developed, very late veining pattern. Within the veins, up to 5 percent pyrite, pyrrhotite and/or chalcopyrite may occur with coarse visible specks of native gold, scattered irregularly throughout.

The lack of close correlation between adjacent areas of mineralization suggests that the QT veining may consist of numerous sporadically mineralized, en echelon structures or very sporadic mineralization within more regionally penetrative vein sets. The veins may bear a strong relationship to QT veins observed in other competent bodies. Late, auriferous QT veins have been recorded within lamprophyre dikes, quartz porphyry dikes (for example, the Windsock porphyry, Figure 3), the Wilmar East Breccia Zone and the Granodiorite Zone (see below).

WILMAR WEST (GRANODIORITE) ZONE

The granodiorite is a nearly vertical, south-dipping dike with a surface strike of 070° (see Figure 3). The dike varies from 170 to 200 m in length and thickens from a maximum of 12 m near surface to between 25 and 40 m on the 1300 level. Limited deep drilling suggests that this gradual increase in horizontal thickness continues to at least the 2050 level (Figure 7). The dike commonly has a wavy, irregular appearance in both plan and sectional views. It wedges out towards the west and degenerates into multiple, narrow interfingering dikes towards the east (Figure 7).

Although the dike has intruded an area of extremely complex geology, the construction and continuous update of a sectional, plexiglass model (Scale 1:12 000) has aided in the interpretation of the area. Apart from clearly depicting the pinches, rolls and swells in the granodiorite dike, the model also clearly shows a 10 to 15° clockwise rotation in azimuth of the body from the surface to the 1300 level (Figure 7). This rotation has not yet been explained or related to any identifiable mineralization trends; however, it may be related to the major, northwesterly trending fault to the east of the granodiorite zone (see Figure 3). The model also shows that the granodiorite transects a subparallel, altered ultramafic dike which dips 45 to 75° south and is 15 to 20 m wide. SC rock (30 to 40 m thick) occurs in a subparallel zone directly above this ultramafic dike. Vertically above the SC unit is a thick

sequence (30 to 100 m) of strongly silicified, pillowed; mafic volcanic rocks. These volcanic rocks were considered to be felsic flows until their primary mafic nature was recognized. They are widespread throughout the immediate area and occur predominantly within the hanging wall of the granodiorite.

Where the granodiorite intrudes the ultramafic dike and SC units (50 to 100 m below surface) it transforms to multiple, interfingering dikes (Figure 7). Quartz-tourmaline veining occurs in this area but contains little auriferous mineralization. The finger zone separates lower and upper zones of mineralization within the granodiorite and also appears to control arsenopyrite mineralization (see below).

The volume of SC and silicified mafic volcanic rocks

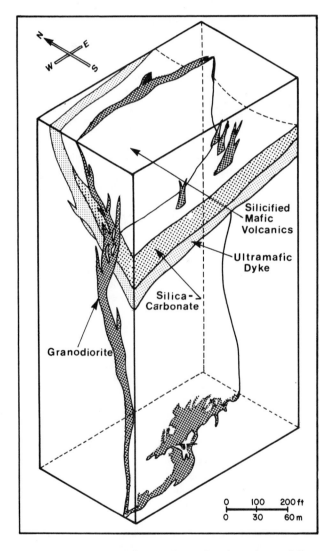

Figure 7. *Simplified, three-dimensional geology of the Wilmar West (Granodiorite) Zone.*

in this area would require a very large volume of silicifying, hydrothermal solutions. It is believed that a major hydrothermal conduit (probably structurally controlled along the upper contact of the ultramafic dike) was the focus of the most intense alteration (SC), with solutions percolating upwards from this channelway, silicifying large volumes of the mafic volcanic rocks above. The genetic relationship between the mineralized granodiorite zone and this hydrothermal system is still a matter of conjecture. However, the spatial association of silicified, mafic volcanic rocks (hanging wall) and higher grade mineralization in the granodiorite along this hanging wall would suggest a genetic relationship.

The granodiorite is medium grained, light to medium grey, with a massive, equigranular texture. Mafic minerals are usually altered to sericite and carbonate; however, irregular patches of less altered, chloritic granodiorite are locally preserved. The granodiorite contains 2 to 5 percent fine grained, disseminated pyrrhotite and 1 percent pyrite. Limited petrographic studies indicate that extensive albitization occurs throughout the lighter coloured, altered parts of the dike.

The granodiorite has been moderately fractured and contains 8 to 13 percent quartz-tourmaline veins. The majority strike 018° and dip vertically to almost horizontally east. These veins vary from 1 cm to 0.5 m in thickness and 1 to over 10 m in length. Detailed fracture analysis has failed to define preferred vein sets. A complicating factor is that down-warping and curving causes strike and dip changes within individual veins. Vein relationships are somewhat ambiguous; however, the available evidence suggests that all veins were about contemporaneous. Vein penetration of wall rocks is minimal (< 15 cm) and only minor increases in vein widths have been observed on the major flat veins adjacent to the hanging wall contacts.

Vein constituents are variable, with 20 to 60 percent quartz, 30 to 70 percent tourmaline and 5 to 8 percent accessory minerals. The accessory minerals, in order of decreasing abundance, are pyrrhotite, pyrite, and chalcopyrite with traces of argentite, ruby silver, native gold, native silver, galena and scheelite. Arsenopyrite is rarely observed within the granodiorite below the level of intersection with the ultramafic dike (Figure 7); however, in the overlying, upper, mineralized zone it occurs as coarse grained crystals forming 2 to 3 percent of vein material.

Gold within the free milling ores of the granodiorite zone occurs in the native state, as fine to coarse, disseminated leaves up to 0.25 cm wide. The gold is generally pale yellow, indicating a high silver content (electrum) and is in frequent association with native silver. A definite association occurs between pyrrhotite and gold within mineralized veins. Qualitatively, the greater the percentage of pyrrhotite, the better the chance of high grade mineralization.

Detailed underground mapping has identified several orientations of tourmaline-slickensided fractures which postdate and slightly offset the QT veining within the granodiorite zone. Further work is required to clarify fracturing and displacement patterns as an aid in identifying block faulting, possibly significant to this zone.

CONCLUSIONS

The Wilmar property in Dome Township has been the focus of a concerted exploration program over the last four years and has involved both surface and underground exploration. Mineralization on the Wilmar property occurs within a sequence of tholeiitic mafic metavolcanics and intraformational metasediments. This sequence is located between two major ultramafic dikes which define a large, canoe-shaped wedge of variably altered volcanic and intrusive rocks in which several types of ore structures have been observed (in some cases, the focus of previous mining activity). Although auriferous mineralization occurs in many different rock types and structural settings, only three major stages of mineralization have been identified to date.

1. A structurally controlled, hydrothermal discharge zone has been identified to encompass the Wilmar East Breccia Zone. This zone of sericitization, carbonatization and silicification occurs along the contact of the northern ultramafic dike and at depth intersects the southern serpentinite dike. This zone is marked by 1 to 2 percent disseminated pyrite, pyrrhotite and rarely chalcopyrite and carries low grade but widespread gold mineralization. A similar, structurally controlled discharge may be proposed for low grade, widespread, patchy, gold mineralization which has been identified within the Rahill Zone and along less-altered, ultramafic contacts throughout the area. The strong alteration and the development of large, open fissure-filling quartz-carbonate (QC) bodies in the Rahill Zone may be interpreted as the result of hydrothermal ponding beneath a widespread, impermeable felsic volcanic cap overlying this area (Figure 4). On the other hand silica-carbonate rock (SC), characterized by sporadic gold values, appears to have formed through the extensive alteration of porous rocks.

2. Mineralization associated with local areas of intense silicification has been identified within the Wilmar East Breccia Zone. Intense silicification appears to overprint earlier hydrothermal alteration in structural traps. This occurs within the central part of the interpreted hydrothermal conduit, adjacent to the major mafic volcanic-ultramafic contact. Original fabrics, often brecciated in appearance, are very poorly preserved as ghostly outlines. The silicified areas are characteristically light green to grey in colour and very fine grained to cherty in appearance. Mineralization is often of very high tenor and spectacular in appearance. This type of mineralization is perhaps economically the most significant.

3. Late, cross-cutting veins occur in numerous competent bodies (diorite, lamprophyre, quartz-porphyry and granodiorite dikes, silica-carbonate, quartz-carbonate and silicified zones) which occur throughout the property. As a regional late vein-set, these veins are usually undeformed, north-trending and contain quartz, or quartz-carbonate. They are characterised by sporadic occurrences

of native gold but do not form economic zones. Within the Wilmar East and Rahill Zones there is good evidence to suggest that this type of mineralization is related to a local remobilization of previously introduced gold. It may be suggested that the more complex, north-trending vein systems within the Granodiorite Zone and possibly the Footwall Diorite Zone may be contemporaneous with this regional late set. The cooling of the intrusive bodies and resulting hydrothermal convective activity may account for the higher degree of fracturing and the more wide-spread mineralization of these areas.

A study of several additional types of mineralization and a detailed fracture analysis have still to be completed on this property. This work may significantly modify the current interpretation.

ACKNOWLEDGEMENTS

The authors wish to thank B. Gillies and J.D. Misiura for their contribution to the geological understanding of the area. Special thanks are extended to I. Watson for his extensive contribution to Wilanour Resources Limited from the very earliest stages of the present work. The authors also wish to extend their gratitude to B.K. Meikle, M.E. Holt, P. Busse and A.R. Hill for their input and support. The Ontario Geological Survey is thanked for allowing the opportunity to present this paper.

SELECTED REFERENCES[1]

Chastko, L.C.
1973: Report on Wilmar Diamond Drilling Program; Unpublished Company Report, November, 1973.
1975: Wilmar Mines Limited, Summary of Results, West Granodiorite Exploration; Unpublished Company Report, January, 1975.

1976: Wilmar Mines Limited; Summary of Exploration and Development 1973 to 1975; Unpublished Company Report, January 1976.

Cossett, D., and David, M.
1980: Geostatistical Study of the Wilmar Gold Deposit, Preliminary Study; Unpublished Report prepared for Wilanour Resources by Mineral Exploration Research Institute.

Ferguson, S.A.
1966: Geology of Dome Township; Ontario Department of Mines, Geological Report 45, 98p.

Gillies, B.
1981: Summary of Surface Exploration 1978-1980, Wilmar-Anco Properties, Wilanour Resources Limited; Unpublished Report, March, 1981.
1981: Progress Report on Diamond Drill Program, Consolidated Marcus Property, Dome Township, Red Lake District, Reports I and II; Wilanour Resources Limited Unpublished Report, July, 1981.

Hutton, D.A.
1973: Wilmar Mines Limited, A Study of Exploration Possibilities and the Potential Economic Objectives; Unpublished Company Report, March, 1973.

Kuryliw, C.J.
1960a: Interior Geological Report on the Wilmar Exploration Drive; Unpublished Company Report, August, 1960.
1960b: Report on the Wilmar Crosscut Exploration; Unpublished Company Report, December, 1960.
1961: Notes on Wilmar Exploration; Unpublished Company Report, December, 1961.
1962: Report of Wilmar Exploration; Unpublished Company Report, October, 1962.

Pirie, J.
1981: Regional Geological Setting of Gold Mineralization, Eastern Red Lake Area, Northwestern Ontario; *in* Genesis of Archean, Volcanic-Hosted Gold Deposits. Symposium Held at the University of Waterloo, March, 1980, Ontario Geological Survey Miscellaneous Paper 97, 175p.

---

[1]Unpublished reports are on file with Assessment Files Research Office, Ontario Geological Survey, Toronto, and Resident Geologist, Ontario Ministry of Natural Resources, Red Lake.

Structural Setting of Vein-Type Gold Mineralization in the Mine Centre – Fort Frances Area: Implications for the Wabigoon Subprovince

K. Howard Poulsen

Department of Geological Sciences, Queen's University, Kingston

ABSTRACT

Laminated, gold-bearing quartz veins in the Mine Centre – Fort Frances area occur in ductile shear zones and as dilations of regionally developed cleavage. These structures are related kinematically to large transcurrent faults in the region. Gold mineralization is thought to be entirely epigenetic and possibly related to seismic pumping of fluids during faulting. A similar spatial relationship between gold and large fault zones exists throughout the Wabigoon Subprovince and recognition of related subsidiary structures should be one objective of an exploration strategy for gold in this region.

INTRODUCTION

Early in this century, geologists were particularly aware of structural controls on vein-type gold deposits. Recent emphasis on the stratigraphic setting of Archean lode gold deposits has resulted in little application of advances in the field of structural geology to this particular problem. Specifically, a variety of structural styles involving diapir folds and shear zones have been documented in the Archean of southwestern Superior Province (Schwerdtner *et al.* 1979; Poulsen *et al.* 1980; Park 1981; Blackburn *et al.* 1982; Borradaile 1982). In all cases, a relative structural chronology has been documented and, where gold-bearing veins can be related to a particular structural episode, they too will be governed by the same chronology. Recognition of the structural association of lode gold deposits not only may provide one component of an exploration strategy for gold but also will be of value in evaluating genetic concepts for this class of deposit. The specific example of gold mineralization which occurs in the Mine Centre – Fort Frances area and the general example of the distribution of lode gold in the Wabigoon Subprovince illustrates this point.

MINE CENTRE – FORT FRANCES AREA

All significant occurrences of base and precious metal mineralization in the Mine Centre – Fort Frances area lie within a wedge shaped fault block along the southwestern margin of the Wabigoon Subprovince. The northern boundary of this block is the mylonite zone comprising the Quetico Fault and the southern margin is marked by the Seine River – Rainy Lake Fault, a phyllonitic schist zone (Figure 1). Internal faults divide the block into individual domains with distinctive structural, stratigraphic and metamorphic characteristics. Two fundamental types of domain are present. To the north and west of Swell Bay (Figure 1) mafic and ultramafic metavolcanics with intercalated gabbroic sills, turbiditic metasediments and iron formations comprise the volcanic sequence which is cut by granodioritic intrusions. The rocks are metamorphosed to assemblages characteristic of the lower to upper amphibolite facies and are folded into antiforms and synforms which do not reflect the stratigraphic order. To the south and east of Swell Bay, the domains are dominated by felsic and intermediate metavolcanic compositions. Subvolcanic sills include gabbro, anorthosite, tonalite and trondhjemite and the volcanic and plutonic rocks are overlain with angular unconformity by conglomerate and arenites of probable alluvial-fluvial sedimentary facies (Wood 1980; Blackburn *et al.* 1982). The rocks in these domains form steeply dipping northward- and southward-facing panels with northeastward strike; steeply dipping cleavage is ubiquitous and greenschist facies metamorphic assemblages predominate.

STRUCTURAL SETTING OF GOLD

Gold-bearing quartz-carbonate veins have been exploited intermittently in this area since 1893. Veins range from a few centimetres to a few metres in width, are notably lenticular and contain localized high grade shoots characterized by uneven distribution of gold. The veins are locally sulphide-rich and sphalerite, galena and chalcopyrite commonly are major components. Tourmaline, arsenopyrite and scheelite are rare accessories. Gold-bearing quartz veins are restricted spatially to the southeast domains which have been metamorphosed at low grade (Poulsen 1981) and are found in two structural associations. Most occur within ductile shear zones in plutonic and massive metavolcanics while some occur in dilatant zones parallel with regionally developed cleavage.

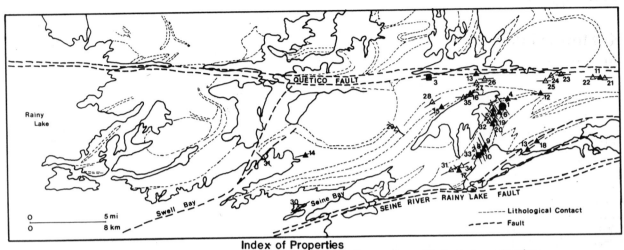

Index of Properties

● **Properties with moderate production**
   (<10,000 oz. Au)
   1. Golden Star mine

■ **Properties with limited production**
   (<10,000 oz. Au) and/or extensive development
   2. Foley mine
   3. Olive mine

▲ **Properties with limited production**
   (<1,000 oz. Au) and/or moderate development
   4. Pacitto mine
   5. Isabella mine
   6. Ferguson mine
   7. Golden Crescent mine
   8. R.C. Cone mine
   9. Cone prospect
   10. Stagge prospect
   11. Alice "A" mine
   12. Turtle Tank prospect
   13. Saundry mine
   14. Young –Corrigan prospect
   15. Stellar mine
   16. South Vermilion mine
   17. McKenzie Gray prospect
   18. Dinosaur –Smylie mine
   19. Lucky Coon mine
   20. Manhattan –Decca mines

△ **Properties with limited production**
   (<100 Au oz. Au) and/or limited development
   21. Emma Abbot occurrence
   22. Gold Bug occurrence
   23. E. Turtle River occurrence
   24. W. Turtle occurrence
   25. Turtle Siding occurrence
   26. McMillan occurrence
   27. Corrigan occurrence
   28. Thomson occurrence
   29. Barber Lake Au occurrence
   30. Scott Island occurrence
   31. Swell Bay occurrence
   32. Emperor mine
   33. Gibson occurrence
   34. Finger Bay occurrences
   35. Stone occurrence

Figure 1. *Geological sketch map of gold properties and major fault structures in the Mine Centre – Fort Frances area. The bars plotted through the symbols reflect the orientation of vein systems on each property.*

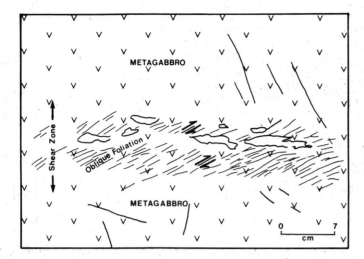

Figure 2. *Ductile shear zone cutting metagabbro, Seine Bay. The asymmetry of foliation oblique to the shear zone indicates a dextral sense of shear.*

Figure 3. *Laminated quartz carbonate in dextral shear zone, Stellar Mine. Note the oblique foliation in carbonate-rich sericite schist derived from the trondhjemite host.*

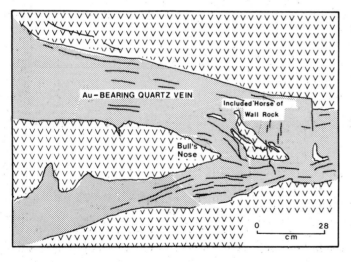

Figure 4. *Branching in a shear zone to create a "bull's nose" structure, Manhattan Mine. A narrow zone of foliated rock adjacent to the veins indicates the same dextral shear sense for both branches.*

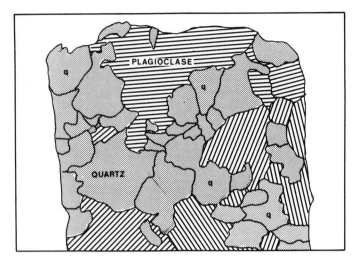

Figure 5. Sketch of thin section of weakly deformed tonalite, Foley Mine area. Note relatively equant and unaltered plagioclase and quartz grains. Width of view approximately 2 cm.

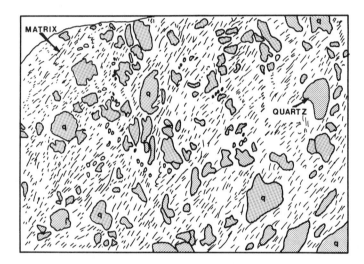

Figure 6. Sketch of thin section of protomylonite from shear zone in tonalite, Foley Mine area. Note the complete absence of plagioclase with fine grain foliated sericitic matrix in its place. Grain size reduction in quartz is due both to cataclastic and recrystallization processes. Field of view as in Figure 5.

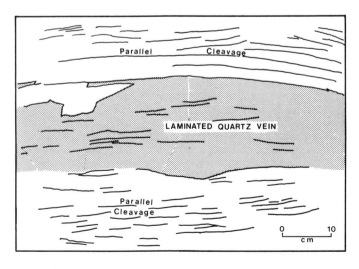

Figure 7. Lenticular, laminated quartz vein parallel to cleavage, Olive Mine.

177

Ductile shear zones (Ramsay and Graham 1970; Ramsay 1980) are common throughout the Rainy Lake area. They are tabular zones, centimetres to metres wide, which contain an oblique internal foliation in contrast to the homogeneous, equigranular rocks which they transect (Figure 2). Asymmetry of foliation, sigmoidal second order vein arrays, discrete slip surfaces with slickensides and rare offset of markers provide evidence for subhorizontal displacements parallel to the shear zone boundaries. The gold-bearing quartz veins most commonly occur in the central part of a shear zone (Figure 3). Branching of shear zones produces the common "bull's nose" structure (Figure 4) and included "horses" of wall rock within veins. The foliated wall rocks which comprise the shear zones show abundant evidence of mechanical and chemical alteration. For example, equigranular tonalites and trondhjemites away from a shear zone (Figure 5) give way gradationally to schists and protomylonites in which feldspars have been converted entirely to foliated sericitic matrix, and quartz porphyroclasts show abundant evidence of grain size reduction (Figure 6). The width of foliated rock developed on either side of a vein varies from centimetres to metres; there is no direct relationship between vein width and shear zone width, yet the widest shear zones appear to be most persistent along strike. Misoriented inclusions of foliated wallrock occur locally within veins and the laminated nature of the veins themselves (see Figure 3) results from narrow sericitic or chloritic inclusions of wallrock incorporated into them. These textures are interpreted to be the result of episodic brittle failure at the interface between early vein material and foliated wallrock followed by new vein filling at that site. Portions of veins which are finely laminated generally are richer in gold than those which are the coarse grained products of a single vein filling episode.

The shear zones are demonstrably related in a kinematic sense to regional wrench faulting. Their vertical orientation, vertical foliation, subhorizontal slickensides and the geometry of sigmoidal vein arrays indicate dominantly transcurrent displacements. Dextral shear zones are most abundant adjacent to the late, bounding dextral faults, and conjugate sinistral structures are found most commonly in the central part of the area (see Figure 1). Westerly striking shear zones are all dextral while northwesterly to northerly striking zones are sinistral, compatible with the overall dextral nature of the regional wrench zone (Poulsen 1981; Blackburn et al. 1982). The shear zones cut all rock types but are found most commonly in tonalite and trondhjemite (Poulsen 1981), an observation which led early workers to relate gold mineralization to emplacement of intrusions of this composition. An important observation, however, is that metamorphosed basalt, diabase and gabbro also host shear zones and veins and that the orientation and shear sense of the zones is independent of the orientation and facing directions of the rock units which they cut; they are, therefore, late, superimposed discordant structures.

A second structural association for gold is exemplified by the Olive Mine and several smaller prospects and occurrences of similar type (see Figure 1). The host rocks, in this case, are tuffs and metasediments with well developed cleavage. Laminated veins parallel this cleavage (Figure 7) and likely result from decoupling of cleavage laminae by shear displacement. Locally, folding and brecciation of the host rock gives rise to irregular vein networks associated with longer, sigmoidal cleavage-parallel veins. While morphologically different from the shear zones, formation of these types of vein is thought to be merely the response of anisotropic host rocks to shear displacement in a tectonic wrench zone.

WABIGOON SUBPROVINCE
GOLD DISTRIBUTION AND FAULT ZONES

Figure 8 shows the distribution of gold deposits of the Wabigoon Subprovince relative to the positions of regional faults. It is evident that the fault network described in the Mine Centre – Fort Frances area extends eastward along the subprovince margin through the Atikokan, Beardmore and Geraldton areas. The bulk of gold production from the subprovince has come from the latter district where the locus of mineralization is the east-striking Bankfield-Tombill Fault (Horwood 1948). A second fault network which lies internal to the subprovince comprises the Miniss-Wabigoon-Manitou Lakes Fault Zone along which there is also a very prominent association of vein-type gold deposits. The fault and shear zone networks of the Wabigoon Subprovince consist of two distinct elements: east-trending dextral faults and conjugate faults striking 030° reflect a late-tectonic shortening of the subprovince about a northwesterly trending axis (Schwerdtner et al. 1979; Park 1981). Shorter faults of differing orientation are likely second-order splays (McKinstry 1953) of the principal fault zones. The localization of gold in subsidiary structures related to the fault zones in the Wabigoon Subprovince implies an equally late timing for their formation.

RECOGNITION OF THE FAULT ZONES

The fault zones identified on Figure 8 come from compilation maps of the Ontario Geological Survey. The most significant of the structures mark dramatic stratigraphic discordances and generally have been recognized as fault zones from the time of earliest mapping. Potential exists, however, for the recognition of new or related structures of lesser dimension. Identification of fault rocks (Sibson 1977) provides a useful criterion for recognition of faults: mylonite, cataclasite, phyllonite and pseudotachylite have distinctive petrographic characteristics. Minor structures such as asymmetric folds and minor sympathetic brittle faults are commonly localized in the vicinity of major faults. Anastamosing fault networks isolate characteristic lozenge-shaped domains (see Figure 1). Electromagnetic anomalies and topographic lineaments also commonly mark fault zones. The above criteria certainly apply in the Mine Centre – Fort Frances area and at other localities in the Wabigoon Subprovince (Blackburn et al. 1982; Poulsen and Franklin 1981).

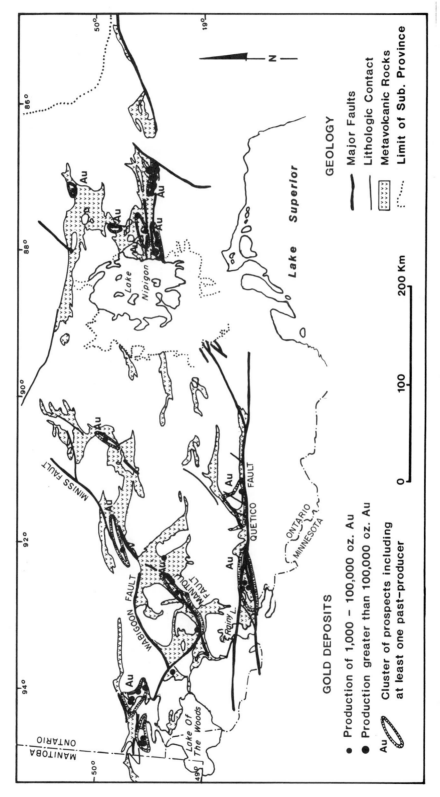

Figure 8. *Distribution of gold deposits and fault zones in Wabigoon Subprovince. Deposits with past production in excess of 1000 ounces of Au are shown.*

IMPLICATIONS FOR EXPLORATION AND GENETIC MODELS

The above observations imply that much of the gold exploited to date in the Wabigoon Subprovince has come from fault-related structures, both on the regional and local scales. While it is not suggested that structural siting is the only requirement for lode gold mineralization, it is proposed that recognition of potential fault structures should represent one criterion in target selection for gold in the Wabigoon Subprovince. The genetic significance of the observed relationship remains speculative. The relationship may be indirect in that the faults and other commonly related features such as shallow-water conglomerate and felsic intrusions merely reflect a common tectonic environment in which gold is localized in passive conduits by other magmatic or metamorphic processes. A more likely relationship is that regional faults are directly responsible for the transport of fluids in their vicinity. Sibson *et al.* (1975) have used theoretical considerations to show that "seismic pumping" is a viable explanation for the direct observation of warm fluids which are commonly expelled from active fault zones. Fluids may be of magmatic, meteoric or metamorphic origin but major fault zones have the potential for involving large fluid volumes including those from deep crustal sources. The apparent control of metamorphic grade on the localization of gold in the Mine Centre – Fort Frances area suggests that fluids derived from metamorphic dehydration (Fyfe and Henley 1973) may be significant in this example. The application of the above model to lode gold deposits of the Mine Centre – Fort Frances area and possibly of the Wabigoon Subprovince as a whole implies that they are relatively late stage epigenetic features.

REFERENCES

Blackburn, C.E., Breaks, F.W., Edwards, G.R., Poulsen, K.H., Trowell, N.F., and Wood, J.
1982: Stratigraphy and Structure of the Western Wabigoon Subprovince and Its Margins, Northwestern Ontario; Geological Association of Canada, Field Trip Guide Book, Winnipeg, 105p.

Borradaile, G.J.
1982: Comparison of Archean Structural Styles in Two Belts of the Canadian Superior Province; Precambrian Research, Vol. 19, p.179-189.

Fyfe, W.S., and Henley, R.W.
1973: Some Thoughts on Chemical Transport Processes, with Particular Reference to Gold; Minerals Science and Engineering, Vol. 5, p.295-302.

Horwood, H.C.
1948: General Structural Relationships of Ore Deposits in the Little Long Lac-Sturgeon River Area; p.377-384 in Structural Geology of Canadian Ore Deposits, Vol. 1, Canadian Institute of Mining and Metallurgy.

McKinstry, H.E.
1953: Shears of the Second Order; American Journal of Science, Vol. 251, p.401-404.

Park, R.G.
1981: Shear Zone Deformation and Bulk Strain in Granite-Greenstone Terrain of the Western, Superior Province, Canada; Precambrian Research, Vol. 14, p.31-48.

Poulsen, K.H.
1981: The Geological Setting of Mineralization in the Mine Centre – Fort Frances Area, District of Rainy River; p.190-195 in Summary of Field Work, 1981, by the Ontario Geological Survey, edited by J. Wood, O.L. White, R.B. Barlow, and A.C. Colvine, Ontario Geological Survey, Miscellaneous Paper 100, 255p.

Poulsen, K.H., Borradaile, G.J., and Kehlenbeck, M.M.
1980: An Inverted Archean Succession at Rainy Lake, Ontario; Canadian Journal of Earth Sciences, Vol. 17, p.1358-1369.

Poulsen, K.H., and Franklin, J.M.
1981: Copper and Gold Mineralization in an Archean Trondhjemitic Intrusion, Sturgeon Lake, Ontario; p.9-14 in Current Research, Part A, Geological Survey of Canada, Paper 81-1A.

Ramsay, J.G.
1980: Shear Zone Geometry: a Review; Journal of Structural Geology, Vol. 2, p.83-99.

Ramsay, J.G., and Graham, R.H.
1970: Strain Variation in Shear Belts; Canadian Journal of Earth Sciences, Vol. 7, p.786-813.

Schwerdtner, W.M., Stone, D., Osadetz, K., Morgan, J., and Stott, G.M.
1979: Granitoid Complexes and the Archean Tectonic Record in the Southern Part of Northwestern Ontario; Canadian Journal of Earth Sciences, Vol. 16, p.1965-1977.

Sibson, R.H.
1977: Fault Rocks and Fault Mechanisms; Journal of the Geological Society of London, Vol.133, p.191-213.

Sibson, R.H., Moore, J.M., and Rankin, A.H.
1975: Seismic Pumping — a Hydrothermal Fluid Transport Mechanism; Journal of the Geological Society of London, Vol.131, p.191-213.

Wood, J.
1980: Epiclastic Sedimentation and Stratigraphy in the North Spirit Lake and Rainy Lake Areas: A Comparison; Precambrian Research, Vol.12, p.227-255.

Gold Mineralization in the Shebandowan Belt and its Relation to Regional Deformation Patterns

G.M. Stott[1] and B.R. Schnieders[2]

[1]Precambrian Geology Section, Ontario Geological Survey, Toronto
[2]Resource Geologist, Ontario Ministry of Natural Resources, Thunder Bay

ABSTRACT

The deformational history of the Shebandowan metavolcanic belt is shown to relate to gold mineralization. All known occurrences are found within or at the margins of structural domains affected by a second deformational episode. Gold mineralization is a structurally late event within the northern portion of the belt and is localized by fracture cleavage and shear zones of the second deformation in metavolcanics, and within and proximal to quartz-feldspar porphyry intrusions near the Shebandowan pluton. This correlation between lode gold deposits and the tectonic framework may serve as a model for other regions of similar setting, near the margins of major sedimentary basins.

INTRODUCTION

The purpose of this paper is to report on the regional state of deformation in the rocks of the Shebandowan metavolcanic belt and show how it relates to the distribution and characteristics of gold mineralization. We shall review the overall tectonic and pluton-emplacement history of the belt and the timing of gold mineralization. We shall also suggest several research topics relevant to the history and genesis of gold mineralization.

The key focus of the paper is to show that almost all known gold occurrences are confined within or at the margin of domains in the belt where a second deformation event is documented. It is concluded that the pronounced fracture cleavage and local shear zone development, characteristic of the domains of the second deformation, have rendered the northern half of the belt more viable for gold concentration in quartz and quartz-carbonate veins.

GENERAL GEOLOGY

The Shebandowan belt is bounded to the north by the Quetico metasedimentary subprovince and to the south by a granitoid complex. The general geology is summarized in Figure 1. The portion of the belt shown in Figure 1 has been mapped by Harris (1970), Giblin (1964), Hodgkinson (1968), Morin (1973) and Srivastava and Fenwick

(1973a,b). Subsequent more detailed field studies have been conducted by Morton (1979, 1982), Stott and Schwerdtner (1981), and Shegelski (1980).

The southern half to two-thirds of the belt is dominated by mafic volcanic rocks locally containing jaspilite ironstone bands; there are also some ultramafic sills and flows. Felsic to intermediate volcanic flows and pyroclastic rocks occur mainly in the northwestern part of the belt. Somewhat bleached and carbonatized, locally fissile, mafic to intermediate volcanic rocks are also found in the northern third of the belt. The distribution of these altered volcanic rocks has not been precisely delineated but a significant proportion occurs within the zone in Figure 1 previously mapped exclusively as felsic volcanic rocks.

Two apparently related zones of younger sedimentary rocks and intermediate to felsic pyroclastic rocks occur south of Lower Shebandowan Lake (Figure 1). At least part of the southernmost zone, the Duckworth group, contains distinctly hematitic intermediate pyroclastic deposits similar to those found just south and east of Lower Shebandowan Lake. This is relevant, in conjunction with other observations described below, to the interpreted overall tectonic history.

Several late- to post-tectonic felsic intrusions invaded the belt and are probably correlative in age with several massive intrusions which are found within the granitoid complex to the south and have intruded the tonalitic terrain that comprises much of the complex. One exceptional syntectonic felsic intrusion is the Shebandowan pluton which will be discussed later.

STATE OF DEFORMATION

In order to propose an interpretation of the distribution and timing of gold mineralization in relation to the tectonic history of the "greenstone" belt, we shall first review the evidence from the structural record as summarized in Figure 2. The regional structure and deformation history have been outlined by Stott and Schwerdtner (1981).

The stratigraphy and mineral foliation is generally vertical to steeply northward dipping. Two domains of deformation have been identified and designated as D_1 and D_2 in Figures 2 and 3. The D_1 domain dominates the southern half of the belt. This region is uniformly characterized (outside of the contact strain aureoles enveloping the late to post-tectonic plutons) by moderately devel-

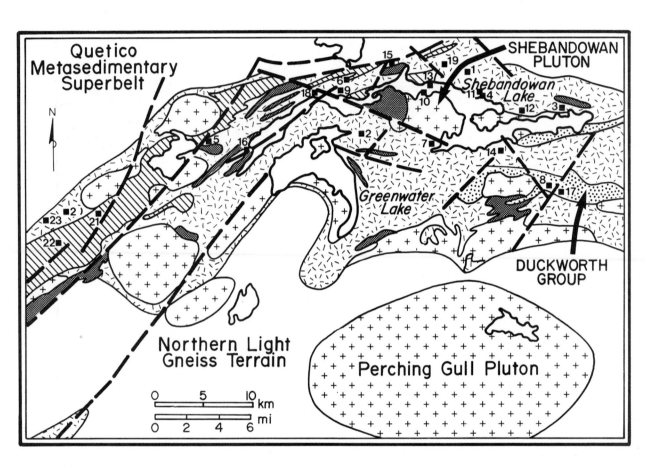

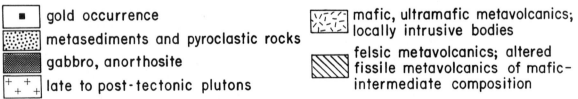

Figure 1. *General geology of the Shebandowan area showing locations of known gold occurrences. Numbers correspond to gold occurrences in Table 2.*

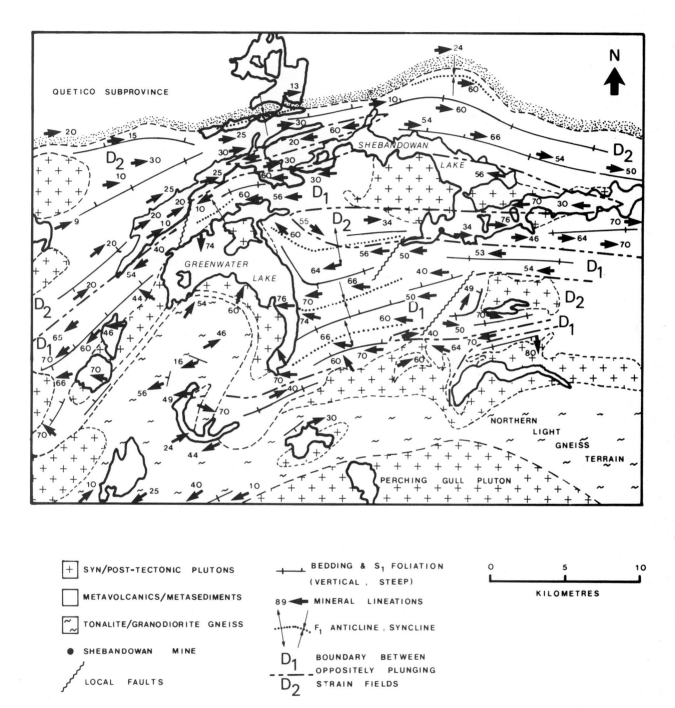

Figure 2. Structural map of the Shebandowan area summarizing the major structural features.

oped westerly to southwesterly plunging mineral lineations (Figure 4) readily observed on the steep, weakly to
moderately developed foliation surfaces. A single generation of folds occurs in the D_1 domain; these folds are up-
right in orientation and plunge westward to southwestward similar to the mineral lineations.

The D_2 domain covers the northern half of the belt,
extending into the Quetico metasedimentary terrain, and
also covers the Duckworth sedimentary group east of
Greenwater Lake along the central part of the Shebandowan belt (Figure 3). This domain possesses a moderately to strongly developed foliation with a weakly developed mineral lineation plunging northeastward to
eastward (Figure 4). The D_2 domain is also widely observed to be characterized by a well developed, fissile
schistosity typically confined to relatively narrow zones.

Folds of the stratigraphy are tight to isoclinal in profile but open folds occur in the sedimentary rocks and
volcanic breccia south and east of Lower Shebandowan
Lake. The axes of these folds plunge eastward, generally
parallel with the mineral lineations.

The boundaries between D_1 and D_2 domains are
sharp, generally with no associated faulting. An exception is the faulted western boundary of the D_2 domain encompassing the Duckworth sedimentary group in the
centre of the belt (Figure 2).

Late asymmetric, "S" and "Z", and conjugate kink
folds are widespread in the northern half of the belt and
are not confined to the D_2 domain. These are most prominent in thinly bedded units and are referred to as D_3
structures.

Overall, the belt possesses a pattern of deformation

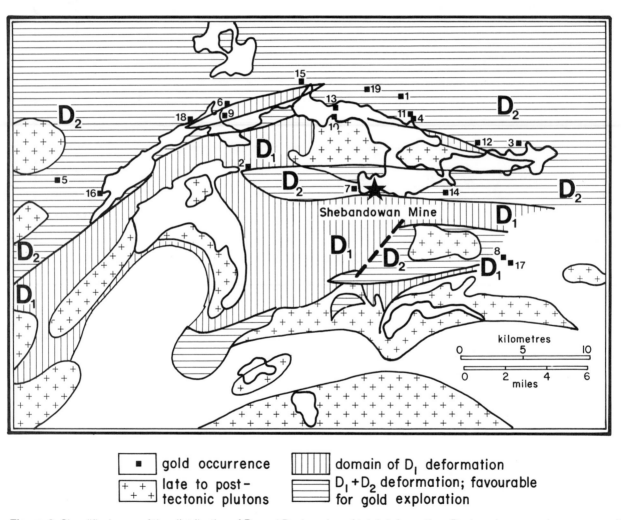

Figure 3. Simplified map of the distribution of D_1 and D_2 domains of total deformation. D_2 domains comprise a composite
of $D_1 + D_2$ deformations. The D_2 domains are the areas proposed as the most favourable for gold exploration. Numbers
correspond to gold occurrences in Table 2.

domains that can be distinguished by the contrasting plunge directions of their mineral lineations (westerly in D_1 and easterly in D_2 domains) and by the more pronounced fissile schistosity or fracture cleavage, and local shear zones in the D_2 domain.

TECTONIC HISTORY

The evidence for the sequence of tectonic events to follow is drawn from observations on the relationships of domains and the plutons within and along the margin of the belt to the D_1 and D_2 domains (Table 1).

Initially the entire width of the belt recorded a regional D_1 deformation that is attributable to a stage of vertical tectonics involving the rise of the tonalitic terrain that now occupies the region to the south of the belt (Schwerdtner *et al.* 1979).

A second period of deformation, D_2, involving subhorizontal shortening, and a significant component of simple shear, developed over the northern half of the belt

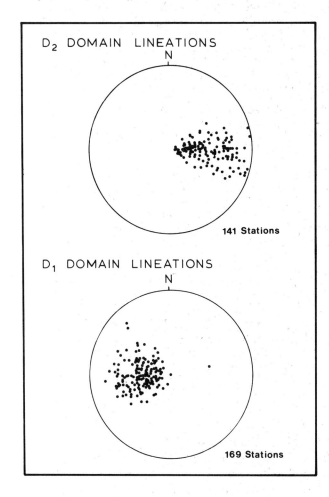

Figure 4. *Equal area stereograms: top, D_2 domain; bottom, D_1 domain from area in Figure 2.*

with corresponding D_2 shortening across the adjacent Quetico Subprovince. This generation of structures in the Quetico metasediments developed prior to the peak of metamorphism in the central core of the Quetico subprovince. But E.W. Sawyer (University of Toronto, personal communication, 1982) has established that southward, closer to the Shebandowan belt, there is less time separation between D_2 structural development and metamorphism.

This supports our interpretation that a tectono-thermal stage evolved within the Quetico Subprovince and affected parts of the Shebandowan belt subsequent to the first generation of structures in the belt. It is this widely distributed stage of deformation, superimposed on the D_1 strain pattern, that produced the composite state of deformation recorded in the D_2 domains. The observable effects of this event are confined to zones given in Figure 2.

The late kink folds of the D_3 phase of deformation are only locally observed and may reflect a progression of the principal flattening component of deformation. During the ductile D_2 phase, flattening was in a north or northwest direction; in the later brittle phase it was in an easterly direction.

A set of plutons has intruded the belt shown in Figure 2. All but one appear to be late to post-tectonic intrusions (i.e. late- to post-D_2) that possess contact strain aureoles and some evidence of contact metamorphic aureoles. The exception is the Shebandowan pluton centred on Shebandowan Lake (see Figure 1). This intrusion lacks a contact strain aureole upon its supracrustal envelope and straddles two structural domains so that the southern half was subjected to localized D_2 shearing and retrograde metamorphism. The northern half of the pluton possesses a primary strain fabric that corresponds in its lineation direction to the westerly stretching of the supracrustal rock fabric in the D_1 domain. The evidence suggests that the Shebandowan pluton intruded during D_1; the northern half effectively escaped penetrative deformation during D_2 but the pluton experienced some bulk flattening and acquired discontinuous narrow shear zones in its southern half in the vicinity of Lower Shebandowan Lake.

Several stocks and sills north of the Shebandowan pluton are probably related to it but lie within the major D_2 domain and display a pervasive fracture cleavage and evidence of shearing. Some of these quartz and/or feldspar porphyry bodies have served as suitable, structurally competent sites for quartz carbonate vein formation parallel to fracture cleavage planes. Their deformed appearance markedly contrasts with the "fresh looking" northern half of the Shebandowan pluton and this might suggest to an observer that the stocks and the pluton are unrelated. The evidence noted above, together with the spatial proximity of the stocks to the pluton, provides circumstantial support for their consanguineous relationship. No geochronological or petrological evidence has been documented to further substantiate this interpretation.

Another, partially related aspect of the overall history concerns the relative age of the red-bed sedimentary rocks and interbedded calc-alkalic volcanic rocks observed south of Lower Shebandowan Lake. Shegelski

Table 1. *Tectonic sequence of events.*

Tectonic Event

D_3 - E-W Compression	- kink folding and extension approx. perpendicular to D_2 cleavage - possible quartz veining along cleavage during extension
D_2 - Regional N-S and NW-SE compression with significant simple shear component (probably dominantly left lateral sense) - D_2 superimposed on D_1 within domains - D_2 dominant in N. half of belt and in structurally less competent groups of sediments and pyroclastic rocks; including Quetico subprovince	- quartz veins associated with late plutons (eg. Gold Creek occurrence) - late felsic plutons and hematitic fine grained dykes - Quartz veining - Quartz-carbonate veins infill along D_2 cleavage surfaces in volcanic rocks and porphyry intrusions. Most are in or near shear zones and some are in en echelon array. (eg. Band Ore, J.F. West) - Sequence of vein generations produced by hydraulic fracturing episodes during on-going ductile D_2 deformation
D_1 - westerly-plunging folding of supracrustal across Shebandowan belt. Record of D_1 unaffected by D_2, is preserved in southern half of belt - major period of volcanism	- sedimentation - red bed deposits, conglomerates - Shebandowan stock intrusion over a protracted period - "Timiskaming" K-rich pyroclastic volcanism

(1980) has demonstrated that there are rocks of high-K shoshonite affinity among these volcanic deposits. Worldwide, the formation of troughs partly filled with terrestrial (alluvial-fluvial red beds fault-margined) deposits, coupled with explosive eruption of alkaline volcanic rocks is indicative of late stage crustal thickening and craton stabilization. Similar "Timiskaming-type" volcanic suites with an alkalic component have been documented by Cooke and Moorhouse (1969) in the Kirkland Lake area, Smith and Longstaffe (1974) in the North Spirit Lake area and Blackburn (1982) in the Manitou Lake area.

Our evidence supports the late timing of this pyroclastic volcanism and concomitant clastic sedimentation. These deposits (the Duckworth group and another zone south of Lower Shebandowan Lake) are weakly deformed and are exclusively confined to D_2 domains. Some of these units display open easterly plunging folds that at-

test to the weak deformation. It is most unlikely that they underwent two phases of deformation (D_1 + D_2). In addition, polymictic conglomerates south of Lower Shebandowan Lake contain jaspilitic ironstone and mafic volcanic clasts derived from erosion of the basaltic platform which contains ironstone beds. The platform metavolcanics comprise the bulk of the D_1 domain. It is also intriguing to note the presence in the conglomerates of quartz porphyritic trondhjemite clasts that resemble part of the Shebandowan pluton. A limited record of the pluton unroofing appears to have been preserved in the conglomeratic deposit prior to D_2 deformation. There is also some evidence for the presence of the calc-alkalic pyroclastic suite north of the pluton as well as south. It is conceivable (although as yet unproven) that the Shebandowan pluton constitutes the parental intrusion to the late calc-alkalic volcanic rocks extruded in this area and further east. The tectonic record is at least consistent with this hypothesis.

The cratonization process may have commenced during the late stage or following D_1. Our evidence and that of Shegelski (1980, personal communication) indicates that an unconformity separates the late calc-alkalic suite and sedimentary rocks from the rest of the volcanic pile. This is also evident for the Duckworth sedimentary group further south.

DISTRIBUTION AND CHARACTERISTICS OF GOLD MINERALIZATION

Virtually all of the known gold deposits in this belt are confined to the D_2 domains or along their margins (see Figures 1 and 3). This also applies, beyond the areas in Figure 2, to the east and southwest parts of the belt (Figure 1). The deposits generally occur within mafic metavolcanics and within or adjacent to quartz and/or feldspar porphyry sills and dikes north of the Shebandowan pluton and southwest of Moss Lake (southwest corner of Figure 1).

The deposits are listed in Table 2 with their structural and mineralogical characteristics. One deposit, the Hayne's Shebandowan occurrence, is found within that part of the Shebandowan pluton that lies in the D_1 domain. However, the auriferous quartz vein is hosted by a 10 m wide shear zone that constitutes a very localized response to the D_2 deformation in an area of the pluton that escaped regional penetrative D_2 deformation.

The limited information available on the gold occurrences suggests that they typically constitute lensic quartz-carbonate veins and younger generations of quartz veins within or adjacent to shear zones that are developed within, adjacent to, or at a distance from feldspar porphyry sills and stocks. In many cases, porphyry sills appear to be incidental to the vein development, appearing to provide a more competent surface against which shearing has developed within the adjacent supracrustal rocks. In other cases, the veins are developed along D_2 fracture surfaces within the porphyry intrusions or along their contacts with the metavolcanics, e.g., J.F. West Prospect. Veins within shear zones are in places parallel to the zone trend and in places arrayed as en echelon lenses, giving a directional sense of the shearing (this is unfortunately rarely recorded). (There is widely distributed but sparsely documented evidence for left lateral shearing in the northern half of the belt. This could imply a regional westward or southwestward sense to the simple shear component of the D_2 deformation.)

Among the several generations of veins observed in some occurrences, the gold tends to be enriched in the younger quartz veins that cut the earlier quartz-carbonate veins; e.g. in part of the Band Ore Prospect.

TIMING OF GOLD MINERALIZATION

As shown in Table 1, the major development of hydrothermal veining is generally concomitant with the D_2 deformation. Veins are seen to have typically developed along fractures parallel or subparallel to and slightly transecting the D_2 foliation. In places, quartz-carbonate veins are boudinaged with inter-boudin nodes filled with quartz. En echelon boudins of veins can give a sense of the shearing component during D_2. There is also, as mentioned above, a spatial correlation between vein development and the presence of D_2 shear zones. Some quartz veins appear to be intimately related to the emplacement of late- to post-D_2 felsic intrusions and it is also possible that hydrothermal veining developed along D_2 foliation surfaces during D_3 compression that produced extension perpendicular to the foliations. This possibility has not been assessed. Indeed, the overall history of veining in this belt has yet to receive careful documentation. We can however point out that the most extensive development of hydrothermal veins is related to the D_2 phase of deformation. This focuses attention on the D_2 domains shown in Figure 3 as the areas of first priority for gold exploration. In essence this simply confirms the distribution of prospecting success over the past century. It does offer a rationale for this distribution and from that vantage, allows us to predict the general areas of most probable exploration success within the belt.

CONCLUSION AND DISCUSSION

We conclude that the structural evidence in the Shebandowan belt indicates auriferous quartz-carbonate vein systems formed during the second period of deformation and appear to be mainly constrained to domains wherein this second deformation is recorded. The veins have most advantageously developed along planar anisotropies, notably fracture cleavages in mafic volcanic rocks and porphyry intrusions. There is however evidence for multiple generations of hydrothermal veins that reflect a history of instances when brittle hydraulic fracturing occurred during penetrative D_2 deformation of the ductile host lithologies.

We also conclude that the field evidence plus regional variations in magnetic susceptibility anisotropy (Stott and Schwerdtner 1981) demonstrate that a sequential tectonic history occurred, comprising a regional D_1 phase, followed and superimposed by localized D_2 deformation. The D_2 phase is recognized to have extended southwards across the Quetico Subprovince into the Shebandowan belt. In the centre of the Quetico metasedimentary terrain, D_2 structures formed earlier than the peak of metamorphism. Farther south, in the Shebandowan belt, metamorphism and D_2 occurred together.

We shall now review several aspects deserving future research consideration. There are regional implications derived from these observations for gold exploration and we shall discuss them briefly. Our work indicates that most if not all of at least the northern half of the Shebandowan belt has experienced a D_2 deformation including a significant component of simple shear. This raises the question: were metavolcanic domains north of and immediately proximal to the Quetico metasedimen-

Table 2. Brief descriptions of properties shown in Figure 1.

Property Name	Discovery Date	Mineralization	Host Rock	Structure	Deformation Domain
1. Anderson Occurrence	1966	–	shear zone in mafic-intermediate volcanics	east-west strike	within D_2 domain
2. Andowan Occurrence	–	pyrite, chalcopyrite galena, sylvanite, gold	felsic volcanics close to faulted margin of late felsic intrusion	east-west strike, dips 80° south	within D_1 domain, close to a major D_2 contact and several narrow D_2 zones in D_1
3. Band Ore Prospect	1936	pyrite, chalcopyrite, gold, silver	quartz carbonate veins in and near shear zones in/near feldspar porphyry; silicification, carbonatization, sericitization and pyritization	east-west strike, dips 80° north; lenticular veins	within D_2 domain, close to D_1-D_2 contact
4. Calvert Occurrence	1947	pyrite, chalcopyrite, malachite, gold	quartz-carbonate veins and younger quartz veins within shear zones in volcanics and quartz-feldspar porphyry	strike 080°, dips 55°S; lenticular veins	within D_2 domain
5. Coldstream Mine (past producer)	1870's	Copper, gold, silver producer; massive sulphide deposit produced approx. 21,950 oz gold as a by-product	chert lens in mafic volcanics close to felsic volcanic contact	lenticular ore bodies plunge 50° east, strike east-west, dip north 80°-90°; eastward plunge related to D_2	within D_2 domain
6. Cornell Occurrence	1980	pyrite, chalcopyrite, pyrrhotite, sphalerite, gold, silver	intermediate to felsic volcanics	discontinuous shear zones strike 080°, dip southward 70° to 90°; quartz veins strike 062°, dip 80° southeast; left lateral sense of shear	within D_2 domain
7. Discovery Bay Occurrence	pre-1928	gold, silver	quartz vein in apparent felsic volcanics	no data	within D_2 domain

Table 2. *Continued.*

8. Gold Creek Occurrence	1896	pyrite, chalcopyrite, galena, possible tellurides, gold, silver	quartz-carbonate and quartz veins within shear zones in feldspar porphyry stock. Stock probably related to late to post D_2- Peewatai Lake pluton nearby. Veins also in adjacent volcanics and metasediments	northeast striking veins may indicate left lateral sense of shear	within D_2 domain
9. Harkness Occurrence	1949	pyrite, chalcopyrite, gold	mafic volcanics	shear zone in diamond drill core	on contact between D_2 and narrow relict D_1 zone
10. Hayne's Shebandowan Occurrence	pre-1928	pyrite, chalcopyrite galena, sphalerite, molybdenite, malachite, gold, silver	biotite granodiorite in Shebandowan pluton; Carbonatization and sericitization of shear zone	quartz vein strike 070°, dip 25° north in shear zone striking 100°, dip 90°	within D_1 domain, near D_1-D_2 contact
11. J.F. West Prospect (Greenwich Lake option)	1947	pyrite, chalcopyrite, malachite, gold	several generations of quartz-carbonate veins in felsic porphyry; quartz and quartz-carbonate veinlet stockwork in carbonatized porphyry intrusion; quartz segregations in felsic volcanic breccia unit	cross-cutting generations of veins and stratiform veins in different environments; stratigraphy strike 150°, dip 90°.	within D_2 domain
12. Lobanor Occurrence	1945	pyrite, chalcopyrite,	feldspar porphyry, bearing a silicified,	extensive overburden	within D_2 domain, near contact
13. Middle Gap Island Occurrence	pre-1928	molybdenite, gold, silver	quartz vein in granodiorite sill	vein cuts through sill; nearby rhyolite is quartz ribboned	within D_2 domain, near D_1-D_2 contact
14. Ourgold Occurrence	1961	no data, minor gold	mafic volcanics	quartz veins in fault planes and tension fracture; orientation unknown	within D_2 domain, near D_1-D_2 contact

Table 2. Continued.

15. Ray Smith Prospect	1954	pyrite, chalcopyrite, sphalerite, gold, silver	altered mafic to intermediate volcanics	veins within shear zones striking 140°, dip 90°, in stratigraphy striking 065°	within D$_2$ domain, near D$_2$ contact with a relict D$_1$ zone
16. Ritchie Estate Occurrence	pre-1961	pyrite, chalcopyrite, molybdenite	quartz-carbonate veins within shear zone at contact between coarse grained anorthositic gabbro and felsic metavolcanics	shear zone strike 050°, dip 90°	within D$_2$ domain
17. Scali Occurrence	pre-1938	pyrite	quartz and quartz-carbonate veins in mafic volcanics near feldspar porphyry dikes; pyrite-rich zones subparallel the dikes	veins are lenticular, bearing volcanic breccia, strike 074°, dip 90°, veins occur in shear zones and fractures	within D$_2$ domain
18. Vanguard Occurrence	1943	pyrite, pyrrhotite, chalcopyrite, gold, silver	shear zone of silicified mafic volcanics near anorthosite intrusion	shear zone strike 060°, dip 90°, parallel to stratigraphy; zone comprises en echelon lenses plunging to southwest	within D$_2$ domain and at the southwest end of a relict D$_1$ domain
19. W.A. Gray Occurrence	1950	no data	porphyry dyke in mafic volcanics	no data	within D$_2$ domain
20. Moss Mine (past producer)	1871	pyrite, chalcopyrite, sphalerite, tellurides, visible gold, silver; gold and silver recovered in proportion of	intermediate to mafic volcanics with en echelon quartz vein lenses, closely associated with feldspar porphyry sill forming a wall to vein in parts of the mine; gold contained in second generation quartz vein	quartz vein generally parallel to schistosity, adjacent to major shear zone trending 055°; en echelon veins indicate left lateral sense of shear;	within D$_2$ domain

190

Table 2. *Continued.*

		1:7; 29,948 oz. gold produced during 1932–1936.		ore shoots plunge 35° northeast, approx. parallel to D$_2$ lineation	
21. Snodgrass Prospect	1936	pyrite, chalcopyrite, gold; higher gold values in Sheared dacitic tuff adjacent to contact with diorite intrusion	dacitic tuff adjacent to small diorite body	mineralization occurs as dis- seminations in massive and sheared tuff, and in quartz veins cutting the sheared tuff	within D$_2$ domain
22. Cominco Occurrence	1966	pyrite, pyrrhotite	graphitic zones in felsic volcanics with calcite veins	drill hole data	within D$_2$ domain
23. Obadinaw Occurrence	1870's	pyrite, galena, chalcopyrite, with gold, silver	felsic and mafic volcanics, sheared near quartz vein	quartz vein strike 060° for length of 100 m	within D$_2$ domain

Note: 1) Data taken from available Ontario Department of Mines Reports, assessment file reports and observations by the second author.

2) Definitions: Occurrence   – having never produced gold and having minimal development work

Prospect   – producing less than 100 ounces of gold and having 30 m of lateral development work or 600 m of diamond drilling.

Past Producer – producing greater than 100 ounces of gold.

tary subprovince similarly affected by a comparable "D$_2$ history"? Most of the Wabigoon-Quetico Subprovince boundary is marked by a mylonitic shear zone or the Quetico Fault and it appears that the bulk of the D$_2$ deformation may be constrained to the Quetico terrain. However it is worth investigating parts of the Wabigoon-Quetico boundary to determine if the metavolcanic domain has experienced a similar D$_2$ deformation with its associated auriferous hydrothermal vein systems. Extensive gold occurrences are found in the Wabigoon supracrustal rocks near Mine Centre, Atikokan and the Beardmore-Geraldton areas, all close to the Quetico metasedimentary terrain. Therefore, can "gold-favourable" structural domains be mapped north and south of the Quetico Subprovince beyond the study area shown in Figure 1?

This leads us to the next question: Is there a correlation (beyond the structural relationships described above) between the proximity of major metasedimentary terrains and the occurrences of lode gold deposits in greenstone belts? Is this correlation a function of primary gold concentration related to paleo-facies changes to sedimentary basins nearby (MacGeehan *et al.* 1982) or is

it mainly a function of large scale metamorphic hydrothermal fluid cycling between the metasediments and the lithologies structurally favourable to hydraulic fracturing? In a differential stress regime during D$_2$ deformation, a rise in the pore fluid pressure will lower the effective normal stress, leaving the component of shear stress unchanged. Hydraulic fractures will develop normal to the least compressive stress when the pore fluid pressure exceeds the combined principal tensile stress plus the tensile strength of the rock. Under these conditions of high pore fluid pressure, which may be cyclically built up and relieved during the deformation, a set of veins may develop with geometries related to the orientation of the principal stresses at the critical moments of fracturing. These veins are indirectly "material snapshots" of the principal stress regime during the increments of the total history when the pore fluid pressure was sufficient to induce hydraulic fracturing. The mechanics of hydraulic fracturing and vein formation are discussed in Hubbert and Rubey (1959), Secor (1968) and Beach (1980). Application of hydraulic fracturing principals to quartz vein formation is very limited in the literature (e.g. Kerrich and

Allison 1978) and warrants more extensive consideration in conjunction with regional structural analyses. Indeed the fundamentals of pore fluid pressure and hydraulic fracturing have been developed extensively by oil geologists but have received little applied consideration by structural geologists in lode gold exploration. It may be feasible in areas of relatively simple tectonic history to predict the distribution and physical shape of the vein systems after a careful analysis of the strain state in the rocks and the tectonic history, coupled with relevant analogue modelling studies. It is not our purpose to review these considerations but simply to point out that structural models should be developed and investigated as predictors to enhance the locating and successful diamond drilling of vein systems. This entire field of study has yet to receive adequate attention.

In this context, it is noteworthy that each underground development of gold deposits in this belt trends in a direction approximately parallel to the local extension direction of cumulative strain in the host rocks, that is, parallel to the mineral lineations. The lenticular boudinaged orebodies of the North Coldstream Cu-Au-Ag Mine plunge eastward at about 50° (Giblin 1964) within an easterly plunging D_2 domain. The long, ribbon-shaped orebody of the Shebandowan Ni-Cu Mine plunges 30° eastward and steepens further eastward, comparable to the 65° plunge of the mineral lineations in the host rocks. The auriferous main vein in the Moss Mine appears to be slightly extended with a rake of 35° northeast, consistent with D_2 mineral lineations.

While pretectonic orebodies have responded to the cumulative deformation by rotation and extension of their shapes, the late tectonic quartz vein systems would tend to conform to the stress regime during the deformation.

The strain patterns in the belt have obvious implications for massive sulphide orebody shapes and orientations. Vein systems require detailed analyses to formulate predictive models at depth; hydraulic fracturing has developed within a progressively evolving differential stress regime and several factors may be involved that affect vein orientations and extension directions.

Finally we note that in a very general sense, the Shebandowan belt possesses several significant features that warrant comparison to those in other gold mining camps:

1. Zones of highly altered fissile mafic to intermediate metavolcanics occur in the Shebandowan belt that generally resemble the rocks of the large alteration zone coinciding with major gold deposits in the Red Lake camp (Pirie 1982). These zones in the Shebandowan belt have not been documented but appear to be confined to the northern part of the belt.

2. There appears to be a tectonic similarity (although a petrologic dissimilarity) between the Shebandowan pluton and the auriferous vein-bearing Bourlamaque batholith and nearby stocks in the Val d'Or area of Quebec (Campiglio 1977; Latulippe 1982), This major gold camp, concentrated near the the Cadillac Fault and a metasedimentary belt (Pontiac Group), bears a striking resemblance to areas of gold occurrences and mining camps

north and south of the Quetico metasedimentary terrain in northwestern Ontario. The same questions posed earlier about tectonic relationships near the Quetico terrain and their relevance to gold mineralization apply equally to the Val d'Or-Malartic district and westwards to the Kirkland Lake area.

In summary, our reconnaissance studies in the Shebandowan belt lead us to conclude that a correlation exists between lode gold deposits and the tectonic framework in the Shebandowan belt and that such a correlation may also exist in other regions of similar setting, near the margins of major sedimentary basins.

REFERENCES

Beach, A.
1980: Numerical Models of Hydraulic Fracturing and the Interpretation of Syntectonic Veins; Journal of Structural Geology, volume 2, p. 425-438.

Blackburn, C.E.
1982: Geology of the Manitou Lakes Area, District of Kenora (Stratigraphy and Petrochemistry); Ontario Geological Survey, Report 223, 61p.

Campiglio, C.
1977: Bourlamaque Batholith; Ministere des Richesses Naturelles de Quebec, E.S. 26, 211p.

Cooke, D.L. and Moorhouse, W.W.
1969: Timiskaming Volcanism in the Kirkland Lake Area, Ontario, Canada; Canadian Journal of Earth Sciences, volume 6, p. 117-132.

Giblin, P.E.
1964: Burchell Lake Area; Ontario Department Mines, Geological Report 19, 39p.

Harris, F.R.
1970: Geology of the Moss Lake Area; Ontario Department Mines and Northern Affairs, Geological Report 85, 61p.

Hodgkinson, J.M.
1968: Geology of the Kashabowie Area; Ontario Department Mines, Geological Report 53, 35p.

Hubbert, M.K. and Rubey, W.W.
1959: Role of Fluid Pressure in Mechanics of Overthrust Faulting; I. Mechanics of Fluid-Filled Porous Solids and Its Application to Overthrust Faulting; Geological Society of America Bulletin, volume 70, p. 115-166.

Kerrich, R. and Allison, I.
1978: Vein Geometry and Hydrostatics during Yellowknife Mineralization; Canadian Journal of Earth Sciences, volume 15, p. 1653-1660.

Latulippe, M.
1982: An Overview of the Geology of Gold Occurrences and Developments in Northwestern Quebec; p.9-14 in Geology of Canadian Gold Deposits, Proceedings of the CIM Gold Symposium, September 1980, edited by R.W. Hodder and W. Petruk, Canadian Institute of Mining and Metallurgy, Special Volume 24.

MacGeehan, P.J., Sanders, T. and Hodgson, C.J.,
1982: Meter-Wide Veins and a Kilometer-Wide Anomaly, Wallrock Alteration at the Campbell Red Lake District, Ontario; Canadian Institute of Mining and Metallurgy Bulletin, volume 75, p. 90-102.

Morin, J.A.
1973: Geology of the Lower Shebandowan Lake Area, District of Thunder Bay; Ontario Division of Mines, Geological Report 110, 45p.

Morton, P.
1979: Volcanic Stratigraphy in the Shebandowan Ni-Cu Mine area, Ontario; Geological Survey of Canada, Current Research Part B, Paper 79-IB, p. 39-43.
1982: Archean Volcanic Stratigraphy, and Petrology and Chemistry of Mafic and Ultramafic Rocks, Chromite and the Shebandowan Ni-Cu Mine, Shebandowan, Northwestern Ontario; Unpublished Ph.D. thesis, Carleton University.

Pirie, J.
1982: Regional Geological Setting of Gold Deposits, Eastern Red Lake area, Northwestern Ontario; p.171-183 in Geology of Canadian Gold Deposits, Proceedings of the CIM Gold Symposium, September 1980 edited by R.W. Hodder and W. Petruk, Canadian Institute of Mining and Metallurgy, Special Volume 24.

Schnieders, B.R., Larsen, C.R. and McConnell, C.D.
1981: Property Visits and Reports of The Atikokan Economic Geologist 1979-1980; Ontario Geological Survey, Open File Report 5334, 103 p.

Schwerdtner W.M., Stone, D., Osadetz, K., Morgan, J., and Stott, G.M.
1979: Granitoid Complexes and the Archean Tectonic Record in the Southern Part of Northwestern Ontario; Canadian Journal of Earth Sciences, volume 16, p. 1965-1977.

Secor, D.T.
1968: Mechanics of Natural Extension Fracturing at Depth in the Earth's Crust; Geological Survey of Canada, Paper 68-52, p. 3-48.

Shegelski, R.J.
1980: Archean Cratonization, Emergence and Red Bed Development, Lake Shebandowan Area, Canada; Precambrian Research, volume 12, p. 331-347.

Smith, T.E., and Longstaffe, F.J.
1974: Archean Rocks of Shoshonitic Affinities at Bijou Point, Northwestern Ontario; Canadian Journal of Earth Sciences, volume 11, p. 1407-1413.

Srivastava, P., and Fenwick K.G.
1973a: Lamport Township, District of Thunder Bay; Ontario Division Mines, Preliminary Map P. 826, Geol. Ser., scale 1 inch to 1/4 mile.
1973b: Duckworth Township, District of Thunder Bay; Ontario Division Mines, Preliminary Map P. 825, Geol. Ser., scale 1 inch to 1/4 mile.

Stott, G.M., and Schwerdtner, W.M.
1981: A Structural Analysis of the Central Part of the Shebandowan Metavolcanic-Metasedimentary Belt; Ontario Geological Survey, Open File Report 5349, 44p.

Gold Deposits in Northwestern Ontario

C.E. Blackburn[1] and D.A. Janes[2]

[1]Resident Geologist, Ontario Ministry of Natural Resources, Kenora

[2]Resident Geologist, Ontario Ministry of Natural Resources, Sioux Lookout

ABSTRACT

Multi-year mapping and synoptic study of some of the metavolcanic-metasedimentary belts in northwestern Ontario have led to documentation of features related to gold deposits. General observations from principal gold-bearing areas, which include the Lake of the Woods and Mine Centre areas as well as the Kakagi-Rowan, Manitou, Eagle-Wabigoon, Sturgeon, Minnitaki-Sandybeach, Pickle and Opapimiskan Lakes areas, suggest a number of common characteristics for the emplacement of gold, summarized as follows.

1. In most cases, preservation of early syngenetic concentrations of gold, under Archean tectono-metamorphic conditions would be unlikely.

2. The source of the gold in the majority of cases is attributed to hydrothermal fluids.

3. Clusters of deposits show common characteristics suggesting related parental systems.

4. The emplacement of gold is controlled by tectono-thermal events, best seen in zones of intense and prolonged activity, characterized by thick stratigraphy, varied lithology, extensive faulting, accompanied by mesozonal to epizonal magmatism and regional metamorphism.

5. The timing of the gold deposition is considered to be post-volcanic and early granitic magmatism, and syn- to post-metamorphism.

It is concluded that the majority of gold deposits studied are structurally controlled and have formed late in the evolution of the metavolcanic belt. The implications of these observations for exploration are that although, in the areas described, gold can be found in a variety of settings, the presence of major faults, internal granitoid bodies, tight isoclinal folds, shear zones and proximity to felsic volcanic centres are strong positive elements. The absence of one or more of these features does not however preclude gold occurrence.

INTRODUCTION

Archean gold deposits occur in a variety of lithological and structural settings in "greenstone" belts of the Canadian Shield. One of the major problems in attempting to understand mechanisms of gold deposit genesis is the lack of regional overviews of these settings. The purpose of this paper is to briefly review the geological associations of selected gold deposits and clusters of gold deposits that lie within a major portion of the Canadian Shield in northwestern Ontario, and to see how well they fit a group of related characteristics that pertain to their genesis.

TOWARD A MODEL FOR GOLD EMPLACEMENT

In developing an overall model for gold emplacement in an Archean greenstone belt, general observation suggests a number of common characteristics, viz:

1. Most gold deposits are late and therefore considered epigenetic. This does not preclude an earlier syngenetic concentration, but given the tectono-metamorphic environment in which they occur, it is unlikely that such deposits would be preserved in their syngenetic form. Also, syngenetic concentration is not a necessary requirement in the development of epigenetic gold deposits.

2. Gold deposits are of hydrothermal origin. Local variability of deposits is accounted for by differing chemistry of the hydrothermal systems, P-T variations, and the nature of wall rocks.

3. Clusters of deposits tend to have common characteristics that may reflect a common parental system. Where markedly different types of mineralization occur in a restricted area, multiple hydrothermal systems may have operated, possibly separated in time.

4. Tectono-thermal events control emplacement of gold deposits. Because volcanism, metamorphism, vertical crustal movements, and granitoid generation and emplacement form a continuum of events driven by heat from the mantle, it is to be expected that gold deposits would be found in the overlying carapace of active tectono-thermal zones. Zones of intense and prolonged activity would be marked by:
   a. thick volcanic-sedimentary assemblages
   b. wide variety of lithologies
   c. profound, wide-spread faulting, some of which is of the vertical type
   d. generation of mesozonal and epizonal felsic melts
   e. regionally developed metamorphism
   f. invasion of late granitoid melts.

5. The timing of gold deposition is important. We know it to be post-volcanic, post-(earlier $\geq$ 2700 Ma) granitoids and syn- to post-metamorphism in studied cases. Hence

we consider that the generation of hydrothermal fluids by metamorphic dehydration and degassing, possibly of greenschist facies rocks at the greenschist-amphibolite transition is the most likely genesis of systems responsible for gold emplacement (Kerrich 1981).

PRINCIPAL GOLD-BEARING AREAS

Gold deposits in the Kenora and Patricia Mining Divisions are clustered in a number of discrete areas, some of which have developed into mining camps. Each of these areas is characterised by lithologic, structural, and gold depositional features that are somewhat unique to that area. In this section, these features will be outlined, and compared with the gold emplacement characteristics outlined above.

LAKE OF THE WOODS

Gold deposits are scattered throughout the northern part of Lake of the Woods. However, they are clustered in three general areas, with a number of isolated, though significant, deposits outside these areas. These three areas are in the vicinity of High Lake, at Shoal Lake, and northeast of Lake of the Woods, around Kenora.

HIGH LAKE

At High Lake, numerous gold occurrences, none of which have come into production, occur in close proximity to and within the High Lake Stock, predominantly near its northeast end (Figure 1). They can be categorised according to one or more of three situations: in quartz veins and silicified zones in the stock; in quartz veins and silicified zones in volcanic country rock near and along the contacts with porphyry of the stock; and in shear zones and fractures as visible gold, within the stock.

Quartz veins and silicified zones in the stock notably carry chalcopyrite and molybdenite, with low tenor of gold. Typical of this situation is the molybdenite property of Eco Explorations Limited, where quartz veins occupy

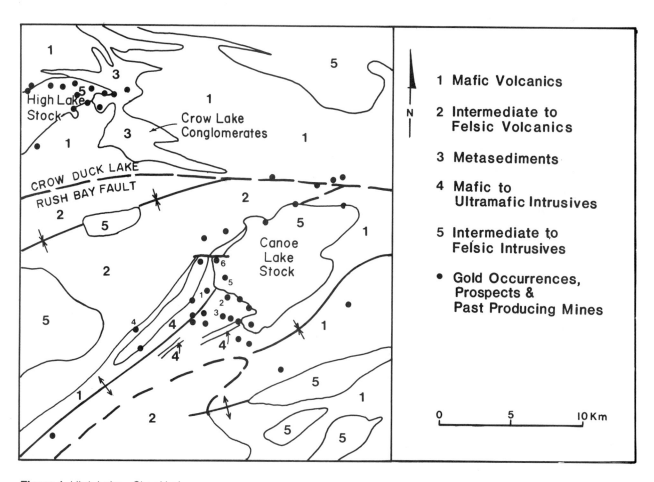

Figure 1. *High Lake – Shoal Lake area.*

fractures in the porphyry. Molybdenite is disseminated in the veins, and along fractures, and associated are pyrite and chalcopyrite. Though detailed study is lacking, gold appears to be associated with the chalcopyrite, and in concentrations of 0.05 ounces per ton and lower.

Quartz veins and silicified zones in country rocks at or near the margin with the stock are typified at properties close to Electrum Lake, such as the Purdex, and the former Electrum Lake Gold Mines Limited property southwest of Electrum Lake. At the latter property gold occurs both in quartz veins and silicified zones within porphyry of the stock, and in basaltic country rocks in pyrite and magnetite-bearing zones. At the Purdex property, gold with pyrite occurs in tourmaline-bearing quartz veins right along the contact with the porphyry. Notable copper or molybdenum are not associated at these properties.

Visible gold has been found along parallel fractures and shear zones within the stock, notably along northeast-trending fractures. Pyrite, pyrrhotite, and chalcopyrite are associated minerals.

The High Lake gold deposits are clearly epigenetic, as shown by their general association in shear zones or within quartz veins in shear zones. It appears also that emplacement was at least in part later than deposition of the overlying Crowduck Lake Conglomerates, since at the east end of the stock gold occurs in quartz veins and shear zones that cut the conglomerates. Mineralization probably either accompanied metamorphism, or postdates it, as shown by its association in amphibolite-grade basaltic flows at the Electrum Lake Gold Mines Limited property. The High Lake Stock is interpreted to have been intruded as two separate phases (Davies 1965), but no radiometric ages are available on either phase. Pedora (1976) has suggested that sulphide species accompanying gold at High Lake define a zonal distribution, which he relates to emplacement of the younger phase of the stock: higher temperature (molybdenite, chalcopyrite) minerals were deposited closest to the younger phase. This could well be the case. Local variation in wall-rock geology could also account for sulphide-species variation, since gold-bearing shear zones locally cut felsic to mafic volcanic and conglomeratic country rocks (see Marmont, this volume).

SHOAL LAKE

The Shoal Lake mining camp saw production in the past from four mines, the Cornucopia at Cedar Island, the Mikado, the Olympia, and the Duport. Numerous other occurrences and prospects are scattered particularly around the southwest end of the Canoe Lake Stock, notably near its margin, but characteristically outside the stock: there are a few exceptions, notably the Tycoon and Crown Point prospects that occur within the stock. Colvine and Sutherland (1979) noted that "gold mineralization is hosted by quartz and quartz-carbonate veins which occupy roughly east-west and north-to-northwest trending fractures [that are] responsible for most of the production from the Cornucopia, Mikado, and Olympia

mines. Accessory vein minerals include pyrite, chalcopyrite, sphalerite, galena, and molybdenite."

Copper and molybdenum mineralization is characteristic of deposits within the Canoe Lake Stock. Gold and silver are associated, and according to Colvine and Sutherland (1979), in exploration by Kerr Addison Mines Limited, "best assays were 0.06 ounces gold per ton and 2.94 ounces silver per ton".

Colvine and Sutherland (1979) concluded that within the stock, "the erratic nature of mineralization and the widespread occurrence of xenolith inclusions suggests possible assimilation of sulphide-bearing wallrocks", while "vein-gold mineralization around the stock margin was probably remobilized from the country rocks". However, this study was of a preliminary nature, and it is equally possible that mineralising fluids entered the stock during or shortly after its emplacement.

At the Duport Mine, on Cameron Island, gold mineralization appears to be in a felsic tuff, in two zones, the Main Zone, and the more recently discovered East Zone. Thomson (1935) described the felsitic Main Zone as containing arsenopyrite, pyrite, pyrrhotite, and chalcopyrite. Gold is closely associated with the arsenopyrite, both in solid solution and as occasional visible gold. The tuff units strike northeasterly, in conformity with regional strike, and the unit comprising the Main Zone has been traced considerably further than the 2400 feet of mineralization outlined by Selco Incorporated in exploratory drilling (The Northern Miner, May 13, 1982). Source of gold in this deposit is as yet undetermined, but it appears likely that the felsic tuff units acted as a favourable, sheared, host for gold-bearing solutions. It is also possible that gold in these felsic units is syngenetic; if this is the case, recognition of the position of these units within the regional stratigraphy may be a valuable exploration guide.

In summary, gold-bearing quartz veins surrounding the southwest end of the Canoe Lake Stock are undoubtedly epigenetic, whether sulphide and gold mineralization within the stock resulted from assimilation of mafic country rock, or from penetration of the stock by hydrothermally generated fluids. The nature of gold deposition at the Duport Mine is less clear, and this may be one exception to the characteristics outlined at the beginning of the paper.

NORTHEAST LAKE OF THE WOODS

Many gold deposits have been found in the general vicinity of the northeast corner of Lake of the Woods, south and east of Kenora. They notably occur in a cluster in close proximity to the contact of metavolcanics with the Dryberry Batholith. They predominantly are within the metavolcanic belt, and in a basaltic sequence centred on Bigstone Bay, but also occur within the batholith. Past-producing mines include four within the metavolcanic belt, the Sultana and Ophir (Figure 2, numbers 1 and 2 respectively), the Gold Hill (3), and the Wendigo (4), and one well within the Dryberry Batholith, the Champion (5).

There appear to be two groupings, that bear some

relationship to stratigraphy. The first grouping includes all those deposits that are located within the Bigstone Bay basalts, and in the immediate adjacent granitoid rocks of the Dryberry Batholith. These would include four of the past producers, the Sultana (Figure 2, number 1), the Ophir (2), the Gold Hill (3), and the Champion (5). Although at present little understood, all these deposits may be related to fracture systems developed in proximity to the metavolcanic-batholith contact, with hydrothermal systems generated by regional metamorphism subsequently responsible for transport and deposition of gold.

The second grouping includes those deposits developed higher in the stratigraphy, near the transition from mafic into intermediate to felsic metavolcanics located at Andrew Bay. A number of differentiated ultramafic to mafic sills intrude the upper part of the Bigstone Bay basaltic sequence at this general stratigraphic level. The Wendigo Mine (4), the largest gold producer on the Lake of the Woods, producing 67,423 ounces of gold and 14,762 ounces of silver, was located within metavolcanics in close proximity to the base of one of these sills, developed on a vein that parallels the stratigraphy. Blackburn (1983) has recently suggested that gold

mineralization in and near the Wendigo Mine may be stratabound and at a specific level in the stratigraphy. It may be of some significance that another past producing mine, the Duport at Shoal Lake, also is located close to differentiated ultramafic sills, and near the transition from a lower, basaltic, volcanic sequence upward into an overlying intermediate sequence.

Gold-bearing quartz veins in the northeast Lake of the Woods area are undoubtedly epigenetic. Available information suggests that those deposits within the Dryberry Batholith are of this type. Wendigo Mine may represent a special case; however, it too is a quartz vein deposit, and it is probable that the fracture into which it is emplaced is a late tectonic feature, thus implying a later, hydrothermal origin for this deposit.

KAKAGI-ROWAN LAKES

Numerous gold deposits, none of which have come to production, are scattered throughout this "greenstone" terrain (Figure 3), but they appear in general to conform to one of three situations: those that occur near or along

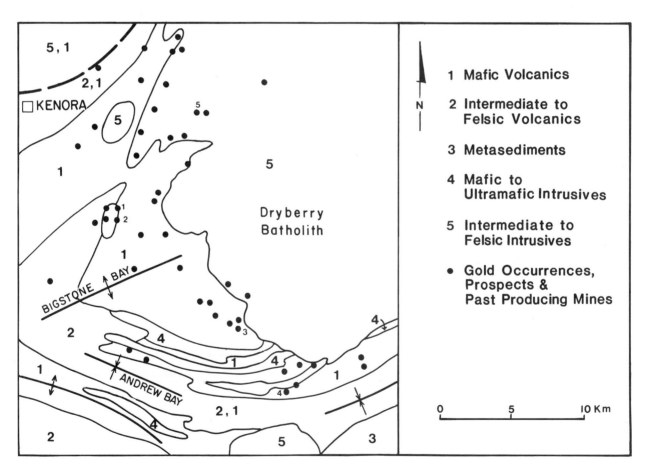

Figure 2. *Area northeast of Lake of the Woods.*

197

the transition from mafic to intermediate volcanism; those that occur in fractures in the differentiated ultramafic to mafic Kakagi sills; and those that occur along extensive shear and fault zones. A number of these occurrences could be grouped under two, or all three of these headings, so that there may be an overall genetic link between all three associations.

Geologic synopsis of a much larger region, that encompasses the Kakagi-Rowan Lakes area (Trowell *et al.* 1980) has led to the suggestion that: (1) at Kakagi Lake a lower mafic, volcanic flow sequence (Snake Bay Volcanics) is overlain by an upper mixed mafic to felsic, predominantly pyroclastic sequence (Kakagi Lake Group); and (2) at Rowan Lake a lower, mafic, volcanic flow sequence (Brooks Lake Volcanics) is similarly overlain by an upper, mixed mafic to felsic, predominantly pyroclastic, sequence (here called Cameron Lake Volcanics). Occurrences numbered 1 through 19 (Figure 3) all occur near this transition, though some of them, for example the

Canadian Arrow (1), the Robertson (3), and the Martin Kenty (5), could also be considered as hosted in Kakagi sills. Although all of these occurrences are quartz vein deposits occupying shears and fractures, their location at a specific level in the stratigraphy suggests that there may have been an original syngenetic gold enrichment.

In addition to the three occurrences noted above, other occurrences numbered 20 through 25 occur in association with Kakagi sills. At the Millree occurrence (Figure 3, number 22) gold-bearing veins occur in a series of northeasterly oriented transverse fractures that cross a Kakagi sill at high angles. Quartz-carbonate veins carry pyrite and molybdenite. All veins carry gold. At the Wensley occurrence (Figure 3, number 23), narrow quartz veins that carry gold strike easterly, within the same sill. Though information is limited, a similar orientation of veins is present at the Wensley-Burnt Peninsula (20) and Martin (21) occurrences. It is suggested that

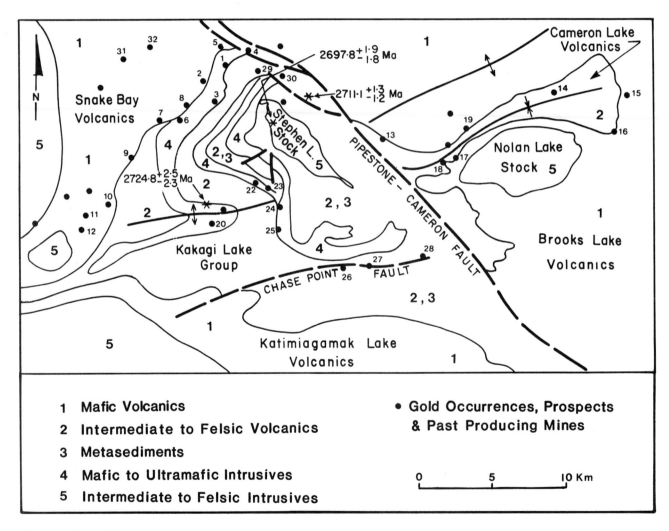

Figure 3. *Kakagi-Rowan Lakes area.*

gold-bearing veins in the vicinity of these four occurrences are occupying fractures opened up in the Kakagi sills where they are tightly folded about an east-trending anticline.

Two prominent faults or shear zones, the Pipestone-Cameron Fault, and the Chase Point Fault, host gold occurrences. Along the former, these include the Caswell Williams (Figure 3, number 29), the Meahan (3) and the Noranda-Beggs Lake (13) occurrences. Along the latter, the Martin (26, 27) occurrences, and the West Otterskin (28) occurrence appear to be along a common linear trend.

Other gold deposits occur within Snake Bay Volcanics, and several, notably the Bag Lake (31) and Frobisher (32) appear to be localised in the vicinity of porphyry intrusions.

Overall, gold deposits in the Kakagi-Rowan Lakes area are fairly widely scattered, and occur in a number of situations. Overall metamorphic grade appears to be greenschist facies. No single concentrating mode can be suggested; it may be that a number of metamorphically derived hydrothermal systems acted at differing times in the evolution of the area. Previous workers (e.g. Davies and Morin 1976; Beard and Garratt 1976) have laid emphasis on the undoubtedly major Pipestone-Cameron Fault as a locus for gold mineralization; examination of Figure 3 suggests that in fact the majority of occurrences are well removed from this structure. The presence of such a major, through-going, fault zone is indicative of profound tectonic events, probably accompanied by a number of ages of emplacement of felsic melts, exemplified by the Stephen Lake or Nolan Lake Stocks.

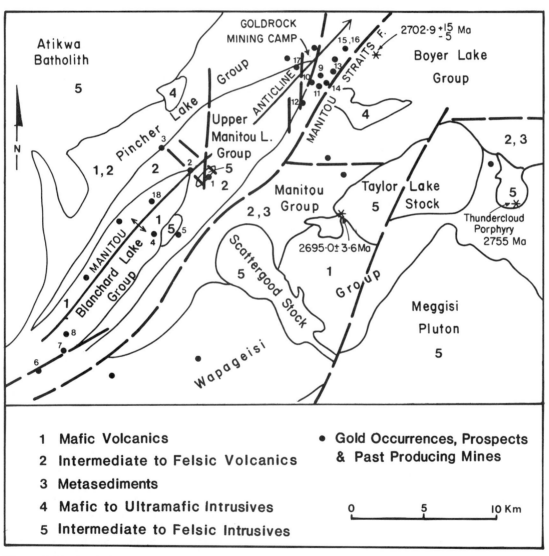

Figure 4. *Manitou Lakes area.*

Zircon U-Pb ages (Figure 3) obtained by Davis and Edwards (1982) put some constraints on time of emplacement of quartz veins. An age of $2724.8 ^{+2.5}_{-2.3}$ Ma from a Kakagi sill gives a maximum age for deposits that occur in these sills. An age of $2711.1 ^{+1.3}_{-1.2}$ Ma from tuff at the top of the Kakagi Lake Group gives a maximum age for deposits in veins that cut at least the upper part of this group. Gold occurrences are not known within the Stephen Lake Stock, although a numbr of mineral deposits, both gold and base metal sulphides, occur in close proximity. A preliminary age of $2697.8 ^{+1.9}_{-1.8}$ Ma from this stock (D. Davis, Jack Satterly Geochronology Laboratory, personal communication, 1982) may well give a minimum age for gold deposition in the Kakagi Lake area.

MANITOU LAKES

Although known occurrences are not numerous in the Manitou Lakes area, the Goldrock mining camp was the site of three past-producing mines, the Laurentian, Elora, and Kenwest (Figure 4, numbers 9, 10, and 11 respectively), while a fourth mine, the Twentieth Century (Figure 4, number 18), was situated southwest of Upper Manitou Lake.

It is immediately evident (Figure 4) that the majority of gold occurrences at Manitou Lakes occur northwest of the through-going Manitou Straits Fault. Blackburn (1982) has demonstrated that northwest of the fault three major lithostratigraphic units, the Blanchard Lake, Upper Manitou Lake, and Pincher Lake Groups, have been tightly folded, with attendant intense shearing, about the Manitou Anticline. Undoubtedly this deformation opened up fractures that would have been favourable to emplacement of gold-bearing quartz veins. Of the occurrences northwest of the Manitou Straits Fault, the majority can be assigned to one or more of three associations: (1) those related to porphyry or granitoid stocks; (2) those controlled by shear zones or faults; and (3) those associated with felsic units at the fold nose of the Manitou Anticline (at Goldrock).

The Frenchman Island (1), Swede Boys (2), Haycock (3), Reliance (4), and Queen Alexandra (5) deposits all occur either in close proximity to, or within, felsic stocks. Gold-bearing quartz veins at Frenchman Island occupy fractures in a subvolcanic microgranodioritic plug. A number of faults and crossfractures (Figure 4) intersect at the plug, and may have acted as channelways for gold-bearing fluids. Pyrite and chalcopyrite are associated at these occurrences, and in addition, pyrrhotite and sphalerite at the Reliance.

At Goldrock, the association of gold-bearing quartz veins with felsic units has been documented by Thomson (1942) and Blackburn (1981). Thomson (1942) placed heavy emphasis on the presence of a "break", the locus of ore-bearing zones at the Elora and Laurentian Mines. The combination of factors such as carbonatized mafic metavolcanics, location at a tight fold nose, and numerous cross-faults, suggests the action of hydrothermal systems in transporting and localizing gold. Associated sulphide mineralization is confined to pyrite in the Goldrock Camp.

Shear zones and faults also appear to play an important role in deposits at Lower Manitou Lake, namely the Gaffney (6), Bee-Hive (7), and Royal Sovereign (8), which occur close to or along a major splay off the Manitou Straits Fault (Blackburn 1976).

At the Gaffney occurrence, lying within the fault splay, gold occurs both in quartz veins that trend at high angles to the fault, and either within or close to felsic porphyry dikes, and in a pyritic sulphide zone that trends parallel to the schist zone. Chalcopyrite is the only other associated sulphide mineral noted. In summary, gold mineralization in the Manitou Lakes area is epigenetic, though at Goldrock syngenetic pre-concentration is a distinct possibility. Blackburn (1981) interpreted the felsite units to be of synvolcanic origin, whether extusive or shallow sills, rather than later dikes, and suggested that these may have been the original gold repositories, later re-mobilizing into quartz veins. As in the Kakagi-Rowan Lakes area, the presence of a through-going, major fault zone in the centre of the "greenstone" belt along with tight folding and accompanying shearing suggests profound tectonic events, that operated over a prolonged time span (see Poulsen, this volume). This latter point is supported by zircon U-Pb dates (Davis *et al* 1982) that suggest a minimum time span of in excess of 55 Ma for deposition of the Manitou Lakes – Stormy Lakes volcanic sequence (measured by a 2755 Ma minimum age on the Thundercloud Porphyry, and a $2702.9 ^{+15}_{-5}$ Ma age on a tuff in the Boyer Lake Group, see Figure 4). An age of 2695.0 ± 3.6 Ma from the post-tectonic Taylor Lake Stock, as suggested for the Stephen Lake Stock at Kakagi Lake, may give a minimum age for gold deposition in the Manitou Lakes area.

EAGLE-WABIGOON LAKES

Gold occurrences in and around Eagle and Wabigoon Lakes are concentrated in two specific areas (Figure 5), and there appears to be stratigraphic control, as yet not clearly understood. Many of the occurrences are located within the Lower Wabigoon Volcanics, a sequence of predominantly intermediate to felsic metavolcanics lying stratigraphically above the predominantly basaltic Eagle Lake Volcanics and underlying the predominantly basaltic Upper Wabigoon Volcanics. Other occurrences are located within the Atikwa Batholith, close to its contact with the Lower Wabigoon Volcanics, especially in the vicinity of Eagle Lake. Zircon U-Pb geochronology studies have shown (Davis *et al.* 1982) that there is a close temporal connection between the emplacement of the Atikwa Batholith and the Lower Wabigoon Volcanics: at Wabigoon Lake ages determined on volcanic and batholitic rocks (Figure 5), dated at $2734.8 ^{+4.0}_{-3.1}$ Ma and 2732.2 ± 2.9 Ma respectively, are within experimental error of each other; at Eagle Lake the batholithic rocks, dated at $2731.8 ^{+1.6}_{-1.3}$ Ma, are somewhat younger than adjacent volcanic rocks dated at $2742.8 ^{+1.4}_{-1.2}$ Ma. It therefore seems probable that Lower Wabigoon Volcanics are at least in part extrusive equivalents of the Atikwa Batholith.

Gold occurrences at Eagle Lake, that include one past producer, the Baden Powell Mine (Figure 5, number 1), are variously in quartz veins, shear, and sulphide zones. Information on many of them is scant, but considerable attention has been paid to the Fornieri (5), Smith (6) and Magdalena (7) occurrences. Gold appears to be widely distributed in the vicinity of these properties, and in two situations: (1) in quartz veins and stringers, mainly in felsic volcanic and porphyry country rocks, and (2) in sulphide zones, probably of replacement type, in mafic metavolcanics. Mineralization includes pyrite, pyrrhotite, sphalerite, galena, chalcopyrite, and bismuthinite, in addition to gold. One of the sulphide replacement zones appears to parallel and be adjacent to an east-striking narrow banded chert unit.

In a report for Magdalena Red Lake Gold Mines Limited (Resident Geologist's Files, Ontario Ministry of Natural Resources, Kenora) it is noted that the felsic rocks that host the gold-bearing quartz veins are considerably altered in places.

At Wabigoon Lake, numerous occurrences are situated within the Lower Wabigoon Volcanics. Most of these occur north and west of the Doré Lake lobe of the Atikwa Batholith. Two of these, the Bonanza (Figure 5, number 2) and Redeemer (3) were producing mines. Description of

the geology of the immediate vicinity of these mines by Bruce (1925) suggests that the quartz veins that hosted the gold are narrow and consistently oriented easterly, with little wall rock alteration, and cross-cut the latest emplacement of felsic porphyry dikes. Further west, at Flambeau Lake, numerous occurrences are situated at a similar stratigraphic level to the Bonanza and Redeemer. The association with intermediate to felsic metavolcanics, and cross-cutting felsic porphyries, is evident, but control of these veins is little understood. It is possible that a shear zone runs westerly through this zone, extending through Larson Bay of Wabigoon Lake, and that these occurrences are located on it.

Gold occurrences at Eagle Lake that occur in quartz veins and stringers cross-cut volcanic stratigraphy, and are therefore younger than about 2740 Ma, and probably younger than batholithic rocks at about 2730 Ma. Although rocks dated at Wabigoon Lake are distant from the cluster of gold deposits, it seems likely that these also are younger than about 2730 Ma.

The clustering of gold deposits at two localities, both adjacent to lobes of the Atikwa Batholith that are of the same age, suggests that similar hydrothermal systems operated at about the same time to concentrate gold mineralization.

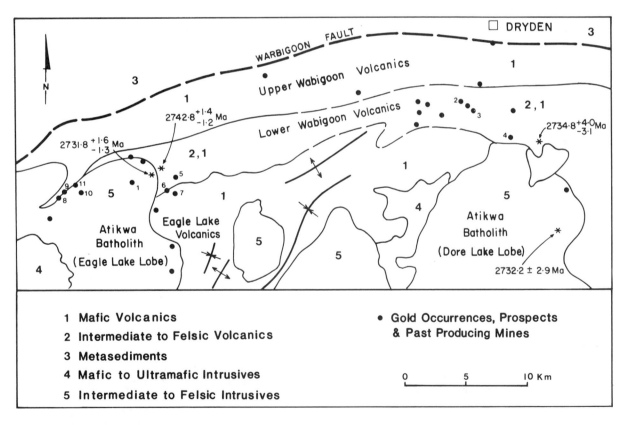

Figure 5. *Eagle-Wabigoon Lakes area.*

MINE CENTRE

At Mine Centre, gold deposits can be assigned to three distinct environments. Three of the former gold mines, the Cone (Figure 6, number 1), the Foley (2), and the Golden Star (3) are located in one of these environments, that is in quartz veins occupying "ductile shear" zones in tonalitic and trondhjemitic intrusions on the northwest and southeast flanks of the Bad Vermilion Lake Anorthosite. Poulsen (1981, this volume) attributes this association more to the mechanical characteristics of these felsic plutons than to a genetic link with the plutons, and has developed an eloquent argument relating "ductile shear" zones to regional deformation patterns expressed by major movement on the Quetico and Seine River Faults.

The second environment is in close proximity to or within the Quetico Fault, and is exemplified in the past-producing Olive Mine (Figure 6, number 4). Information on this environment is scant, but it appears that gold-bearing quartz veins lie within highly deformed rocks resulting from movement along the fault. At many places the fault zone is mylonitic; at the Olive Mine a unit of silicic rock with strong banding is bound on either side by metavolcanics. Bruce (1925) termed these quartzites, but a photograph in his report (p.29) strongly suggests that they are mylonitic rocks. The single gold-bearing quartz vein from which 3572 ounces of gold were won lies between and parallel to the banding.

The third environment is in the volcanic sequence fault-bounded within the Seine Group, north of the Seine River Fault. Two occurrences that characterise this environment are the Dinosaur (14) and the Smylie (15), but information on them is again scant. According to mapping by Wood (1980), they lie in a zone of felsic metavolcanics, consisting of siliceous sericitic altered rock, with chloritoid present in places. The area is sufficiently removed from the main Mine Centre area to be categorised as a separate environment.

Sulphide mineralization associated with gold deposits includes pyrite, sphalerite, galena, and chalcopyrite, and Poulsen (1981) mentioned arsenopyrite and argentite in addition.

Undoubtedly all those deposits that occur as quartz-vein hosted in "ductile shear" zones in felsic plutons, and also those, like the Olive, that are located within or in proximity to the Quetico Fault, are epigenetic. Zones of alteration have been outlined in the tonalite, and appear to be pervasive over large areas, but not necessarily in close proximity to the known gold-bearing quartz veins. Within the "ductile shears", alteration of feldspars is pervasive; this strongly supports a hydrothermal mode of emplacement for these veins, and that this system was common to all of the shear zone related deposits, and possibly also those at the Quetico Fault.

STURGEON LAKE AREA

This area has a long and interesting history of gold exploration dating back to 1898. Episodic exploration and development has continued from 1901 to the present.

There are many prospects, showings and properties and new ones have been discovered, or rediscovered, at the rate of several per year for the last three years. The St. Anthony Mine is the sole successful past producer although several other properties have produced limited amounts of gold.

Sturgeon Lake (Figure 7) is an excellent study area due to a combination of many gold prospects, good outcrop density and well defined age relationships. The southern half of the 50 km long lake is better known for the presence of three base metal mines, but only one significant gold deposit, the Darkwater Mine, is located near this part of the lake.

The northern portion of the lake hosts more than twenty gold occurrences, aligned along several structural trends. The area is underlain by a roughly north-trending band of mafic to felsic volcanic extrusive and intrusive rocks with trends roughly parallel to the belt boundaries. This trend is truncated at East Bay and King Bay where the foliation and formational boundaries swing to an east-west direction. The section exposed between North and Northeast Bays of Sturgeon Lake consists of a basal basaltic unit overlain to the east by an andesitic to felsic tuffeous assemblage. A major fault with a well defined mylonitic zone extends down Northeast Bay and may extend the length of Sturgeon Lake. A secondary fault or shear zone extends through East Bay and is host to a sulphide zone. Shearing is widespread in King Bay but is not localized in a defined zone. The volcanic rocks have been intruded by sills and stocks of alkalic syenite and nepheline syenite to the south of East Bay. Minor ultramafic sills and at least one possible ultramafic extrusive or fragmental

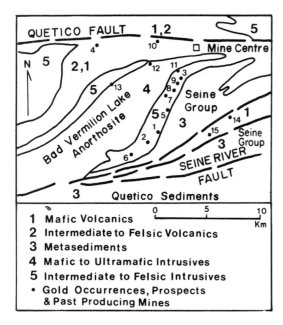

Figure 6. *Mine Centre area.*

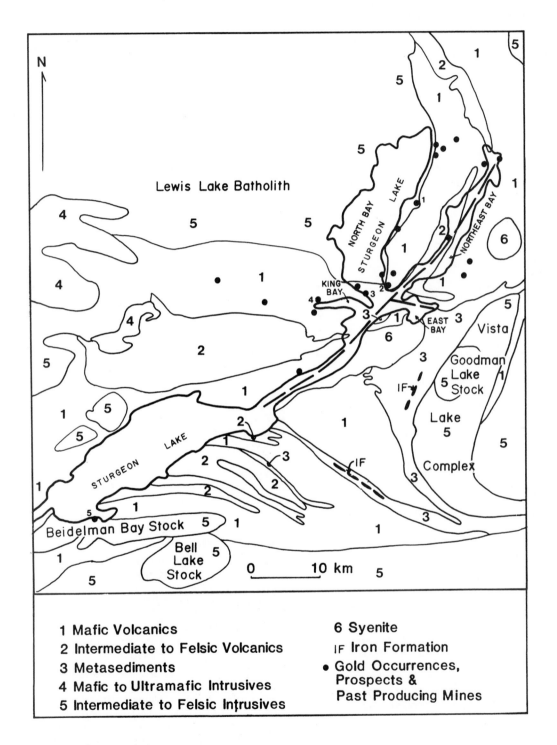

N

Lewis Lake Batholith

NORTH BAY
STURGEON LAKE
NORTHEAST BAY
KING BAY
EAST BAY
Vista
Goodman Lake Stock
Lake Complex

STURGEON LAKE

IF

Beidelman Bay Stock

Bell Lake Stock

0   10 km

1 Mafic Volcanics
2 Intermediate to Felsic Volcanics
3 Metasediments
4 Mafic to Ultramafic Intrusives
5 Intermediate to Felsic Intrusives

6 Syenite
IF Iron Formation
• Gold Occurrences, Prospects & Past Producing Mines

Figure 7. Sturgeon Lake area.

rock has been found in Northeast Bay. The base of the mafic section has been intruded by the Lewis Lake Batholith along North Bay. The batholith is a composite body containing migmatitic, gneissic and leucocratic-equigranular granodiorite phases. Undoubtedly several intrusive phases are present, possibly differing considerably in age, and detailed mapping will be required if reliable age relationships are to be defined. The relative ages of the various phases of the batholith are important because of the structural control of several gold deposits at the granodiorite-volcanic contact.

The gold deposits of Sturgeon Lake can be grouped into four categories (Janes 1981). While these groups are convenient for classification, no claim as to common age of emplacement is made. However, a number of characteristics are common to all deposits.

1. No other rock has been seen which cuts the gold-bearing veins, so the veins appear to be the youngest rocks in the area.
2. Some, if not all, of the veins postdate the latest phases of the Lewis Lake Batholith.
3. Gold-bearing veins appear to be later than metamorphism. Where well developed, alteration haloes cut metamorphosed rocks and local superimposed hornfelsic haloes at granitoid contacts.
4. Minor quartz-gold veins postdate the faulting in Northeast Bay.

Deposits examined are classed in four categories.

1. *Dilatant zones at granitoid-volcanic rock contacts.* These zones may host one, several or many quartz veins with simple mineralogy. Typical minerals are galena, sphalerite, pyrite and gold, but not arsenopyrite. These veins frequently have an envelope of sericitized and carbonate-veined wall rock. Veins may extend into the volcanic or granitoid rocks for some distance from the contact. At least one of the veins is silver-rich and is more properly termed a silver-bearing vein. Except where there is an irregularity to the granitoid/volcanic contact, the veins tend to be narrow and produce little ore. The quartz is white, the principal mineral is pyrite and the veins locally cross the volcanic-granitoid contact at a small angle. The St. Anthony Mine (Figure 7, number 1) falls into this category and has produced approximately 63,000 ounces of gold and 13,000 ounces of silver with an overall grade of 0.19 ounces Au per ton.

2. *Shear-zone-hosted sulphide deposits and associated quartz veins.* Several of these deposits, the Iron Duke and the "Triangle" zone, are located on the peninsula separating the Northeast and North Bays of Sturgeon Lake. These appear to occupy fault splays and minor faults at or near granitoid-volcanic rock contacts. The deposits have massive sulphide zones of simple mineralogy consisting of pyrite and pyrrhotite. The companion quartz veins are sparsely mineralized with pyrite and chalcopyrite and run from trace to 0.04 ounces of gold per ton. These occurrences do not appear to have economic potential at this time.

3. *Grey-to-black quartz veins located at granitoid contacts and breaks in volcanic stratigraphy.* These veins

have simple mineralogy of pyrite and minor chalcopyrite. All the occurrences found to date trend east and are associated with carbonate alteration or carbonate breccias in the wall rocks. The Rainbow Island (Figure 7, number 2), Armstrong-Best (3) and L.W. Green (4) deposits fall into this category.

4. *Quartz-tourmaline veins in the Beidelman Bay Granodiorite.* These veins are located within the granodiorite near the contact with the volcanic rocks. The Beidelman Bay body is considered to be a subvolcanic sill and a possible feeder to the overlying felsic volcanic edifice hosting the base metal deposits on south Sturgeon Lake (Poulsen and Franklin 1981). The veins contain varying amounts of tourmaline and pyrite with traces of sphalerite and chalcopyrite. The Darkwater property (Figure 7, number 5) was developed on these veins which were reported to die out at depth (Horwood 1937). Other similar veins have been reported to the west of the Darkwater Mine.

MINNITAKI LAKE – SANDYBEACH LAKE AREA

This portion of the Wabigoon Subprovince is underlain by a basal assemblage of mafic volcanic rocks (Northern Volcanic Belt) overlain by a transitional sedimentary sequence. These rocks are overlain in turn by the Central Volcanic Belt which contains mafic to felsic volcanic rocks and derived sedimentary rocks. To the south, the Central Volcanic Belt is in fault contact with the Southern Volcanic Belt so that exact relationships are unclear. Bedding and foliation trends are roughly parallel to the major unit boundaries. The structural alignment of the gold deposits parallel to the major faulting direction is apparent in Figure 8. This fault system runs from Miniss Lake in the north through Minnitaki Lake and Sandybeach Lake to the south where it bends to the west to join the Wabigoon Fault (Trowell *et al.* 1980). In the Minnitaki Lake area, the fault system splits into a series of parallel faults with a number of companion fault splays at acute angles to the main faulting direction.

E.O. Chisholm (1951) described the gold occurrences under four groups and these serve today as a good basis for description.

1. *Quartz and carbonate fissure-veins and stockworks in lavas, tuff, agglomerate and intrusive rock types.* Several properties fall into this class, namely the Quyta property (Figure 8, number 1), and gold veins in the east end of the Pickerel Arm Porphyry (2). In both locations brittle fracturing has produced veins to stockworks in a felsic body. Tourmaline-quartz veins have sericitic alteration haloes and carry gold associated with sparse pyrite.

2. *Cross-fractures in lavas, tuff and intrusive rock types.* The most important example of this type is the fractured 'granodiorite' of the Goldlund Mines Limited (Figure 8, number 3) and Windfall Mines Limited (4) properties. This series of dikes or sills has been soda-metasomatized, fractured and intruded by quartz-pyrite-gold veins along a series of relatively flat-lying tension gashes. The dikes

or sills, which intrude mafic volcanic rocks, have been traced intermittently along a 15 km arc trending roughly parallel to the main faulting direction. The dikes or sills are essentially vertical and vary from 10 to 30 m in width. The fractures are contained within the dikes and the quartz veins vary from millimetres to as much as a metre. Ore zones occur where clusters of these fractures are found. Approximately 1800 m of strike length has been developed on the Goldlund and Windfall properties; the Goldlund Mine is currently operating at a rate of 200 tons per day. In addition to quartz and pyrite, the ore zones contain varying amounts of carbonate, ilmenite, magnetite, lead telluride and up to 1 percent iron-rich sphalerite in several areas. Scheelite is a ubiquitous but minor mineral in the ore zones. There does not appear to be any direct correlation between the thickness of quartz veins

and the width of the alteration halo but gold is found within the alteration halo associated with pyrite and tellurides. Gold grade within a zone is dependent on the density of fractures. While the country rocks surrounding the deposit are mafic volcanic lavas, tuff and porphyry units are present and the ore zones are within 500 m of the contact with a felsic volcanic unit to the east.

3. Carbonate replacement zones in mafic volcanic and sedimentary rocks. These gold occurrences are found in several areas on Minnitaki Lake and similar zones are found on Neepawa Island (Figure 8, number 5) where an extensive carbonate replacement zone occurs within mafic lavas and agglomerate. Several narrow veins carry spectacular gold values in a quartz-carbonate gangue with sparse pyrite as the only sulphide. The veins have

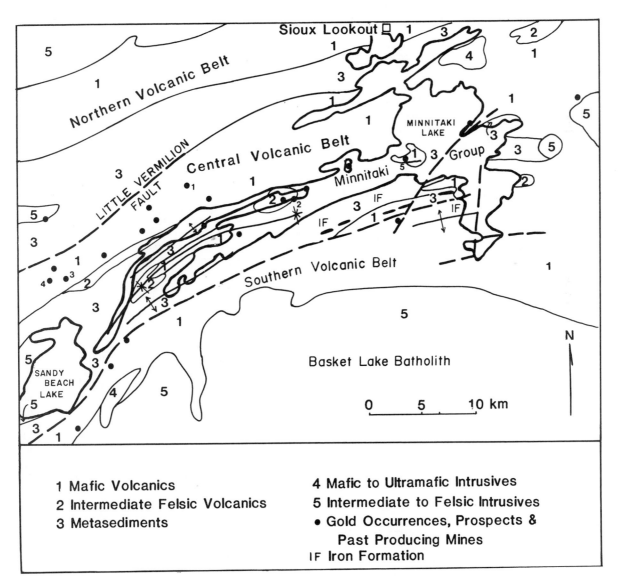

Figure 8. *Minnitaki-Sandybeach Lakes area.*

narrow alteration haloes rich in light green chlorite. While spectacular, these veins are of very limited extent.

4. Silicified shear zones in tuff and lavas. A number of these zones are known to the south of the Goldlund Mine. They are found in sheared mafic lavas, schistose greywacke and most recently, in silicified felsic tuff and agglomerate near pyritic horizons at interflow contacts. Narrow quartz veins cut these zones but carry little if any gold. The gold appears to be associated with the pyritic inter-unit contacts and has also been found associated with biotite-rich zones in dacitic tuffs where the only sulphides are pyrite and pyrrhotite veinlets on shear planes. While these occurrences are interesting, the grades are low, generally less than 0.05 ounces Au per ton. Occasional intersections with economic grades have been reported but not with sufficient width for mining.

In general, all of the deposits known within this area have these common characteristics:
1. They appear to be epigenetic.
2. The veins are structurally controlled and generally follow trends parallel to major fault directions.
3. The veins postdate all rocks in the area with the exception of the granites; no contacts with the granites are known precluding definition of age relationships.
4. The deposits postdate regional metamorphism in that, where alteration haloes are present, they appear to be fresh, unaffected by regional metamorphism.

DEPOSITS RELATED TO IRON FORMATION

Most of the discussion in this paper has dealt with lode quartz-gold veins. It would not be proper to neglect the deposits of northwestern Ontario that are spatially related to iron formation. In fact, outside of the Red Lake camp, the Central Patricia Mine at Pickle Lake produced more gold than any other mine, and the camp as a whole produced over 2.2 million ounces during its active life; the area is presently being re-investigated. In the past several years, interest in gold deposits associated with iron formation has sharply increased with the realization of the size and grade potential of these targets. The commercial development of the Contwoyto Lake deposits in the Northwest Territories and the discovery of the Musselwhite deposits of Opapimiskan Lake in northwestern Ontario have pointed up this potential.

It is useful to compare the two areas in northwestern Ontario that host major iron formation related gold deposits and to see if they have characteristics in common with other gold areas within the region.

PICKLE LAKE AREA

The Pickle Lake area was prospected from 1928 to 1930. Two main properties were outlined and became the Pickle Crow and Central Patricia Mines. The Central Patricia Mine (Figure 9, number 1) started commercial oper-

ations in 1934 and the Pickle Crow Mine (2) started up in 1935. All gold mining in the camp had ceased by 1967.

The Pickle Lake area is underlain by a northeast-trending belt of mafic volcanic rocks and chemical and clastic sedimentary rocks, metamorphosed to greenschist facies. A small felsic volcanic centre is located near the Pickle Crow Mine. The Hooker-Burkoski Stock, a sodic granodiorite, intrudes the volcanic-sedimentary assemblage to the south of the felsic volcanic centre.

The Pickle Lake area is heavily covered with drift and outcrop is limited. Most of the information used for this paper was obtained from published reports of the Ontario Geological Survey (formerly Ontario Department of Mines) (Pye 1976) and from field notes on the area kindly donated by E.G. Pye. One of us (D.S.J.) has benefited from discussions with R. Shegelksi (Newmont Exploration of Canada Limited) on iron formation and the geology of Pickle Lake and his contributions are acknowledged.

Both the Central Patricia and Pickle Crow Mines obtained ore from several deposits on their properties. Only the Central Patricia No. 1 operation could be technically termed to be hosted by iron formation and even here the best ore was obtained in heavily mineralized quartz veins localized in brittle fractures and cross structures in the iron formation. The Central Patricia No. 2 operation produced ore from low sulphide content quartz veins associated with structural deformation in the iron formation. The Pickle Crow ore zones were fairly typical quartz-gold veins which cut the iron formation in structurally disturbed areas. While gold tenors were greatest in the vein where it crossed the iron formation, the iron formation itself was lean ore at best. The mineralogy of the various deposits is highly variable with pyrrhotite, arsenopyrite and pyrite predominating in the veins with high sulphide content. Lesser amounts of chalcopyrite, galena, and sphalerite are found in varying amounts. The gangue is commonly quartz–iron carbonate ± albite, sericite, and tourmaline. Scheelite has been found and was briefly recovered during World War II.

To summarize, in the Pickle Lake camp, the majority of gold occurrences and all past producing mines are associated with quartz veins introduced into structurally deformed iron-rich sedimentary rocks and greenschist metavolcanic rocks. The major deposits are located in cross-structure faults and shears near or in felsic centres or in iron formation, in these zones. The deposits, in their present location, are clearly epigenetic and later than metamorphism. Several faults parallel the ore zones and predate the cross-faults that host the ore zones. Several gold occurrences are found within the Hooker-Burkoski Stock and thus at least some of the veins postdate the emplacement of this stock. In fact, the Pickle Lake deposits are not markedly different from other vein systems found in northwestern Ontario and differ only in their association with iron formation (see Macdonald, this volume).

OPAPIMISKAN LAKE

The main deposit in this area is the Musselwhite property (Figure 10, number 1) owned by a consortium of several

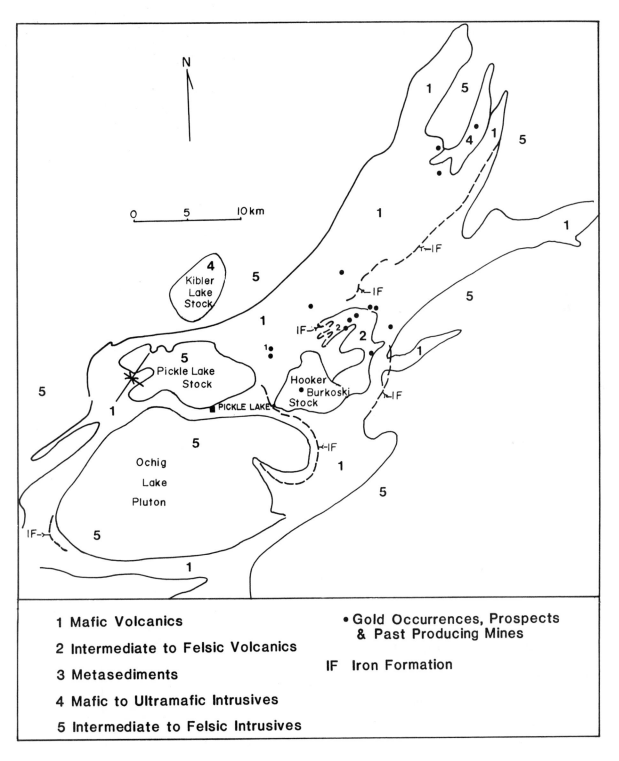

Figure 9. *Pickle Lake area.*

companies; Dome Exploration Limited is the operator. Other properties are found on Liebert Lake (2) and Forrester Lake (3). Geologically, the North Caribou Lake Volcanic Belt, in which these properties are located, forms a narrow, synclinal band oriented roughly north-south in the central portion and swinging to an easterly trend at both extremities of the belt. Basal mafic volcanic rocks are overlain by chemical and clastic sedimentary rocks containing iron formation and chert beds. Known and inferred cross faults transect the synclinal structure. While metamorphic grade has been reported to be lower amphibolite (Satterly 1939; Andrews *et al.* 1981) one of the authors (D.A.J.) has traversed a portion of the belt to the north of Opapimiskan Lake which appears to be, at most, greenschist metamorphic grade. However, towards the north shore of Akow Lake, cross folding becomes evident and

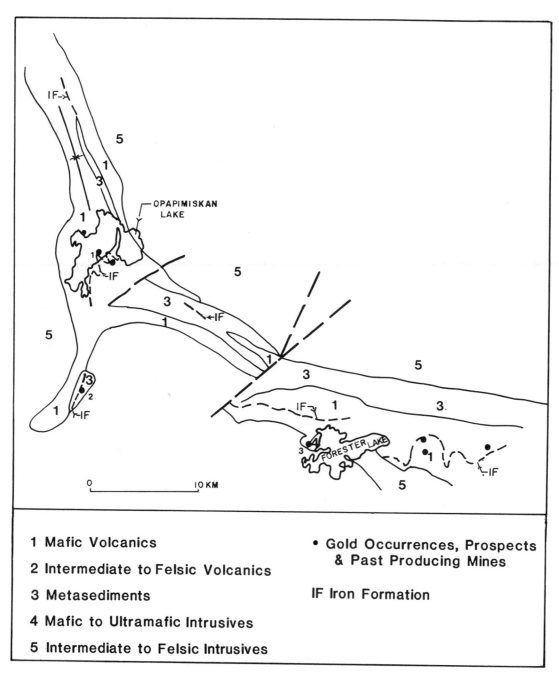

Figure 10. Opapimiskan Lake area.

1 Mafic Volcanics
2 Intermediate to Felsic Volcanics
3 Metasediments
4 Mafic to Ultramafic Intrusives
5 Intermediate to Felsic Intrusives

• Gold Occurrences, Prospects & Past Producing Mines

IF Iron Formation

the metamorphic grade abruptly increases to amphibolite facies. A similar metamorphic facies transition is inferred to occur under Opapimiskan Lake. From outcrop examination and magnetic and electromagnetic surveys, it appears that the thin metasediment bands and iron formation have been complexly folded and thickened to form an "interference dome". Antiformal folds in iron formation have been mineralized by heavy concentrations of pyrrhotite, and lesser amounts of pyrite, chalcopyrite and arsenopyrite. The interlayered basalt has been metamorphosed to amphibolite grade with the development of large garnet porphyroblasts. Gold is associated with heavy sulphide mineralization in the fold crests, where zones from 5 to 12 m thick and 60 m wide dip shallowly to the north and northwest. Separate quartz veins do not occur in these zones and thin, vermiform quartz veinlets may represent deformed, 'lean' iron formation units. Approximately 1 million tons of mineralization grading roughly 0.20 ounces Au per ton have been outlined by vertical drilling (The Northern Miner, March 5, 1981).

This type of deposit contrasts sharply with the Pickle Lake camp. Quartz veins, if they existed, are not now evident. A case could probably be made for syngenetic gold deposition in the metasediments remobilized by deformation and metamorphism into the present location. However, preliminary studies on sedimentary rocks and iron formation at other locations within the belt show that gold tenors in the iron formation are very low (< 2 ppb; Andrews *et al.* 1981), and that the only anomalous gold values occur in brittle, pyritic fractures normal to bedding planes and parallel to the cross-folding directions. These, then are epigenetic concentrations and the iron formation is not considered to be a source of the gold. A similar pattern was found in minor mineralized structures on the Musselwhite property where minor folds in 'lean' iron formation have low gold concentrations in veins within fold axial planes but the gold content in the limbs of these folds is at background level. For this reason, the gold deposits of Opapimiskan Lake are considered to be epigenetic in their present location and the origin of the gold is most likely to have been hydrothermal.

CONCLUSIONS

The great majority of deposits in the studied areas are vein deposits with strong structural control. The veins appear to have formed late in the evolution of the "greenstone" terrain and where known, are younger than metamorphism and postdate many if not all of the internal syntectonic granitoid rocks.

IMPLICATIONS FOR EXPLORATION PROGRAMS

In the portions of northwestern Ontario described here, gold deposits can be found in many diverse sites, and in general the areas with the highest density of gold occurrences have certain characteristics:

1. the presence of major through-going, faults that are medial to metavolcanic belts, or along subprovince boundaries;

2. the presence of internal granitoid stocks and plugs which were probably generated within the volcanic pile;

3. the presence of tight, commonly isoclinal folding, and attendant shearing and fracturing; and

4. the presence of felsic volcanic centres.

The absence of one or another of these features does not preclude gold occurrence, but in the authors' opinion, diminishes the probability of finding economic concentrations.

REFERENCES

Andrews, A.J., Sharpe, D.R., and Janes, D.A.
1981: A Preliminary Reconnaissance of the Weagamow-North Caribou Metavolcanic-Metasedimentary Belt, including the Opapimiskan Lake (Musselwhite) Gold Occurrence; p.203-213 *in* Summary of Field Work 1981, by the Ontario Geological Survey, edited by J. Wood, O.L. White, R.B. Barlow and A.C. Colvine; Ontario Geological Survey Miscellaneous Paper 100, 255p.

Beard, R.C., and Garratt, G.L.
1976: Gold Deposits of the Kenora-Fort Frances Area, Districts of Kenora and Rainy River; Mineral Deposits Circular 16, 46p.

Blackburn, C.E.
1976: Geology of the Lower Manitou - Uphill Lakes area, District of Kenora; Ontario Division of Mines, Report 142, 81p. Accompanied by Map 2320, scale 1:31,680.
1981: Geology of the Boyer Lake - Meggisi Lake Area, District of Kenora; Ontario Geological Survey Report 202, 107p. Accompanied by Maps 2437 and 2438, scale 1:31,680 (1 inch to ½ mile).
1982: Geology of the Manitou Lakes Area, District of Kenora (Stratigraphy and Petrochemistry); Ontario Geological Survey Report 223, 61p. Accompanied by Map 2476, scale 1:50,000.
1983: 1982 Report of the Kenora Resident Geologist; *in* Annual Report of the Regional and Resident Geologists, 1982, edited by C.R. Kustra, Ontario Geological Survey Miscellaneous Paper 101.

Bruce, E.L.
1925: Gold Deposits of Kenora and Rainy River Districts; Ontario Department of Mines, Volume 34, Part 5, p.1-42.

Chisholm, E.O.
1951: Recent Activities in the Sioux Lookout Area, Ontario; The Precambrian, Volume 24, p.10-14.

Colvine, A.C., and Sutherland, I.G.
1979: Early Precambrian Porphyry Deposits; p.230-243 *in* Summary of Field Work, 1979, by the Ontario Geological Survey, edited by V.G. Milne, O.L. White, R.B. Barlow, and C.R. Kustra, Ontario Geological Survey, Miscellaneous Paper 90, 245p.

Davies, J.C.
1965: Geology of High Lake - Rush Bay Area, District of Kenora; Ontario Geological Survey Report 41, 57p. Accompanied by Maps 2068 and 2069, scale 1:31,680.

Davies, J.C., and Morin, J.A.
1976: Geology of the Cedartree Lake area, District of Kenora; Ontario Geological Survey Report 134, 52p. Accompanied by Map 2319, scale 1:31,680.

Davis, D.W., and Edwards, G.R.
1982: Zircon U-Pb Ages from the Kakagi Lake Area, Wabigoon Subprovince, Northwest Ontario; Canadian Journal of Earth Sciences, Volume 19, p.1235-1245.

Davis, D.W., Blackburn, C.E., and Krogh, T.E.
1982: Zircon U-Pb Ages from the Wabigoon-Manitou Lakes Region, Wabigoon Subprovince, Northwest Ontario; Canadian Journal of Earth Sciences, Volume 19, p.254-266.

Horwood, H.C.
1937: Geology of the Darkwater Mine; Ontario Department of Mines, Volume 46, Part 6, p.26-35.

Janes, D.A.
1981: Report of the Sioux Lookout Resident Geologist; p.30-42 in Annual Report of the Regional and Resident Geologists, 1980, edited by C.R. Kustra, Ontario Geological Survey Miscellaneous Paper 95, 158p.

Kerrich, R.
1981: Archean Gold-Bearing Chemical Sedimentary Rocks and Veins: A Synthesis of Stable Isotope and Geochemical Relations; p.144-168 in Genesis of Archean Volcanic-Hosted Gold Deposits, edited by E.G. Pye and R.G. Roberts, Ontario Geological Survey, Miscellaneous Paper 97.

Moore, E.S.
1911: The Sturgeon Lake Gold Field; Ontario Bureau of Mines, Volume 20, Part 1, p.133-157, accompanied by Map, scale 1:31,680.

Pedora, J.M.
1976: Mineralization of the High Lake Pluton and Adjacent Country Rocks; Unpublished M.Sc. thesis, University of Manitoba, 60p.

Poulsen, K.H.
1981: The Geological Setting of Mineralization in the Mine Centre-Fort Frances Area, District of Rainy River; p.190-195 in Summary of Field Work, 1981, by the Ontario Geological Survey, edited by John Wood, O.L. White, R.B. Barlow, and A.C. Colvine, Ontario Geological Survey, Miscellaneous Paper 100, 255p.

Poulsen, K.H., and Franklin, J.M.
1981: Copper and Gold Mineralization in an Archean Trondhjemite Intrusion, Sturgeon Lake, Ontario; Geological Survey of Canada, Paper 81-1A, p.9-74.

Pye, E.G.
1976: Geology and Mineral Deposits of the Crow River Area, District of Kenora, Patricia Portion; Ontario Division of Mines, Open File Report 5152, accompanied by Preliminary Map P.1009, scale 1:12,000.

Satterly, J.
1939: Geology of the Wendigo-North Caribou Lakes Area; Ontario Department of Mines, Annual Report, Volume 248, Part 9, 32p. Accompanied by Map 38h, scale 1:63,360, and Map 48j, scale 1:126,720.

Thomson, J.E.
1935: Gold Deposits on the Lake of the Woods; Ontario Department of Mines, Volume 44, Part 4, p.29-52.
1942: Some Gold Deposits near Goldrock, Upper Manitou Lake; Ontario Department of Mines, Annual Report for 1938, Volume 47, Part 6, p.1-10. Accompanied by Map 47k scale 1:4,800 (1 inch to 400 feet).

Trowell, N.F., Blackburn, C.E., and Edwards, G.R.
1980: Preliminary Synthesis of the Savant Lake - Crow Lake Metavolcanic, Metasedimentary Belt, Northwestern Ontario, and its bearing upon Mineral Exploration; Ontario Geological Survey, Miscellaneous Paper 89, 30p.

Wood, J.
1980: Mine Centre Area (Eastern Half), District of Rainy River; Ontario Geological Survey, Preliminary Map P.2202, Scale 1:15,840.

The Structure and Geological Development of the Porcupine Camp — A Re-Evaluation

C.J. Hodgson
Department of Geological Sciences, Queen's University, Kingston

ABSTRACT

A review of published geological data for the Porcupine camp indicates that the Tisdale Group volcanic rocks and conformably overlying sedimentary rocks were tilted into subvertical attitudes (probably as a result of listric normal faulting in an extensional tectonic regime) and eroded before the deposition of the younger (Timiskaming) sedimentary strata. Both sequences were then folded, after which they were cut by major faults which served as loci of carbonatization, shearing, porphyry intrusion, and gold mineralization. Partly overlapping with but continuing after faulting, intense deformation resulted in the development of a penetrative schistosity and east-plunging lineation in the rocks. Abundant evidence indicates the gold mineralization was emplaced late in the geological development of the area after, but broadly in association with the porphyry-forming magmatic event and the major deformation which succeeded this. There is little persuasive evidence for the presence of syngenetic chemical sedimentary gold mineralization in the camp.

INTRODUCTION

The gold production of the Porcupine camp (Figure 1) is more than 50 million ounces, larger than any other lode gold camp in North America. Despite the unparalleled economic significance of the camp, and the many hundreds of man years of geological work which have been done in it during the 75 years of continuous mining, there are still many aspects of the structure, stratigraphy, and geological development of the area which are poorly understood. In particular, the time of emplacement and controls on gold mineralization remain contentious.

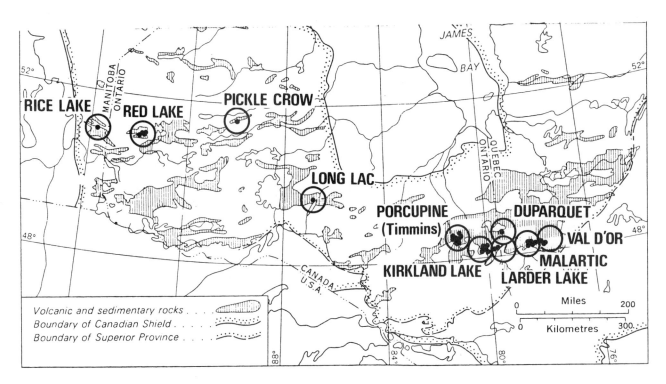

Figure 1. *Location of Porcupine Camp in relation to other major gold producing camps of the Superior Province of the Canadian Shield.*

Table 1. *Main geological features of the Porcupine Camp.*

STRATIGRAPHY		"YOUNGER" SEDIMENTS
		"OLDER" SEDIMENTS
	TISDALE GROUP	(KRIST FELSIC UNIT (THOLEIITIC UNIT (KOMATIITIC UNIT
INTRUSIONS		QUARTZ-FELDSPAR PORPHYRIES
MINERALIZATION		GOLD-QUARTZ VEINS
		AURIFEROUS INTERFLOW SEDS
		CU-AU STOCKWORK PIPES
STRUCTURES	FOLDS	(PORCUPINE SYNCLINE (SOUTH TISDALE ANTICLINE (SOUTH TISDALE SYNCLINE (HOLLINGER-McINTYRE FOLD ZONE
	LINEAR ZONES OF CARBONATIZATION, HIGHLY FISSILE ROCKS AND PORPHYRY	
	PENETRATIVE SE LINEATION AND NE TO NW FOLIATION	
	UNCONFORMITY AT BASE OF YOUNGER SEDIMENTS	

The geology of the area was reviewed by the writer in the course of a compilation study of the gold deposits of the larger Timmins-Kirkland Lake area (Hodgson 1982). The purpose of this paper is to point out certain geological facts which are well documented in the literature, and to suggest a partly new (but also in large part traditional!) hypothesis for the geology and geological development of the area which is consistent with these facts. Several critical features of the hypothesis can be readily tested by field work, and this will be initiated in the coming season.

The writer would like to acknowledge his debt to the many geologists who through their field work have provided the documentation upon which this paper is based. The report of Ferguson *et al.* (1968) stands as the most important compilation of the field work done up to the time of its publication, and is based on the detailed mapping, on a day-to-day basis, by a very large number of mine and exploration geologists. More recently, major contributions have been made by Karvinen (1981), who recognized and traced out the large scale linear zones of carbonatization, and who drew attention to the quantita-tive importance of carbonatization in the mines, Pyke (1982), who recognized the difference between the komatiitic and tholeiitic formations of the Tisdale Group, and Roberts (1981), who mapped for the first time the penetrative fabric of the rocks in the area and also documented a number of features in the area of the "Greenstone Nose" of the Dome Mine which must be explained by any viable hypothesis for the genesis of the gold mineralization.

GEOLOGICAL SETTING OF THE AREA

The gold deposits of the Porcupine camp are hosted mainly by volcanic rocks of the Tisdale Group (Table 1), which occur as a lens-shaped enclave bounded on all sides by sedimentary rocks, except locally along its southwest side, where the boundary is the Porcupine-Destor Fault (Figure 2). The sedimentary rocks form part of a major east-trending belt which mainly lies along the north side of the Porcupine-Destor Fault. The camp also lies on a major cross-lineament which extends southwest from the Kidd Creek massive sulphide deposit, and includes the Burrows-Benedict fault system (Figure 3), the Porcupine camp and Tisdale enclave, the Shaw Dome, the Montreal River fault system, the Matachewan gold camp, and several major structures further south in the Proterozoic sequence (Figure 2).

MAIN GEOLOGICAL FEATURES OF THE PORCUPINE CAMP

The main geological features of the area are outlined on Table 1 and shown on Figure 3. Detailed descriptions of the stratiform and intrusive rock units, the mineralization

and alteration types, and the structures are given in the extensive literature on the area (see in particular reviews and bibliographies presented by Pyke 1982; Roberts 1981; Karvinen 1981; Ferguson *et al.* 1968; and Dunbar 1948), and will not be repeated here, except in very brief outline.

The stratigraphic sequence in the Tisdale Group and overlying sedimentary rocks is well exposed in a north-trending homoclinal section in the vicinity of the Whitney-Tisdale Townships boundary (Figure 3). The relation of the Tisdale Group to the enveloping units to the south of the Porcupine-Destor Fault, to the west in Mountjoy Township, and to the north and apparently beneath the Tisdale Group, is essentially an unsolved problem, and will not be

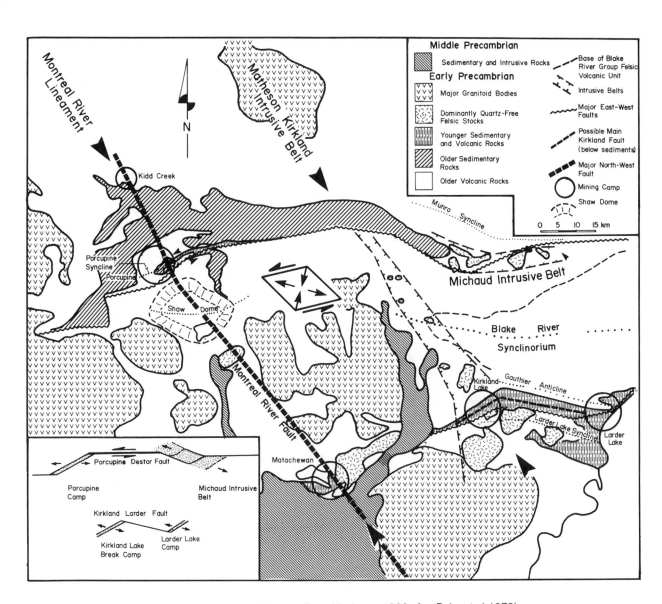

Figure 2. Geology of the Timmins-Kirkland Lake area (from Hodgson 1982 after Pyke et al. 1973).

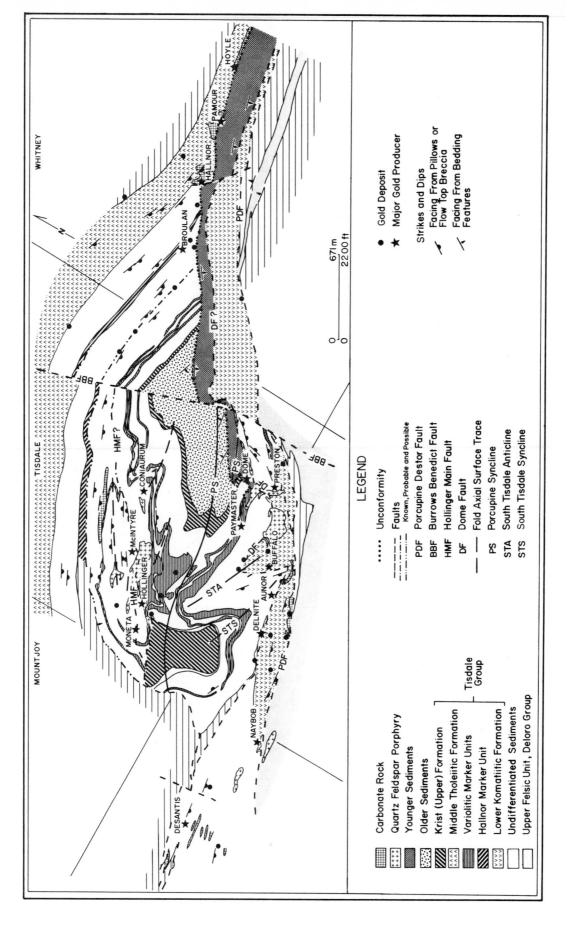

Figure 3. *Generalized geology of the Porcupine camp. Compiled from Ontario Geological Survey 1 inch to 1000 feet and 1 inch to ¼ mile scale maps of Tisdale, Whitney, Deloro, Ogden and Mountjoy Townships.*

LEGEND

Carbonate Rock

Quartz Feldspar Porphyry

Younger Sediments

Older Sediments

Krist (Upper) Formation

Middle Tholeiitic Formation

Variolitic Marker Units

Hallnor Marker Unit

Lower Komatiitic Formation

Undifferentiated Sediments

Upper Felsic Unit, Deloro Group

Tisdale Group

······ Unconformity

– – – Faults
        Known, Probable and Possible

PDF   Porcupine Destor Fault

BBF   Burrows Benedict Fault

HMF   Hollinger Main Fault

DF   Dome Fault

—— Fold Axial Surface Trace

PS   Porcupine Syncline

STA   South Tisdale Anticline

STS   South Tisdale Syncline

● Gold Deposit

★ Major Gold Producer

   Strikes and Dips

   Facing From Pillows or
   Flow Top Breccia

   Facing From Bedding
   Features

671 m

2200 ft

0

0

considered in any detail here. Extensive discussion of the problems, and a suggested stratigraphic interpretation are given by Pyke (1982).

The sedimentary rocks of the area have been subdivided into a number of formations, and all have been assigned to the Porcupine Group by Pyke (1982). Since some of Pyke's correlations are contentious, and furthermore are unnecessary for the purposes of this discussion, the older scheme of subdividing the sedimentary rocks is used here. That is, the rocks stratigraphically overlying the Tisdale Group (which are the only sedimentary rocks considered here) are divided into an "Older" sequence (originally termed Keewatin) and an unconformably overlying "Younger" sequence (originally termed Timiskaming, implying they correlate with the type Timiskaming in the Kirkland Lake area) (Table 1).

Locally intrusive into all of the stratiform rocks are distinctive quartz-feldspar porphyry bodies. These may not, however, all be of the same age, since at least one of the bodies, the Crown Porphyry (see Ferguson *et al.* 1968) appears to merge upwards into the upper felsic unit (the Krist Formation) of the Tisdale Group. Most, however, seem to have been emplaced relatively late in the geological development of the area (see below).

The three main mineralization types are extensively described in the literature (see, in particular, Griffis 1962; Fryer *et al.* 1979; Karvinen 1981, Roberts 1981) and will not be considered further here.

The fold structures listed on Table 1 and labelled on Figure 3 are of at least two ages (Roberts 1981) and the relationship of these represents one of the major geological problems discussed in this paper.

The genesis and significance of the lithologically distinctive linear zones in the area is also highly controversial. In texture these range from zones of carbonatization, in which the original rock textures are well preserved, to highly fissile zones consisting of various proportions of rusty weathering (normally) carbonate, chlorite, talc, and a number of other minerals. Gold is spatially associated with many of these zones, particularly where they are high in Fe- and/or Mg-rich carbonate. However, it should be emphasized that the most carbonate-rich rocks contain no significant gold, and long sections of these linear zones are essentially barren of gold mineralization. In general, porphyry intrusions and the best gold-rich zones are those most closely associated with the more fissile carbonate-rich zones.

All of the rocks in the area have a penetrative foliation and lineation, although the extent to which this is developed varies widely. This penetrative fabric clearly overprints all of the rocks, and at least some of the mineralization, but is approximately axial planar to major folds like the South Tisdale Anticline, the Northern Anticline, McIntyre Syncline and Coniaurum Anticline (Figures 3 and 4). The fabric also appears to overprint the Porcupine Syncline (Roberts 1981, see Figure 4).

There is one major unconformity in the area, at the base of the Younger Sediments.

The pattern of these features, as shown on Figure 3,

and on sublevel plans and sections from the mines, published by Ferguson *et al.* (1968), are the basis for the interpretation of the area outlined in the following sections.

INTERPRETATION

The sequence of geological events suggested here for the Porcupine camp is outlined on Table 2. The interpretation is discussed in terms of geological field evidence in the following sections.

1. *Tisdale volcanism followed by deposition of Older Sediments.* The Tisdale volcanic sequence appears to overlie a sedimentary sequence lying to the north of it, but the nature of the contact, although apparently broadly stratiform, is not known. However, stratigraphically upwards from this contact, the sequence appears to be continuous to the base of the overlying Younger Sediments, as indicated by the parallelism of at least four internal contacts (the Lower-Middle Formation contact, the Hallnor Marker Unit, the V8-V10B Variolitic Marker Units, and the Krist (Upper)-Middle Formation contact, see Figure 3), and the well documented consistent south-facing of the well exposed section near the Whitney-Tisdale Townships boundary. However, there appears to be at least one bedding-parallel fault in the sequence which is marked by a discontinuous zone of carbonatization and a line of gold deposits, as shown on Figure 3 and discussed below.

2. *Rotation of strata into subvertical attitudes on listric normal faults, followed by erosion and deposition of the Younger Sediments.* The high angle of truncation of the Tisdale Group and concordantly overlying Older Sediments by the unconformably overlying Younger Sediments indicates that the Tisdale Group was rotated into steeply dipping attitudes and eroded before the Younger Sediments were deposited. Thus, in the 7.6 km between the Burrows-Benedict Fault and the base of the Middle Formation of the Tisdale Group near the Broulan Mine, the unconformity cuts down through about 5.6 km of section in the sequence below the Younger Sediments. This indicates a dip of at least 40° in the Tisdale Group when the Younger Sediments were deposited (assuming they were deposited on a horizontal surface), and probably more, since later deformation has flattened the sequence in a north-south direction, and extended it in an east-west direction, which would tend to decrease the apparent angle of truncation by rotating the unconformity surface towards parallellism with bedding in the Tisdale Group.

The unconformity similarly cuts down stratigraphy in the Older Sediments, the Krist, and through the upper part of the underlying Middle Formation of the Tisdale Group as it is traced westwards from the Burrows-Benedict Fault. Since the direction of downcutting of the unconformity is down section both east and west of the Burrows-Benedict fault, the sequence beneath the Younger Sediments must have had a different orientation on either side of this fault at the time the Younger Sediments were deposited.

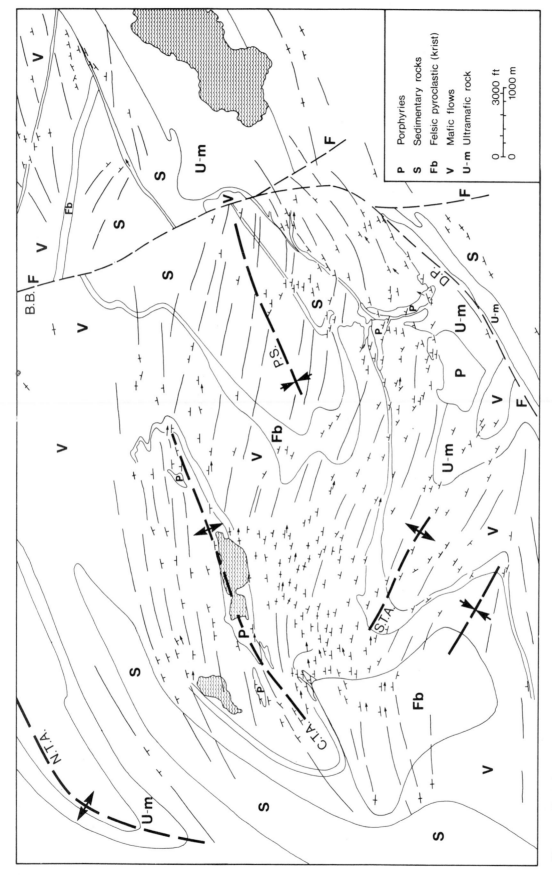

Figure 4. Foliation in relation to major folds in Tisdale Township (after Roberts 1981).

Table 2. *Interpolated sequence of events in the Porcupine camp.*

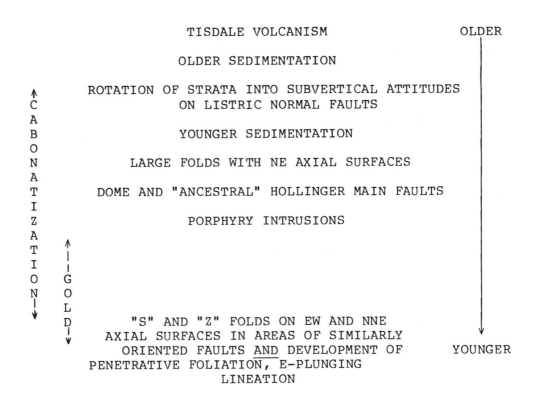

The suggestion that the steep attitudes of the Tisdale Group were the result of listric normal faulting in an extensional tectonic regime is based on both local and regional geological considerations, and was very briefly presented by Hodgson (1982). A more complete discussion of the model is presently in preparation.

3. *Development of the Porcupine Syncline.* Hodgson (1982) suggested that the Porcupine Syncline began to form before the deposition of the Younger Sediments, since the change in direction of stratigraphic downcutting away from the Burrows-Benedict Fault corresponds to a shift of the unconformity from the north to the south limb of the Porcupine Syncline across the fault, and because the unconformity does not show any evidence of folding where it passes from one limb of the syncline to the other. However, it was pointed out by K.H. Poulsen (Queen's University, personal communication, 1982) that (1) the change in downcutting direction across the Burrows-Benedict Fault indicates only that the rocks lying below the unconformity were oriented differently on either side of the fault at the time of Younger sedimentation, and not that the difference in orientation was due to the presence of the Porcupine Syncline, and (2) the expected pattern when unconformably related sequences are folded together is for the axial surfaces of the basement and cover sequences to be displaced laterally from each other as in

fact is the case for the Porcupine Syncline, where it is outlined by the unconformity and by the bedding in the sequence below the unconformity (Figure 5). Therefore, it is suggested here that rather than the Porcupine Syncline pre-dating the deposition of the Younger Sediments, as suggested by Hodgson (1982), the structure post-dates this event. This interpretation greatly simplifies the interpreted geological history of the area, since it involves only one, rather than two, periods of early folding (i.e. only post-Younger Sediment folding to produce Porcupine Syncline vs. early phase of Porcupine Syncline, then erosion and deposition of Younger Sediments, then later phase of Porcupine Syncline to tilt the Younger Sediments into subvertical attitudes).

However, there is one problem with this interpretation which suggests that some type of "ancestral" Porcupine Syncline existed before Younger Sediment deposition. This is that the "ancestral" Hollinger Main Fault, which appears to have cut through the sequence after it had been bent into a curved shape similar to that which now defines the Porcupine Syncline, appears to be truncated on its eastern extension by the unconformity (see below and Figure 3).

As noted by Roberts (1981), there is no penetrative fabric axial planar to the Porcupine Syncline, and therefore the structure appears to have predated the deforma-

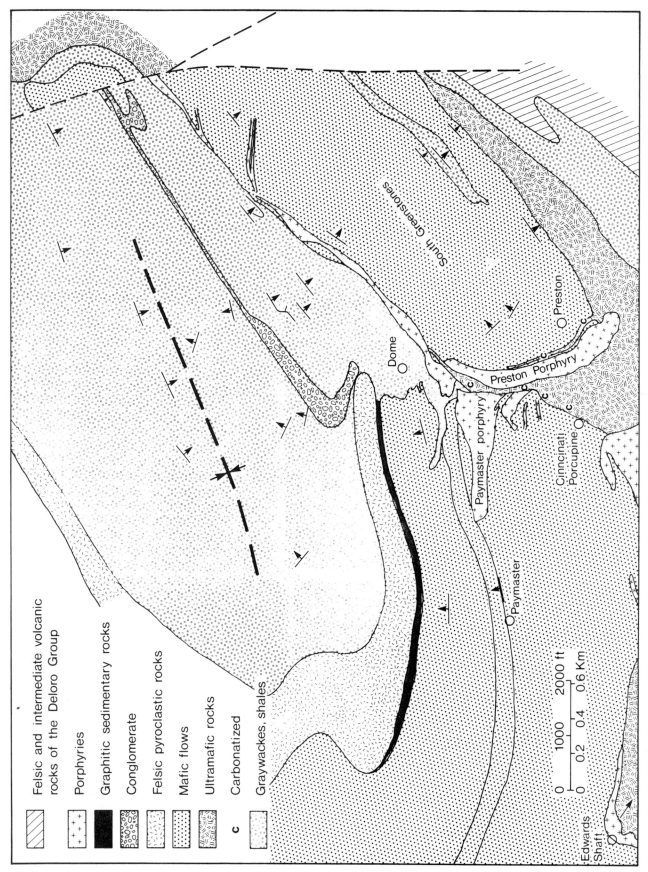

Figure 5. Detail of the geological relations in the vicinity of the Dome Mine (after Roberts 1981).

Felsic and intermediate volcanic rocks of the Deloro Group

Porphyries

Graphitic sedimentary rocks

Conglomerate

Felsic pyroclastic rocks

Mafic flows

Ultramafic rocks

Carbonatized

Graywackes, shales

South Greenstones

Dome

Preston

Preston Porphyry

Paymaster porphyry

Cinncinati

Porcupine

Paymaster

Edwards Shaft

0   1000   2000 ft

0   0.2   0.4   0.6 Km

C.J. HODGSON

tional event which gave rise to the foliation and lineations in the rocks of the area.

4. *Dome and ancestral Hollinger Main Faults; some carbonatization.* The Dome Fault truncates the south limb of

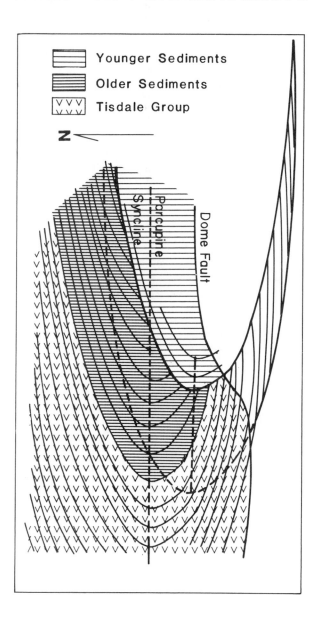

Figure 6. *Idealized north-south cross-section looking east through the Porcupine Syncline, showing the offset of the axial surface in the unconformity from that in the sub-unconformity sequence, and the refraction of the Dome Fault where it passes from the Younger Sediment – South Greenstone contact into the South Greenstone – Tisdale Group contact in the Dome Mine. Modified only slightly from an idealized diagram in Ramsay (1967) given to illustrate the geometrical consequences of folding unconformably related sequences.*

the Porcupine Syncline (Figures 5 and 6), and juxtaposes against the Younger Sediments a south-facing section of mafic volcanic rocks, termed the South Greenstones, which probably belongs to the lower part of the Middle Formation of the Tisdale Group (Pyke 1982). West from the Younger Sediment–South Greenstone contact, the Dome Fault appears to be refracted southwards across the strike of the Tisdale Group volcanic rocks in the Dome Mine, then it veers westwards again to a stratifrom position and can be followed west around the nose of the South Tisdale Anticline and South Tisdale Syncline and westwards from there as shown on Figure 3. The trace of the fault is marked by variable degrees of carbonatization and shearing, local porphyry intrusions, and a line of gold deposits. West of the Buffalo Mine, the fault marks the boundary between a sequence of south-facing rocks of komatiitic affinity which appear to belong to the Lower Formation of the Tisdale Group (Pyke 1982) and the north-facing rocks of the Middle Formation of the Tisdale Group (Figure 3).

Where the fault changes orientation from stratiform to cross-cutting stratigraphy in the Dome and Preston Mines, it has several northwest-trending splays, and is intruded by an unusually large volume of porphyry, including the large Preston, Preston West and Paymaster Porphyries (Figure 7). The porphyries are intruded both along the main Dome fault and the splay faults. The splay faults fade out into S- or Z-shaped folds (Figure 7). This area, where the main fault is refracted and numerous splays branch off it, is by far the most gold-rich part of the entire structure, as well as being the main locus of porphyry intrusive activity. A second major zone of gold mineralization, intense alteration, highly fissile rocks, and porphyry intrusions occurs along the line of the Moneta, Hollinger, McIntyre and Coniaurum Mines (Figure 3). The area is geologically extremely complex, and there are several interpretations of the structure. All incorporate the idea that the broad structure is anticlinal, with the hinge defined by the Variolitic Marker Unit in the vicinity of the Moneta shaft, and with the axial surface approximately parallel to, and the limbs offset slightly in a left hand sense on, the Hollinger Main Fault. The difference between the interpretations involves where the north limb of the anticline is projected to the east (Figure 8). Dunbar (1948) showed the variolitic markers curving back to define a synclinal hinge north of the McIntyre shaft, then being truncated on a fault. However, mapping underground in the Hollinger and McIntyre Mines in the years subsequent to Dunbar's paper indicated that the sequence continues eastwards well past where Dunbar proposed a synclinal hinge, and does not double back on itself to the west, as he suggested. Subsequently Ferguson et al. (1968) suggested that the north limb variolitic marker sequence, after bulging northwards around the porphyry complexes in the Hollinger and McIntyre Mines, veered southwards to come within a few hundred metres of the south limb, just north of the Coniaurum Mine shaft, and from there eastwards, the north and south limb sequences continued parallel to where they are truncated by the unconformity at the base of the Younger Sediments. This interpretation implies a major facing change

219

within the marker unit sequence east of the Coniaurum Mine, with the units north of the northernmost marker facing north to the next synclinal hinge which Ferguson *et al.* (1968) placed about 500 m to the north in the centre of the Hallnor Marker Unit. However, between these two proposed hinges, the rocks face uniformly south, rather than north as implied by the fold interpretation. Furthermore, there is no evidence for the tight isoclinal style of folding in the volcanic units which Ferguson *et al.*'s (1968) interpretation involves.

Finally, Pyke (1982) has suggested a third alternative, in which the north and south limb markers are joined both on the west and east ends of the line of mineralization, to define a doubly plunging anticlinal structure. This interpretation implies that the Variolitic Marker Units in Whitney and eastern Tisdale Townships do not correlate with those on the south side of the Moneta-Coniaurum

line of mineralization, and on the south limb of the Porcupine Syncline. Considering that the marker units are exposed almost continuously over a substantial strike length, best seen (along the line of the highway) from Whitney Township into the area south of the Coniaurum Mine, and are everywhere at about the same stratigraphic distance from the Krist unit, this seems an unlikely interpretation.

As an alternative to all of these interpretations, it is suggested here that the overall structure in the area is not anticlinal, but the two "limbs" of the suggested anticline are in fact repetitions of the marker units caused by north-side-down faulting along a fault system which coincided approximately with the Hollinger Main Fault in the west, and extended eastwards to become a bedding-parallel structure northeast of the Coniaurum Mine, its trace being marked by the discontinuous line of carbonatized zones

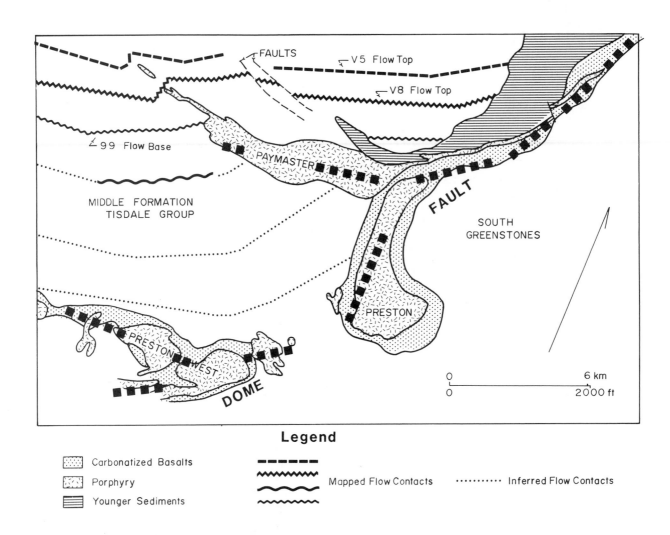

Figure 7. *Compilation based on the geology of the 1587-foot Level, Dome Mine; 1425-foot Level, Preston Mine and 1575-foot Level, Paymaster Mine, showing the relationship of volcanic stratigraphy, faults, carbonatization and porphyry (after Chart D, Ferguson et al. 1968).*

and gold deposits in Whitney Township which trends into the unconformity just west of the Broulan Mine (Figure 3). In order for the marker unit sequence to be truncated on the north block of the fault, and to run parallel to the fault on the south block, it is necessary that the fault or the beds or both be curved. The simplest explanation for the pattern is that the faulting post-dated the Porcupine Syncline, i.e. the beds were curved as a result of their being bent around the syncline as shown in Figure 9. Furthermore, the Dome Fault, which appears to be of the same type as the "ancestral" Hollinger Main Fault proposed here, clearly post-dates the Porcupine Syncline, which would be consistent with this suggested sequence of events.

However, a problem with this interpretation, noted above, is that while the Porcupine Syncline appears to post-date the deposition of the Younger Sediments, the fault proposed here appears to be truncated by, i.e. to predate, the unconformity. This ambiguity cannot be resolved without further field data.

The interpretation shown on Figure 9 implies that the dip of the marker beds where they curve around the South Tisdale Syncline was steep enough that the markers show a truncation at the present level of exposure on

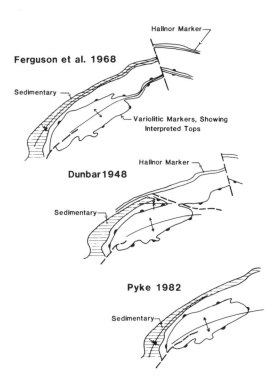

Figure 8. *Diagrammatic representation of the structural interpretations of Ferguson et al. (1968), Dunbar (1948), and Pyke (1982) in the area of Moneta, Hollinger, McIntyre and Coniaurum Mines. Solid half circles on stratigraphic-top side.*

the south block. However, there is no north block equivalent of this structure, nor is the Krist unit repeated in the north block.

To explain these two, probably related, problems, it is suggested that the west end of the north block was sliced off on another fault, perhaps following approximately the base of the Hallnor Marker Unit. A fault roughly in this position is also suggested by the abrupt apparent thickening to the west, in the vicinity of the Tisdale-Mountjoy Townships boundary line, of the thin sedimentary unit into which the Hallnor Marker passes (Figure 3).

On the basis of the pattern indicated by the relationships between faults and porphyries in the Dome Mine area (described above), it is suggested that the complex of porphyry bodies in the area under consideration were emplaced into the "ancestral" Hollinger Main Fault and a system of splay faults as shown in Figure 10.

5. *Emplacement of gold, further carbonatization.* The gold mineralization has been at least partly, and probably entirely emplaced after, but perhaps not long after, the porphyry intrusions. The evidence for this is that a large amount of gold ore is hosted by porphyry in the area (e.g. Preston Mine, Hawley and Hart 1948; McIntyre Mine, Griffis 1962), and there is a general close spatial association of porphyry and ore in many (although not all) of the mines. Certainly a very considerable proportion of the ore in the camp post-dates the Younger Sediments, since it is hosted by them (e.g. Dome Mine, Holmes 1948 and Ferguson *et al.* 1968; Pamour Mine, Price and Bray 1948; Hallnor Mine, Bell 1948). Perhaps the best evidence for the relatively late age of gold mineralization in the area is its close association with the linear zones of distinctive, mostly carbonate-rich, altered rocks which appear to mark fault zones that formed after the Younger Sediments and Porcupine Syncline in which these are involved, and which clearly controlled the emplacement of many of the porphyry bodies in the area. Most gold veins in mafic volcanic rocks away from the pervasively carbonatized zones are enveloped by zones of carbonatization, indicating some of the carbonatization in the area formed synchronously with gold emplacement.

6. *Development of a penetrative schistosity, east-plunging lineation, and associated S and Z folds.* The main period of intense penetrative deformation in the area clearly post-dated the porphyries but appears to be synchronous with much of the economically significant mineralization (Griffis 1962, Roberts 1981). Roberts has shown that the foliation in the area is axial planar to the South Tisdale Anticline, as well as the Northern Anticline, McIntyre Syncline and Coniaurum Anticline (Figures 4 and 10). On this basis he suggested that the repetition of the Krist unit in the South Tisdale Syncline was the result of the Porcupine Syncline being refolded on the South Tisdale Anticline. This explanation presents one problem for the present interpretation of relations in the area of the Moneta Mine (Figure 3), where it is proposed that the truncation of the marker units on the south side of the Hollinger Main Fault is due to the effect of the South Tisdale Anticline and Syncline on the disposition of the units, as shown on Fig-

ure 9. Perhaps there was a precursor cross-fold in approximately the same position as these two late structures at the time the "ancestral" Hollinger Main Fault formed. Indeed, the limited overall extent, in an east-west direction, of the Tisdale Group within the larger sedimentary rock belt (Figure 2), and the alignment of this feature along the northwest trending linear which includes the Shaw Dome just to the south, could indicate an overall domal structure in the camp of relatively early origin. It is also significant, with regard to this possibility, that Roberts' map (1981, Figure 4) shows the foliation crossing the axial trace of the South Tisdale Syncline. More field work is needed to resolve the problem, particularly in the complex area where the South Tisdale Syncline is intersected by the Hollinger Main Fault.

If the rocks on the north side of the "ancestral" Hollinger Main Fault do face south, as suggested here, then the Northern Anticline and McIntyre Syncline are misnamed, since the stratigraphy is upside down in these folds. Thus the Northern Anticline should be renamed the "northern antiformal syncline" and the McIntyre Syncline the "McIntyre synformal anticline".

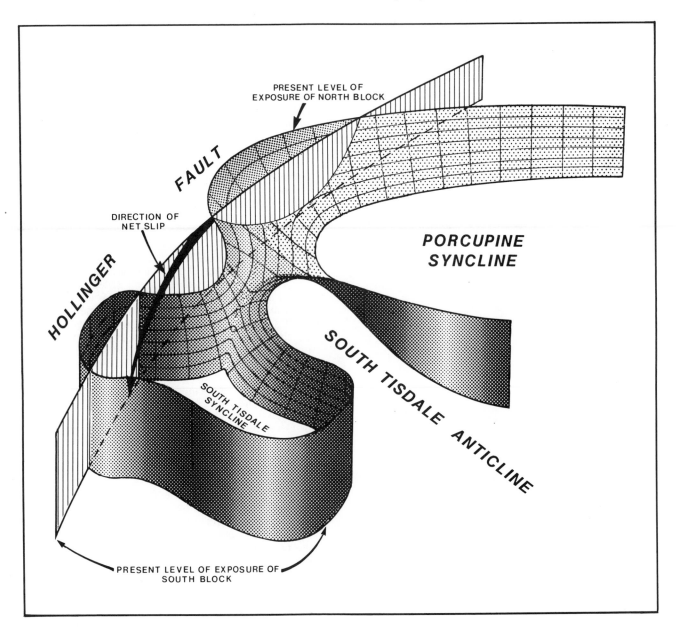

Figure 9. *Suggested geometrical relationship of the proposed "ancestral" Hollinger Main Fault in relationship to the Porcupine Syncline, South Tisdale Anticline, and South Tisdale Syncline.*

DISCUSSION

The sequence of geological events suggested here is based on evidence for the superposition of geological effects. This type of evidence is not readily interpreted in terms of the absolute time frame involved, which must remain a subject for speculation until precise direct dating can be carried out. However, the apparent overlapping of effects gives some indication of the inter-relatedness of the specific events. In this regard, the distribution of carbonatized rocks and porphyry appears to be significant. Carbonatized clasts have been reported from the basal conglomerates of the Younger sedimentary sequence (Pyke 1982), and carbonatized rocks are clearly of regional extent, are in spatial (and presumably temporal) association with the major fault structures in the area, and also occur closely spatially and temporally associated with individual auriferous quartz veins. These relationships suggest that carbonatizing fluids were circulating through the rocks within the time interval bracketed by Tisdale volcanism and the gold-depositing event.

Porphyry magmatism may similarly span a consider-

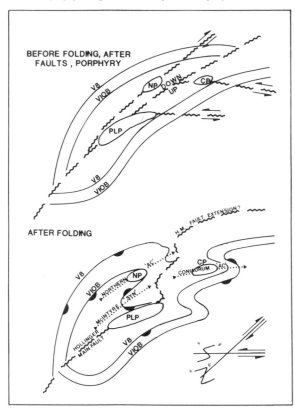

Figure 10. *Control of porphyry bodies by "ancestral" Hollinger Main Fault and related splay faults, and subsequent deformation to produce penetrative fabric and associated folds in the rocks. V8 and V10B, Variolitic Marker Units with solid half circles on stratigraphic top side; NP, Northern Porphyry; CP, Coniaurum Porphyry; PLP, Pearl Lake Porphyry.*

able part of the history of the area shown on Table 2, since (1) there are indications that the Crown Porphyry on the southwest side of the Hollinger property feeds up into the overlying Krist unit (Upper Formation) of the Tisdale Group; (2) the Krist unit is a felsic porphyry itself, although not normally quartz-phyric like the clearly intrusive porphyries in the area; (3) porphyry fragments are abundant in certain parts of the basal unit of the Younger Sediments in the Dome Mine, although it is uncertain if these are fragments of the Krist unit or of the intrusive-type porphyries (if, indeed, there is any significant lithological and genetic difference between these); and (4) porphyry clearly is emplaced into, and its distribution is controlled by, the major faults, such as the Dome Fault, which in turn post-dates the Porcupine Syncline. These relationships suggest the felsic porphyry magmatism started late in Tisdale time, and continued until after major faulting.

Finally there is the evidence of the gold mineralization. It has been suggested (Fryer *et al.* 1979; Roberts 1981; Karvinen 1981) that the main period of gold introduction into the rocks was during the deposition of the Middle and Upper Formations of the Tisdale Group, at which time (Karvinen 1981) the bulk of the auriferous porphyries were emplaced. One of the key items of evidence for the early introduction of gold is the interpretation of the stratiform ankerite veins in the Dome Mine as chemical sedimentary ores of volcanic exhalative origin. Similarly interpreted gold ore is hosted by interflow sedimentary rocks in the Middle Formation of the Tisdale Group in the Hollinger and Moneta Mines (Karvinen 1981). The evidence is unambiguous that these ore zones are largely hosted by interflow sedimentary rocks. However as shown in Section K in Ferguson *et al.* (1968), which is through the Paymaster Mine just west of the Dome Mine, the ankerite vein system forms an anastomosing network which in part cuts across well defined mappable flow units, and one of the ore zones closely follows the contact of a porphyry dike which itself appears to be controlled by an oblique fault, like that which controls the west extension of the Paymaster Porphyry shown on Figure 7. The possibility of chemical sedimentary gold was carefully considered by Hollinger mine geologists but was rejected because it was noted that pyritic interflow sedimentary rocks were auriferous only where they are cut by clearly epigenetic quartz vein systems (Ferguson *et al.* 1968). A further problem with the exhalative theory for the ankerite veins in the Dome Mine is their relationship to the unconformity at the base of the Younger Sediments. Roberts (1981) has mapped the ankerite veins as cross-cutting this surface. On this basis, and on evidence for the orientation of what he interprets as primary bedding and certain other features in the area of the Greenstone Nose in the Dome Mine, he has interpreted at least the lower part of the Younger Sediment unit as a time-stratigraphic equivalent of the Middle and Upper Formations of the Tisdale Group. However, as noted above, this surface appears to be a very significant unconformity farther to the east, and it would seem highly unlikely that a major facies boundary and a major unconformity coincided almost exactly both in space and in orientation. If the Greenstone Nose is in fact an unconformity surface, as it has traditionally been interpreted (see Ferguson *et al.* 1968) then the cross-cutting relationship of the ankerite veins to this surface, as mapped by Roberts (1981), must be taken as evidence that the veins are in fact veins, and not chemical sedimentary rocks, although they coincide with interflow sedimentary rocks over much of their length.

The fact that very large volumes of gold ore in the camp occur in the Younger Sediments and in late porphyries (Figure 7) establishes clearly that much of the gold is late. Although the ill-defined process of "remobilization" is commonly appealed to as an explanation of geologically late gold, it is the writer's opinion that when the volume of "remobilized" mineralization types equals or exceeds the volume of the source or primary mineralization, then it is no longer feasible to think in terms of local remobilization as a process of ore generation.

Finally, the evidence that the major faulting may have started before the deposition of the Younger Sediments has already been described, although it is clear that the Dome Fault, at least, post-dates the Younger Sediments. From the geometrical relationship of the Dome Fault and the Porcupine Syncline, it seems likely that the two are expressions of the same deformational event. At the other end of the time interval, there could well be an overlap between the formation of the faults and the development of a penetrative fabric and Z and S drag folds in the rocks, since in many areas the folds are geometrically related to the faults (Figure 7) and the penetrative schistosity parallels the faults (Figures 4 and 10).

In summary, the evidence suggests that felsic magmatism and the distinctive carbonate-rich alteration of the area started in late Tisdale time and continued until after the major period of faulting. The bulk, if not all, of the intrusive porphyries appear to post-date the faults, although there is still a problem of when the major faulting was initiated. Thus the question of whether the felsic rocks are all comagmatic and were emplaced in a single protracted event, or whether two events, one extrusive and the other intrusive, were involved remains unknown.

In the writer's opinion, the geological evidence indicates that the greater bulk, and probably all, of the gold was introduced relatively late in the history of the area, after the faults and the porphyries, although the problem with dating these features qualifies the term "late". Much more work needs to be done to describe the geological relationships in the area, including in particular the facing directions and internal stratigraphy of the domains separated by major faults, and the mineralogy, chemical alteration and other zoning of the mineralization on a mine scale. However, perhaps the highest priority of research is a thorough investigation of the absolute age relationships of the rocks, using direct dating methods, to provide a time framework of the geological history.

CONCLUSIONS

The sequence of geological events in the area is, in the main, well established by the geological observations of the last 75 years, although there appears to be at least some overlap in the time of emplacement of porphyries and gold, and the development of structures. The evidence indicates that the gold was mostly, and probably entirely, emplaced relatively late in the history of the area, although it appears to be in part overprinted by the last major geological effect, the development of a penetrative foliation and strong east-plunging lineation in the rocks. The most significant research project which could be done at this time is a thorough direct dating study.

REFERENCES

Bell, A.M.
1948: Hallnor Mine; p.547-553 in Structural Geology of Canadian Ore Deposits, Canadian Institute of Mining and Metallurgy, Jubilee Volume, 948p.

Dunbar, W.R.
1948: Structural Relations of the Porcupine Ore Deposits; p.442-456 in Structural Geology of Canadian Ore Deposits, Canadian Institute of Mining and Metallurgy, Jubilee Volume, 948p.

Ferguson, S.A., Bufam, B.S.W., Carter, O.F., Griffis, A.T., Holmes, T.C., Hurst, M.E., Jones, W.A., Lane, H.C., and Longley, C.S.
1968: Geology and Ore Deposits of Tisdale Township, District of Cochrane; Ontario Department of Mines, Geological Report 58, 173p. Accompanied by Map 2075, scale 1:12,000 or 1 inch to 1000 feet.

Fryer, B.J., Kerrich, R., Hutchinson, R.W., Peirce, M.G., and Rogers, D.S.
1979: Archean Precious Metal Hydrothermal Systems, Dome Mine, Abitibi Greenstone Belt, I. Patterns of Alteration and Metal Distribution; Canadian Journal of Earth Sciences, Volume 16, p.421-439.

Griffis, A.T.
1962: A Geochemical Study of the McIntyre Mine; Canadian Institute of Mining and Metallurgy, Bulletin, Volume 55, p.76-83.

Hawley, J.E. and Hart, R.C.
1948: Preston East Dome Mine; p.528-538 in Structural Geology of Canadian Ore Deposits, Canadian Institute of Mining and Metallurgy, Jubilee Volume, 948p.

Hodgson, C.J.
1982: Gold Deposits of the Abitibi Belt, Ontario; p.192-197 in Summary of Field Work, 1982, by the Ontario Geological Survey, Edited by John Wood, O.L. White, R.B. Barlow, and A.C. Colvine, Ontario Geological Survey, Miscellaneous Paper 106, 235p.

Holmes, D.T.
1948: Dome Mine; p.539-547 in Structural Geology of Canadian Ore Deposits, Canadian Institute of Mining and Metallurgy, Jubilee Volume, 948p.

Karvinen, W.O.
1981: Geology and Evolution of Gold Deposits, Timmins Area; p.29-46 in Genesis of Archean, Volcanic-Hosted Gold Deposits, Symposium Held at the University of Waterloo, March 7, 1980, Ontario Geological Survey, Miscellaneous Paper 97, 175p.

Price, P., and Bray, R.C.E.
1948: Pamour Mine; p.558-565 in Structural Geology of Canadian Ore Deposits, Canadian Institute of Mining and Metallurgy, Jubilee Volume, 948p.

Pyke, D.R.
1982: Geology of the Timmins Area, District of Cochrane; Ontario Geological Survey, Report 219, 141p. Accompanied by Map 2455, Scale 1:50,000.

Pyke, D.R., Ayres, L.D. and Innes, D.G.
1973: Timmins-Kirkland Lake, Cochrane, Sudbury, and Timiskaming Districts, Ontario; Ontario Department of Mines, Map 2205, Geological Compilation Series, Scale 1 inch to 4 miles.

Ramsay, J.G.
1967: Folding and Fracturing of Rocks; McGraw-Hill Book Company, 568p.

Roberts, R.G.
1981: The Volcanic-Tectonic Setting of Gold Deposits in the Timmins Area, Ontario; p.16-28 in Genesis of Archean, Volcanic-Hosted Gold Deposits, Symposium Held at the University of Waterloo, March 7, 1980, Ontario Geological Survey, Miscellaneous Paper 97, 175p.

Exploration History in the Hemlo Area

G.C. Patterson

Resident Geologist, Ontario Ministry of Natural Resources, Thunder Bay

ABSTRACT

In the Hemlo area, gold deposits outlined to date by International Corona Resources Limited, Long Lac Mineral Exploration Limited, and Goliath Gold Mines Limited are portions of one large deposit. The combined published tonnage is 13,534,080 tons at 0.236 ounces of gold per ton. The deposits consist of disseminated pyrite, gold, and molybdenite in siliceous and sericitic altered metasediments. There is a strong stratigraphic control on the position of the deposit, which on a regional scale is situated at the contact between felsic metasediments (derived from the reworking of tuffs) and pelitic metasediments.

Exploration in the Hemlo-Heron Bay area dates back to 1869 when gold-bearing veins were discovered near Heron Bay. Since then the area has been explored intermittently, mostly for gold. The deposit presently held by International Corona Resources Limited was drilled extensively in the late 1940s and early 1950s but was dropped and restaked a number of times before the current development began in 1980.

INTRODUCTION

The purpose of this paper is to review the information on the Hemlo gold deposit which is available to the public in the form of newspaper articles, assessment file reports and government reports.

The Hemlo area is located 35 km east of Marathon adjacent to the Trans-Canada Highway (17), 4 km west of the Manitouwadge Highway (614).

Exploration in the area began in 1869, near the present town of Heron Bay, where two veins were discovered by Moses Pe-Kong-Gay. These were shown to A. Cyrette and W. Pritchard in 1872, who reported the occurrence to Captain W. Frue. A number of shafts were sunk and some ore shipped (McKellar 1874).

In the 1920s, J. LeCour, station agent at Hemlo, sank a number of test pits on a mineralized shear zone (currently the Bel-Air Resources Limited property) just north of the Hemlo station. At about the same time, a series of trenches were dug to the north of Mile Post 38 on the Canadian Pacific Railway mainline by persons unknown (currently the eastern showing of Goliath Gold Mines Limited).

The region was first mapped by J.E. Thomson of the Ontario Department of Mines in 1931. He recommended two areas for exploration: Manitouwadge, and northeast of Hemlo.

In 1981, International Corona Resources Limited announced the discovery of a significant deposit. This spurred the staking of approximately 7000 claims, 4300 claims in the Ministry of Natural Resources' North Central Region and 2700 claims in the Northeastern Region.

Forty to fifty companies are currently carrying out active exploration programs in the area. These include: International Corona Resources Limited, Golden Sceptre Resources Limited, Goliath Gold Mines Limited, Teck Corporation Limited, Noranda Exploration Company Limited, Bel-Air Resources Limited, Long Lac Mineral Exploration Limited, Interlake Development Corporation Limited and Harlin Resources Limited.

GENERAL GEOLOGY

The area has been mapped by the Ontario Geological Survey and the former Department of Mines (Thomson 1931; Milne 1968; Muir 1980, 1982). This mapping has defined an east-trending belt of Archean metasediments and metavolcanics (a portion of the Wawa Subprovince) forming a broad synform, with granitic intrusions along the axis. The Quetico gneiss belt lies to the north and the Pukaskwa gneiss complex to the south. Muir (1982) divided the belt into two main sequences near the town of Heron Bay. The northern Heron Bay sequence consists predominantly of intermediate to felsic metavolcanics and metasediments. The metavolcanics consist of flows, pyroclastic breccia and tuff. The coarsest pyroclastic rocks occur near Heron Bay. Towards the east, the pyroclastic rocks gradually become finer-grained with a higher component of reworked material (tuffaceous fragments). Near Hemlo, pelitic metasediments begin to interfinger with the tuffs and tuffaceous metasediments. Further to the east near Struthers the pelitic metasediments predominate. The southern sequence, the Playter Harbour sequence, consists of mafic pillowed metavolcanics (high-iron tholeiites) which have been intruded by ultramafic sills. The geology of this area is further described by Muir (this volume).

PROPERTIES

INTERNATIONAL CORONA RESOURCES LIMITED

The property is located 5 km east of the settlement of Hemlo. It was originally staked by T. Page, M. Bartley (both geologists), Moses Fisher (who had guided J. E. Thomson to Manitouwadge), A. Halliday and J.K. Williams (who also staked the Long Lac property). A company, Lake Superior Mining Corporation Limited, was formed in 1947 to develop the property with W. Toms as president. Between 1947 and 1951, the company performed geological mapping and 6000 feet of diamond drilling (The Canadian Mines Handbook, 1950). In 1951, the property was optioned to Teck-Hughes Gold Mines Limited. Apparently, an additional 6000 feet was drilled before Teck-Hughes dropped the property. The tonnage (west zone of Corona) was estimated at 89,000 tons at 0.27 ounces of gold per ton (Canadian Mines Handbook, 1961). Further drilling was undertaken in 1957 and 1959. The company was dissolved in February, 1965.

During the period 1965 to 1973, the property was staked and held for short periods of time by four individuals: J.W. O'Brien (April 5, 1964 to May 25, 1965), L. Schneider (December 17, 1965 to January 19, 1967), A. Hopkins (July 3, 1970 to January 14, 1971) and A. Schwartz (November 23, 1972 to April 13, 1973). No exploration work was filed for assessement credits.

The property was then staked by J.E. Halonen in April of 1973 for Ardel Exploration Limited. They completed a further three diamond drill holes (229 m) and revised the tonnage (west zone of Corona) to 150 000 tons at 0.21 ounces of gold per ton (The Northern Miner, February 14, 1974). The property was then restaked by R.G. Newman in 1975 although the Canadian Mines Handbook (1976) reported that it was optioned. The property was dropped in January of 1978.

The deposit remained open until March of 1980, when it was staked by J. Larche in partnership with D. McKinnon, who optioned the property to Corona Resources Limited (M. Pezim, President, Vancouver) in October, 1980. They carried out a program of geophysics (electromagnetic and magnetic surveys) in October and November of 1980. The first drill hole was started on January 15, 1981, under the direction of D. Bell, geological consultant. It was not until the 75th hole that the east zone of Corona was discovered. By October, 1981, 150 drill holes had been completed at a cost of $1,475,000. In November, 1981, the property was optioned to Teck Corporation Limited who continued drilling and undertook a feasibility study.

In short, since the commencement of exploration 37 years ago, the deposit has been held by 15 individuals and 5 companies to reach the present state of development.

GEOLOGY OF THE DEPOSIT

The geology of the deposit is described in the 1982 annual report of International Corona Resources Limited:

The gold values are associated within a mineralized siliceous and sericitic altered metavolcanic sediment. The zone is moderately sheared parallel to the bedding on the limb of a steeply dipping homocline 45-60 degrees north and striking 107 degrees east. The west and east zones are within the same stratigraphic horizon which has been intersected by a 250-foot wide diabase

dike that did not offset the zone of mineralization. The gold is in a sulfide-pyrite ore — is evenly distributed — fine-grained and is visible in many of the cores.

Teck Corporation Limited described the deposit in The Northern Miner, June 17, 1982, as:

East Zone: 800 feet wide (east-west), averaging 10 feet thick, extending to a vertical depth of 1300 feet, and open to extension; containing an estimated "geological mineral reserve" of 1,300,000 tons, grading 0.30 ounce per ton gold.

West Zone: containing 325,000 tons of open pit reserves to 125 feet, grading 0.095 ounces per ton gold and 213,000 tons of "undergound reserves" grading 0.129 ounces gold per ton.

A longitudinal section published in the 1982 annual report of International Corona Resources Limited showed the east zone to plunge 70 degrees to the east. The mineralization also has significant molybdenum values that may be recovered (The Northern Miner, November 11, 1982). The molybdenum grade of the east zone is 0.08 percent MoS_2 (M. Blecha, Teck Corporation Limited, personal communication, 1982). A second mineralized horizon parallel to the west zone occurs 300 feet to the south. It was discovered by Lake Superior Mining Corporation Limited (Resident Geologist's Files, Ontario Ministry of Natural Resources, Thunder Bay).

LONG LAC MINERAL EXPLORATION LIMITED (WILLIAMS OPTION)

The property is adjacent to the west boundary of the International Corona Resources Limited claim block, 4 km east of the settlement of Hemlo.

A gold occurrence was discovered during 1944 by Peter Moses of Heron Bay. He showed the property to a Mr. Ollmann of Heron Bay. A block of 11 claims was staked by J.K. Williams of Maryland, apparently in partnership with Ollmann, in September of 1945. Exploration work, consisting of geological mapping, trenching and diamond drilling, was done by 1948 under the direction of T. Page. The property was then optioned by the Williams family to Long Lac Mineral Exploration in 1981. Drilling of 18 holes during the winter of 1982 outlined a deposit near Moose Lake.

The geology has been described by Page (Resident Geologist's Files, Ontario Ministry of Natural Resources, Thunder Bay). The property is underlain predominantly by metasediments striking east. A "major break" with mafic metasediments to the south and felsic metasediments to the north occurs near Highway 17.

A quartz porphyry unit trending 107 degrees occurs in felsic metasediments to the north of the break. The quartz porphyry unit is "250 feet thick in the east and 1,000 feet thick in the west". Both margins of the porphyry are sheared, silicified and mineralized with pyrite, molybdenite and gold. The early work conducted by J.K. Williams was carried out in the western portion of the claim group along the southern contact of the quartz porphyry.

The deposit drilled by Long Lac Mineral Exploration Limited occurs on the east side of the claim block, to the east of Moose Lake and north of Highway 17. The deposit is on strike with the west zone of International Corona Resources Limited. The dimensions of the deposit were reported in The Northern Miner, August 19, 1982: the deposit had been drilled to a depth of 150 m, averaged 23.7 m in width, and was estimated to contain 1.8 million tonnes grading 0.175 ounces of gold per tonne. The deposit is open to depth.

GOLIATH GOLD MINES LIMITED

The Goliath Gold Mines Limited property surrounds the International Corona Resources Limited property on three sides (east, north and south).

The property was first staked in 1945 by T. Page and was then incorporated into the Lake Superior Mining Corporation claim block. It was patented in 1959 but subsequently allowed to come open. The ground was held by A. Hopkins from July 16, 1968, to January 14, 1971. In July of 1980, it was staked by G. Coyne for D. McKinnon who transferred it to Goliath Gold Mines Limited in September of 1982. A deep drill program under the direction of D. Bell, geological consultant, intersected the down dip extension of the Long Lac deposit in September 1982. In November 1982, the property was optioned to Noranda Exploration Company Limited.

Drilling by Goliath Gold Mines Limited and Noranda Exploration Company Limited has outlined a deposit extending along strike for 1,000 feet. The mineralized zone is bounded by the Long Lac Mineral Exploration Limited deposit to the west along strike and to the south up dip.

According to The Northern Miner, January 6, 1983, the deposit has an estimated potential of 4,493 tons per vertical foot (from 800 to 3000 feet, giving a vertical depth of 2,200 feet and a tonnage of 9.88 million tons) with a grade of 0.249 ounces of gold per ton.

Another occurrence on Goliath Gold Mines Limited's claims is located to the east of International Corona Resources Limited, 100 m south of Struthers. Mapping has indicated the presence of molybdenite and pyrite in sericite schist on strike with the Corona east zone (Resident Geologist's Files, Ontario Ministry of Natural Resources, Thunder Bay). This appears to coincide with the "Mile 38 Occurrence" reported by Thomson (1931).

GOLDEN SCEPTRE RESOURCES LIMITED

The Golden Sceptre Resources Limited property is an east-trending claim group, 3.2 km wide by 9.7 km long, to the west of the properties of Long Lac Mineral Exploration Limited and International Corona Resources Limited.

The property was first staked in 1945 by C. Edward. He completed 40 days work (not in Assessment Files) before dropping the claims in 1950. It was then held by D. Michano and H. Hanson for brief periods from 1960 to 1964. In 1975, the ground was staked by R.G. Newman who conducted geological and geochemical surveys. The property came open in July of 1979. It was then staked in January 1980 by E.B. Neill for D. McKinnon who then transferred it to Golden Sceptre. Under the direction of D. Bell, geological consultant, a program of sampling, trenching, geophysics (electomagnetic, magnetic, and induced polarization surveys), geochemistry and drilling was carried out. The property was optioned to Noranda Exploration Company Limited in November 1982.

Exploration has discovered three mineralized zones. Trenching in July 1982, exposed the "fracture zone" 800 m north of Highway 17 , on the east boundary of the claim group, adjacent to the property of Long Lac Mineral Exploration Limited. Drilling revealed the "north zone" in August 1982. The "highway zone" was discovered in the summer of 1978 by T. Muir (Ontario Geological Survey).

The fracture zone is hosted in quartz veins which cut a quartz porphyry, and appears to be on strike with mineralization discovered in the 1950s on the west side of what is now Long Lac Mineral Exploration Limited's property (Resident Geologist's Files, Ontario Ministry of Natural Resources, Thunder Bay). The mineralization consists of native gold, molybdenite, pyrite, petzite, hessite and altaite. Initial drilling has intersected a number of high grade zones (up to 3.36 ounces of gold per ton) over narrow widths (1.6 to 4.9 feet; George Cross Newsletter No. 204, October 25, 1982).

The north zone is located 150 m north of the fracture zone. It is defined by an east-trending soil geochemical anomaly. Drill results were: hole 4 – 0.33 ounces of gold per ton over 21 feet; and hole 19 – 0.325 ounces of gold per over 36 feet ton (The Northern Miner, November 18, 1982).

The highway zone was sampled by Muir (1980) and assayed 0.32 ounces of gold per ton. The mineralization, consisting of pyrite and native gold with minor molybdenite, is hosted in volcaniclastic metasediments. The unit is up to 2 m wide and can be traced from Moose Lake to Finger Lake, a distance of 3 km. The volcaniclastic metasediments are made up of 50 percent fragments of feldspar porphyry, chert, and altered volcanic rocks, 2 mm to 5 cm in size, which have been stretched up to 15:1 parallel to foliation. The matrix contains sericite, green mica and tourmaline.

PRYME ENERGY RESOURCES LIMITED – MARCH RESOURCES LIMITED (MCINTYRE CUNI SHOWING)

The property is located 10 km northeast of the Trans-Canada Highway and the Manitouwadge Highway. The area was first staked by C. Von Klein in 1962 and optioned to

McIntyre-Porcupine Mines Limited, who performed geophysical surveys (electromagnetic and magnetic), geological mapping and drilled 28 holes. In 1964, Caravelle Mines Limited gained control of the group and optioned it to Falconbridge Nickel Mines Limited. It was staked by Pryme Energy Resources Limited and March Resources Limited in July 1982, and was then optioned to Noranda Exploration Company Limited.

Exploration of the property defined six Cu-Ni and Cu-Zn occurrences on the ground; the most significant is showing No. 2. Two drill holes cut sulphide mineralization in "andesite". Assays were as follows. (Assays by Falconbridge Nickel Mines Limited in 1970; Resident Geologist's Files, Ontario Ministry of Natural Resources, Thunder Bay.)

Hole A_2 — 8.2 feet, Cu 1.05%, Zn 0.8%, Ag 0.40 oz/ton, Au 0.24 oz/ton

Hole W_1 — 7.0 feet, Cu 2.94%, Zn 2.12%, Pb 0.14%, Au 0.094 oz/ton, Ag 1.54 oz/ton

A semi-quantitative spectrographic analysis showed the presence of molybdenum.

SUMMARY

The three deposits outlined thus far (International Corona Resources Limited, Long Lac Mineral Exploration Limited, and Goliath Gold Mines Limited) are portions of one large deposit. The combined published tonnage is 13,534,080 tons at 0.236 ounces of gold per ton. The mineralization, consisting of disseminated pyrite, gold, and molybdenite, is hosted in siliceous and sericitic altered metasediments. There is a strong stratigraphic control on the position of the deposit. This unit can be traced from Golden Sceptre Resources Limited's property in the west, across Long Lac Mineral Exploration Limited's property to International Corona Resources Limited's property, to Goliath Gold Mines Limited's property, a distance of 6 km. On a regional scale, the deposit is situated at the contact between felsic metasediments (derived from the reworking of tuffs) and pelitic metasediments. At least two possible origins have been suggested by workers in the area, as follows.

1. Mineralization was concentrated during volcanism in a manner similar to that proposed for the Bousquet deposits in Quebec (Valliant and Hutchinson 1982).

2. Mineralization was concentrated within a shear-zone-related structure (Page 1951 *in* Resident Geologist's Files, Ontario Ministry of Natural Resources, Thunder Bay).

The description and metallogenesis of these deposits will be the topic of a research project by the author.

REFERENCES

McKellar, P.
1874: Mining on the North Shore, Lake Superior; *on file in Library,* Resident Geologist's Office, Thunder Bay, Ontario, 26p.

Milne, V.G.
1968: Geology of Black River Area; Ontario Department of Mines, Geological Report 72. Accompanied by Maps 2143, 2144, 2145, 2146, 2147, scale 1 inch to ½ mile.

Muir, T.L.
1980: Geology of the Hemlo Area, District of Thunder Bay; Ontario Geological Survey Open File Report 5280, 78p.
1982: Geology of the Heron Bay Area, District of Thunder Bay; Ontario Geological Survey Report 218, 89p. Accompanied by Map 2439, scale 1 inch to ½ mile.

Thomson, J.E.
1931: Geology of the Heron Bay Area, District of Thunder Bay; Ontario Department of Mines, Volume 40, pt. 2, p.21-39. Accompanied by Map No. 40d, scale 1 inch to 1½ mile.

Valliant, R.I., and Hutchinson, R.W.
1982: Stratigraphic Distribution and Genesis of Gold Deposits, Bousquet Region, Northwestern Quebec; p.27-40 *in* Geology of Canadian Gold Deposits, Canadian Institute of Mining and Metallurgy, Special Volume 24.

Geology of the Hemlo-Heron Bay Area

T.L. Muir

Precambrian Geology Section, Ontario Geological Survey, Toronto

ABSTRACT

The Hemlo-Heron Bay area, extending east from the northeast shore of Lake Superior, contains what may prove to be a major gold camp. The area is underlain by generally east-trending, Archean metavolcanics and metasediments which have been intruded by Archean granitic rocks and a Proterozoic alkalic complex, as well as numerous dike rocks. The metavolcanics have been assigned to two tentative stratigraphic groups, one predominantly calc-alkalic and consisting of fragmental rocks, the other predominantly tholeiitic and consisting of flows.

There is an eastward facies change from coarse fragmental volcanic rocks near Heron Bay to finer-grained fragmental volcanic rocks to volcaniclastic sedimentary rocks and epiclastic sedimentary rocks in the Hemlo area. Stratigraphic correlations may relate units in the Hemlo area with units near the Lake Superior shore.

Three main gold discoveries near Hemlo appear to be parts of the same deposit. The gold mineralization appears to be related to the facies change between volcaniclastic sedimentary rocks to the west and southwest and epiclastic rocks to the east and northeast. The deposits consist of pyrite, gold, and molybdenite in sheared volcaniclastic metasediments which are sericitic and locally contain green mica. The volcaniclastic units have been intruded by feldspar and quartz-feldspar porphyry bodies and by diabase dikes.

INTRODUCTION

Over two years ago a group of claims was staked east of Hemlo, Ontario. Subsequent exploration on a partially outlined gold deposit has led to the delineation of what may be a major gold camp in Ontario. Current interest in these gold deposits has sparked considerable attention and speculation as to the extent, type, and origin of the mineralized zones. This paper describes the geology of the area based on previous mapping, supplemented by updated information. The Hemlo deposits are also discussed within the context of data available to the public.

LOCATION AND PREVIOUS WORK

The Hemlo-Heron Bay area lies east of the town of Marathon which is located on the northeast shore of Lake Superior (Figure 1). The area described extends from Mara

thon, 37 km east to within 4 km west of the highway turnoff to Manitouwadge. The Hemlo deposit is crossed by the Trans-Canada Highway, and lies 6 km east of the hamlet of Hemlo, which was in the past a pulp and paper, railway, and Ministry of Natural Resources base.

Previously the area around Heron Bay and west of Hemlo was mapped by Thomson (1931); the area to the north was mapped by Milne (1967, 1968). Recently the west half of this area was mapped for the Ontario Geological Survey in 1977 as the Heron Bay Area (Muir 1982a). The east half of this area was mapped in 1978 as the Hemlo Area (Muir 1982b).

GENERAL GEOLOGY OF THE HEMLO-HERON BAY AREA

The Hemlo-Heron Bay area is partly underlain by supracrustal rocks which are part of the east-trending Schreiber – White River section of the Wawa Subprovince of the Superior Province. Sections of these Archean metavolcanics and metasediments are separated by four granitic bodies and one alkalic intrusive body (Figure 2).

Figure 1. *Location of the Hemlo-Heron Bay area. Shaded areas represent "greenstone" belts.*

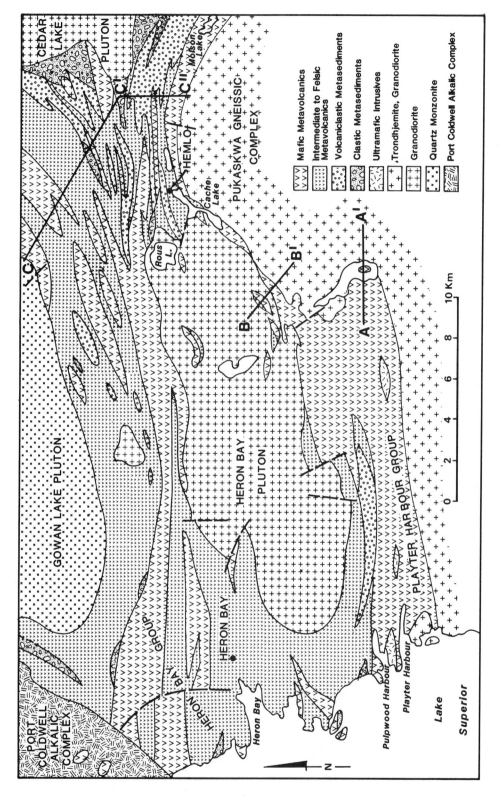

Figure 2. Simplified geology of the Hemlo-Heron Bay area after Muir (1982a, 1982b). Cross-sections shown in Figure 3.

In simple terms, the Gowan Lake Pluton, Heron Bay Pluton, and Pukaskwa Gneissic Complex divide the supracrustal rocks into two small belts which join in the west near Lake Superior and which appear to join in the east. The volcanic rocks of these belts are tentatively subdivided into two groups: the southern, Playter Harbour group, and the northern, Heron Bay group. The division, best distinguished in the west part of the area, is based on limited chemical analyses and is not well defined nor necessarily applicable in the eastern half of the area.

The Playter Harbour group consists largely of high-iron tholeiitic basalt flows and pillowed flows in both variolitic and non-variolitic forms. Feeder dikes have locally been identified. A number of relatively thin, intercalated, discontinuous units of intermediate to felsic tuff and lapilli-tuff as well as siltstone were found along the Lake Superior shoreline. These units were rarely found inland. Minor amounts of poorly banded chert, amphibolite, and magnetite ironstone also occur in the west. Isolated lens-shaped bodies (sills?) of pyroxenite and lherzolite are found within the mafic flows in the Pulpwood Harbour area and throughout the group, east to Mussy Lake. In the Pulpwood Harbour area there are several very thin units of altered graphitic mudstone which contain various amounts and combinations of pyrrhotite, chalcopyrite, and pyrite.

The bulk of the Heron Bay group comprises dacitic and rhyolitic calc-alkalic pyroclastic breccia, tuff-breccia, lapilli-tuff, and tuff; rocks of rhyolitic composition are minor and restricted to the vicinity of Heron Bay. The remainder of the group consists of calc-alkalic basalts as pyroclastic rocks, pillow breccia, and some flows. There are also some tholeiitic basalt flows which become more prevalent than calc-alkalic basalts in the area northwest to east-northeast of Rous Lake.

The southern part of the area is underlain by the Pukaskwa Gneissic Complex which consists of lineated and foliated to weakly gneissic biotite-hornblende trondhjemite and granodiorite (plagioclase-porphyritic and nonporphyritic) with later small bodies and dikes of massive pegmatite and aplite. Locally within the older granitic rocks there are small areas with well-developed gneisses, or amphibolite inclusions, or bodies which may represent recrystallized and moderately assimilated remnants of intermediate to felsic metavolcanics and metasediments. Within about 1 km of the supracrustal rocks the trondhjemitic and granodioritic rocks show a weak to moderately developed mylonitic texture with a trend that parallels the contact, except in Mussy Lake area.

The north-central part of the area is underlain by the Gowan Lake Pluton which is a marginal unit of the Quetico Gneiss Belt. This pluton consists of lineated and microcline-porphyritic varieties of biotite-hornblende quartz monzonite. The lineated hornblende appears to be a primary texture. The central part of the area is underlain by massive and microcline-porphyritic varieties of hornblende-biotite granodiorite. A poorly defined border zone of foliated plagioclase-porphyritic biotite-hornblende granodiorite is locally adjacent to the Pukaskwa Gneissic Complex. The northeastern part of the area is underlain by the Cedar Lake Pluton which consists of massive to foliated hornblende-biotite granodiorite, similar to that of the Heron Bay Pluton. The northwest corner of the area is underlain by part of the Port Coldwell Alkalic Complex, which, in this area, consists of olivine gabbro, biotite gabbro, pyroxene monzonite, and pegmatitic hornblende quartz syenite.

An extensive number of relatively late alkalic and subalkalic dikes are present along the Lake Superior shoreline area; they decrease in abundance along the southern parts of the shoreline and rapidly become scarce inland. These dikes, which are probably associated with the Port Coldwell Alkalic Complex, strike, on average, south-southeast and may be a result of crustal extension as part of the Lake Superior Rift Structure. A few dikes were found west of the Hemlo deposits. Most dikes post-date the subalkalic ('normal') diabase dikes (which have at least two ages; quartz-bearing predates olivine-bearing), and comprise gabbro, porphyritic gabbro, diabase, porphyritic diabase, lamprophyres, porphyritic syenite, carbonatite, and diatreme-like intrusion breccia. Some of these types of dikes have a number of subtypes; overall age relationships are complex.

GEOLOGICAL OVERVIEW

There is a general facies change in the supracrustal rocks across the area. In the general vicinity of Heron Bay the pyroclastic breccia is coarsest, with some blocks measuring up to 2 m in diameter. Bedding is poorly developed or absent and is commonly at a moderate to shallow angle to the schistosity. The average fragment size decreases eastward and lapilli-tuff is more common. In the area north of Rous Lake, lapilli-tuff and tuff predominate; pyroclastic breccia and tuff-breccia are found locally, and some moderately to well-bedded volcaniclastic sedimentary rock units are present. East of Rous Lake there is a gradual but distinct increase in the abundance of volcaniclastic sedimentary rocks; east of the area around the main Hemlo deposit well-bedded epiclastic wacke predominates. Figure 2 is a simplified map showing these relationships.

The overall facies change, coupled with other characteristics seen in the field, suggests that (1) the coarse breccias represent proximal deposits from a major volcanic centre within the vicinity of Heron Bay or possibly under what is now Lake Superior; (2) the finer pyroclastic rocks represent distal deposits from the same sources; (3) the volcaniclastic metasediments represent deposits of the slightly reworked unlithified volcanic tephra; and (4) the erosion of lithified rocks was taking place, possibly to the east of the area, with deposition of epiclastic sediments into a moderately deep basin environment.

Rocks located along Playter Harbour, through the Mussy Lake area, and east of Cache Lake have been interpreted to belong to a unit of mafic metavolcanic flows with medium to very large plagioclase phenocrysts (Muir 1982b). If these rocks represent a time stratigraphic unit or a unit of flows with a close temporal relationship, then a plausible stratigraphic correlation with the Playter Harbour group and the metavolcanics south of the Hemlo deposit may be possible over a strike length of more than 40 km. It is also possible that the wedge of metasedi-

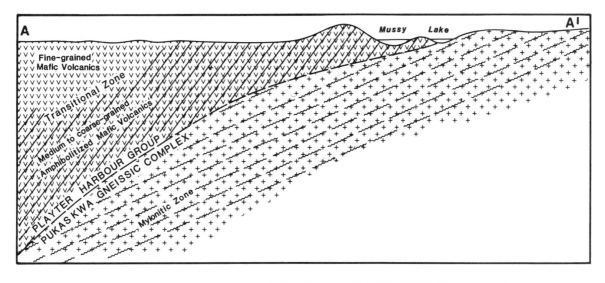

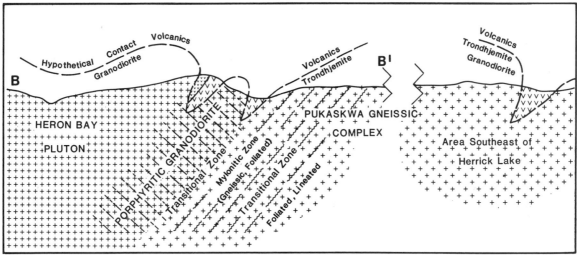

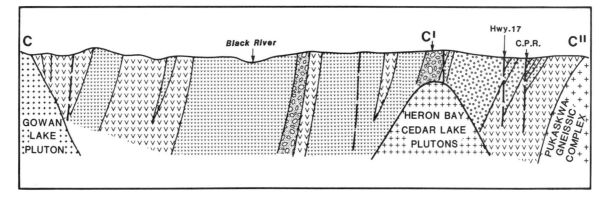

Figure 3. *Cross-sections through selected parts of the Hemlo-Heron Bay area. Sections A-A' and B-B' after Muir (1982b); not to scale. Section C-C'-C'' derived from Map 2452 (Muir 1982b); horizontal component, surface structure measurements, and topography to scale; depth not to scale. Dashed lines represent lineaments and/or faults.*

ments shown east-northeast of Playter Harbour may not pinch out as shown but may extend eastward, offset by a fault, under a largely sand-covered area, and may be correlative with metasediments in the vicinity of Hemlo (personal communication, G. Patterson, Resident Geologist, Ontario Ministry of Natural Resources, Thunder Bay, 1982). These two extrapolations, if correct, would significantly aid in understanding the stratigraphy of the Hemlo-Heron Bay area which would be an advantage in extending exploration westwards from the Hemlo deposit.

Three hypothetical cross-sections through various parts of the supracrustal rocks are shown in Figure 3 and located in Figure 2. Section A-A' depicts the relationship between the Playter Harbour group and the Pukaskwa Gneissic Complex near Mussy Lake and is drawn through, and parallel to, the axis of an interpreted synform. About 1.5 km from the contact the mafic metavolcanics are fine-grained; these grade into medium- to coarse-grained amphibolite closer to the complex. The mylonitic zone of the complex generally consists of weakly to moderately developed mylonitized plagioclase-porphyritic granodiorite and trondhjemite.

Section B-B' depicts the relationship between the Heron Bay Pluton and the Pukaskwa Gneissic Complex in a section southeast of Campfire Lake. The main part of the Heron Bay Pluton is hornblende-biotite granodiorite, whereas plagioclase-porphyritic granodiorite predominates along the boundary between the pluton and the gneissic complex. The configuration of the mafic metavolcanics along the boundary between these two granitic bodies, and the intermediate and mafic metavolcanic bodies within the Heron Bay Pluton, which are interpreted to be pendants, suggests that the Playter Harbour and Heron Bay groups were originally much more extensive.

Section C-C'-C" is a major section through the supracrustal rocks from the Gowan Lake Pluton to the Pukaskwa Gneissic Complex and passes through a spot about 1.6 km west of the main Hemlo showing. Based on currently available information, the supracrustal rocks are presently oriented in a moderately to steeply north-dipping homoclinal sequence. The importance of the faults and granitic bodies will be discussed in the section on the geology of the Hemlo deposit.

HEMLO DEPOSITS

The area around the Hemlo deposits was mapped at a scale of 1 inch to ¼ mile in 1978. The information presented here is largely based on that mapping and more detailed mapping will inevitably result in some changes. Some of these changes are known at the present time but cannot yet be published. A simplified geological interpretation of the vicinity of Hemlo is shown in Figure 4. The dominant lithology at any given locality is shown; many more interdigitations of rock units actually exist. Figure 5 shows the claim groups currently held in the vicinity of the Hemlo deposits.

At the scale shown the 'original' Hemlo deposit (International Corona Resources Limited deposit, located east of Moose Lake) appears to be closely associated with a facies change between epiclastic sediments to the northeast and east, and volcaniclastic sediments[1] to the west and southwest. The diabase dike shown in Figure 4 separates the deposit of International Corona Resources Limited into the "west zone" and the "east zone"; it has not offset the deposit (International Corona Resources Limited Annual Report, 1982). A very general description of the geology of the deposit and surrounding rocks, as seen along Highway 17 (Trans-Canada Highway) follows.

At the east end of the area (see Figure 4), there are moderately deformed, well-bedded, feldspathic wackes which have been folded and which form a small, overturned synform along part of the highway. At the bend in the highway, to the west, is a highly deformed unit of pelitic schist with middle to upper amphibolite facies metamorphic mineral assemblages. Individual beds have characteristic mineral assemblages, which collectively include biotite, muscovite, garnet, staurolite, anthophyllite, and cordierite; chloritoid and kyanite have been reported in drill core specimens (personal communication, K.H. Poulsen, Queen's University, 1982). These mineral assemblages need to be studied further because some minerals should be incompatible and some could indicate a narrow range of pressure-temperature conditions of formation, such as staurolite and chloritoid (Winkler 1976). Elsewhere in the area in other pelitic units, sillimanite and andalusite, as well as some of the above minerals, are found. The deformed schists by the highway show slightly deformed, boudined blocks of competent beds (calc-silicate units?) within a strongly deformed schistose pelitic matrix.

The next significant unit is deformed, schistose, felsic to intermediate volcaniclastic metasediments (equivalent to lapilli-tuff) hosting the ore zone. The matrix is sericitic and the rock contains pyrite, gold and molybdenite. To the west lies a mylonitized[2] package of intermediate to felsic bedded volcaniclastic metasediments. Mylonitization has been parallel and subparallel to the bedding and although the degree is believed to be considerable, it is difficult to quantify. Adjacent to the mylonitized rocks is a package of fractured and foliated intermediate to mafic volcaniclastic metasediments, as seen along the highway. South of the highway there are mafic flows.

Feldspar and quartz-feldspar porphyry dikes and sills have intruded the volcaniclastic units; the porphyries have been deformed and faulted thus predating some of the deformation. Their exact relationship with the mineralized zones is not yet clear. About 4 km to the west of the main Hemlo deposit, along the highway near a feldspar porphyry body (shown exaggerated on the map, see Figures 4 and 5) is a mineralized volcaniclastic unit in which values of 0.32 ounces Au per ton, and 0.48 ounces Ag

---

[1]Volcaniclastic sediments, as used here, refers to sediments with lithic clasts mostly of intermediate, felsic, and/or mafic volcanic material which is interpreted to be derived mostly from unlithified volcanic deposits.
[2]The term is used in the sense of displaying reduced grain size with accompanying overall extension of fragments and matrix.

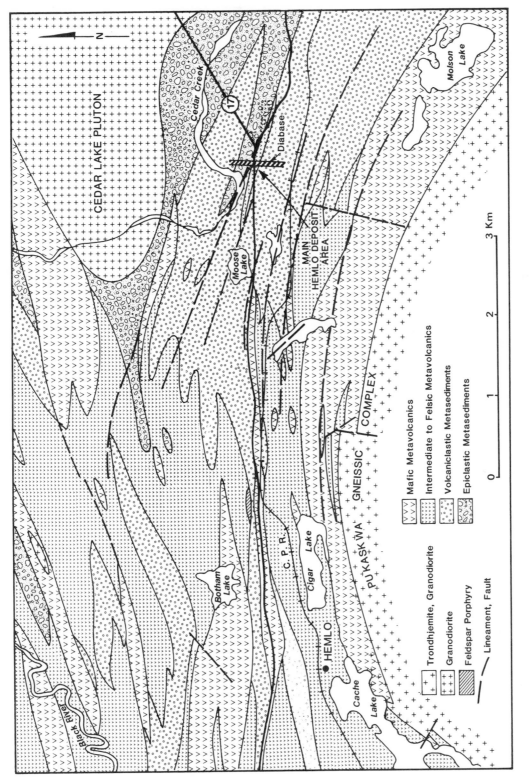

Figure 4. Simplified geology of the Hemlo vicinity modified after Muir (1982b). Units of metasediments and adjacent metavolcanics show the dominant lithology; other units are locally present. Lineaments may be faults.

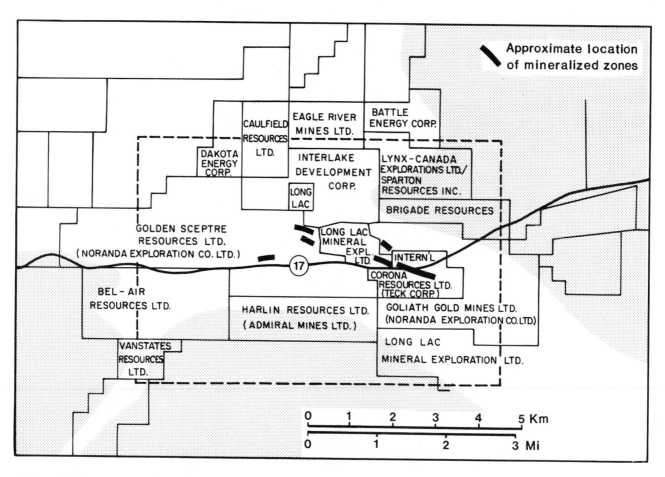

Figure 5. *Current properties in the Hemlo vicinity (after Northern Miner, January 13, 1983, p. 12,13). Area within dashed outline equivalent to area shown in Figure 4.*

per ton were reported from an assayed grab sample (assay by Geoscience Laboratories, Ontario Geological Survey, Toronto) collected in 1978 (Muir 1982b). It is possible that this mineralized zone is related to the Hemlo deposit to the east (see paragraph on Golden Sceptre Resources Limited, next section).

SUMMARY OF GEOLOGY OF GOLD DEPOSITS

The detailed geology of mineralized zones on the various properties is sketchy and/or confidential; information presented here is based on published material (The Northern Miner; George Cross Newsletter; International Corona Resources Limited, Annual Report).

The deposit held by International Corona Resources Limited (presently optioned to Teck Corporation Limited) is in part the 'original' Hemlo deposit outlined a number of years ago (see G.C. Patterson, this volume) and is

crossed by the Trans-Canada Highway (see Figure 5). It has been described as a "mineralized, siliceous, sericitic, altered, metavolcanic sediment" and locally contains green mica. For logistical purposes it has been divided into west and east zones (separated by a diabase dike) both of which appear to be in the same stratigraphic horizon. The zones are moderately sheared parallel to bedding and are on the limb of a steeply to moderately north-dipping homocline which strikes 107 degrees and dips 45 to 60 degrees north-northeast. The mineralization consists of pyrite, gold, and molybdenite. The gold is fine grained, evenly distributed, and visible in some of the drill cores. A parallel mineralized zone lies 300 feet south of the west zone (Resident Geologist's Files, Ontario Ministry of Natural Resources, Thunder Bay).

The deposit of Long Lac Mineral Exploration Limited (Williams option) (see Figure 5) lies to the west of the Corona west zone and east of Moose Lake. It appears to be on strike with the Corona zone. Assessment work filed in a report in 1951 by T. Page (Resident Geologist's Files,

Ontario Ministry of Natural Resources, Thunder Bay) refers to work in the west part of the claim block where a moderate-sized quartz porphyry body (not shown in Figure 4) with sheared mineralized and silicified margins containing pyrite, gold and molybdenite was outlined west of the current main zone of Long Lac Mineral Exploration Limited.

Goliath Gold Mines Limited (see Figure 5) (property presently optioned to Noranda Exploration Company Limited) has a mineralized zone which appears to be the down-dip extension of the deposit of Long Lac Mineral Exploration Limited. To the east of the International Corona Resources Limited deposit, just south of Struthers (Figure 6) a unit of sericitic schist contains pyrite and molybdenite (Resident Geologist's Files, Ontario Ministry of Natural Resources, Thunder Bay).

The property of Golden Sceptre Resources Limited (presently optioned to Noranda Exploration Company Limited) lies to the west of that of International Corona Resources Limited (see Figure 5) and has at least three mineralized zones, one of which (the southerly of the two easterly zones shown in Figure 5) may be on strike with the mineralized zone on the property of Long Lac Mineral Exploration Limited, described in the 1951 report by T. Page (see paragraph on Long Lac Mineral Exploration Limited). This mineralization is within a number of narrow zones which consist of quartz veins within a quartz porphyry; mineralization consists of pyrite, gold, and molybdenite, as well as some tellurides (personal communication; G. Patterson). The second zone lies to the north. The third zone, to the west and just north of the highway (see Figure 5) is in a highly stretched mineralized volcaniclastic (felsic) metasedimentary unit which is traceable easterly 3 km to Moose Lake. This unit consists of abundant feldspar porphyry fragments, and fragments of chert and altered volcanic rocks in a sericitic matrix with green mica and tourmaline (personal communication, G. Patterson, Ontario Ministry of Natural Resources, Thunder Bay).

In summary, it appears that the deposits of International Corona Resources Limited, Long Lac Mineral Exploration Limited, and Goliath Gold Mines Limited may all be part of one deposit. These deposits have a combined published tonnage in excess of 13 million tons with an average grade of about 0.236 ounces of gold per ton. Depth and strike limitations of mineralization have not yet been defined. Mineralized rocks occur over a distance of about 6 km, although they may not all be connected.

There are at least two models for the origin of the Hemlo deposits proposed by workers in the area. In general they propose a volcanogenic gold deposit or a mineralized shear zone possibly associated with porphyry dikes. It is perhaps pertinent to also consider a combination of the two models, namely a syngenetic deposit modified by a tectonic overprint. In any event, careful attention to the geology of the surrounding area as well as to the mineralized zones and their associated minerals and trace elements is fundamental to developing a credible model.

SYNTHESIS

It is of interest to consider the Hemlo deposit in its local setting, its general setting in the Hemlo-Heron Bay area, and its regional setting as part of the Schreiber-White River belt.

Although the Hemlo deposit appears to be associated with a facies change in the east, it does not appear to be so in the west, and although it has some strike length continuity, these features may be superficial. Mineral assemblages indicate that metamorphism has reached a maximum grade of middle to upper amphibolite facies. There are a number of strong linear deformation zones with both shearing and mylonitization which are parallel and subparallel to the stratigraphy. Porphyry dikes are also present.

The cross-section C-C'-C'' shown in Figure 3 may relate some of the above features. The section, derived from Map 2452 (Muir 1982b), shows some of the lineaments and the shear zones that transect it. Although this cross-section is somewhat hypothetical and preliminary, it may be inferred that the supracrustal rocks are in a homoclinal sequence, that the Cedar Lake Pluton and Heron Bay Pluton lie at a shallow depth connected to each other, that Highway 17 and the Canadian Pacific Railway follow shear zones (at least locally), and that some of the units may be repeated. The latter might have some bearing on the search for mineralized zones as it is known that other shear zones exist in the vicinity. The proposed shallow depth of the granodiorite pluton may account for the relatively high metamorphic grade which may have affected or have been related to the mineralization. More detailed work may show that (1) tight isoclinal folding may have taken place because many of the sparse stratigraphic top determinations are as yet equivocal, and (2) repetition of units caused by faulting, as shown in Figure 3, may not have taken place.

In terms of the general setting of the Hemlo-Heron Bay area, important features are: (1) the mafic metavolcanics abutting the Pukaskwa Gneissic Complex may be correlative throughout this area; (2) in the western part of the area there is a tholeiitic Playter Harbour Group and a calc-alkalic Heron Bay Group; and (3) the distinction outlined in (2) may not be possible in the east because of intermixing of the two groups.

In terms of mineralization in the area, a number of occurrences are known. A molybdenite deposit lies about 2 km east of Playter Harbour. The molybdenite is within quartz veins which are possibly associated with a small granodiorite dike (Resident Geologist's Files, Ontario Ministry of Natural Resources, Thunder Bay). The country rocks consist of pyroxenite, lherzolite, and some tuffaceous units (observed in on-site diamond drill core). Maximum grades are 0.28 percent MoS_2 over 8.2 m (Resident Geologist's Files, Ontario Ministry of Natural Resources, Thunder Bay). Gold content is not known. A grab sample from a small sugary pyrite-bearing rock within intermediate pyroclastic breccia on the Lake Superior shoreline returned a value of 0.03 ounces Au per ton (Muir 1982a) A grab sample of rusty sulphides from an old trench in tuff-breccia of intermediate composition west-southwest of

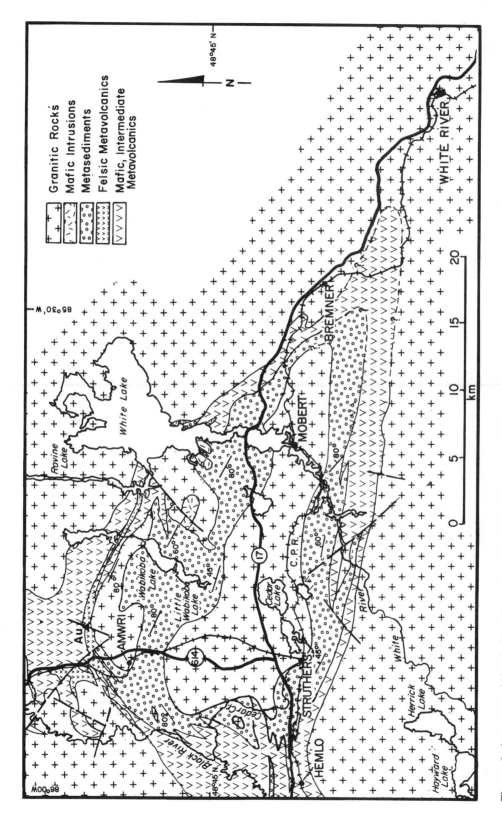

Figure 6. Area east of Hemlo (modified after Map 2220, Milne et al. 1972) showing possible regional synform. Dip measurements supplied by G. Patterson, Resident Geologist, Ontario Ministry of Natural Resources, Thunder Bay.

the town of Heron Bay returned values of 0.15 ounces Au and 2.45 ounces Ag per ton, in addition to well above background levels of Cu, Pb, and Zn (Muir 1982a). Quartz-tourmaline veins in metavolcanics are exposed on the shoreline of Lake Superior south of Marathon; gold content is not known. The metavolcanic-metasedimentary belt in this area thus demonstrates promise on a number of fronts. In addition there is Cu-Ni-Pt-bearing massive and disseminated sulphide mineralization associated with some of the gabbroic rocks of the Port Coldwell Alkalic Complex.

The regional picture is of interest especially with respect to extending exploration for gold beyond the area around the Hemlo deposit. Figure 6 shows the geology of the area from Hemlo to White River based on Map 2220 (Milne *et al.* 1972) and modified by the recent mapping in the Hemlo-Heron Bay are. The figure shows an apparently closing synformal structure just west of White River, based on a number of preliminary field measurements (personal communication, G. Patterson, Resident Geologist, Ontario Ministry of Natural Resources, Thunder Bay). The extent of the synformal axis to the west is not known because of a lack of information. One other known gold occurrence is shown on the map; the location of other occurrences can not presently be released. Their positions suggest that there is an interesting possible stratigraphic relationship with the gold occurrences near the mafic metavolcanic-metasedimentary contact. However, the importance of this relationship is unknown because the deposit at Hemlo has not been proven to be stratabound.

Nevertheless, as the above relationship cannot be rejected at this stage, it is important to point out that a number of isolated exposures throughout sand-and silt-covered areas show that a possible stratigraphic unit of metasediments (either continuous or discontinuous), may lie along the north side of the mafic metavolcanics which are south of the Gowan Lake Pluton (see Figure 2 and Maps 2439 and 2452, Muir 1982a,b). This unit may connect with the unit of metasediments lying in the northwest corner of the area, thereby extending possible exploration targets west of Hemlo. Overall, the regional view provides a favourable outlook for exploration in the Hemlo area.

REFERENCES

Milne, V.G.
1967:Geology of Cirrus Lake-Bamoos Lake Area, District of Thunder Bay; Ontario Department of Mines, Geological Report 43, 61p. Accompanied by Map 2099, scale 1 inch to ½ mile.
1968:Geology of Black River Area, District of Thunder Bay; Ontario Department of Mines, Geological Report 72, 68 p. Accompanied by Maps 2143 to 2147 inclusive, scale 1 inch to ½ mile.

Milne, V.G. *et al.*
1972: Manitouwadge-Wawa Sheet, Algoma, Cochrane, Sudbury, and Thunder Bay Districts; Ontario Division of Mines, Geological Compilation Series, Map 2220, scale 1 inch to 4 miles.

Muir, T.L.
1982a:Geology of the Heron Bay Area, District of Thunder Bay; Ontario Geological Survey Report 218, 89 p. Accompanied by Map 2439, scale 1:31,680.
1982b:Geology of the Hemlo Area, District of Thunder Bay; Ontario Geological Survey Report 217, 65 p. Accompanied by Map 2452, scale 1:31,680.

Thomson, J.E.
1931:Geology of the Heron Bay Area, District of Thunder Bay; Ontario Department of Mines, Annual Report, Vol. 40, pt. 2, p. 21-39. Accompanied by Map No. 40d, scale l inch to 1½ miles.

Winkler, Helmut G.F.
1976:Petrogenesis of Metamorphic Rocks; Springer-Verlag, New York, fourth edition, 334p.

Invisible Gold

Janet Springer
Mineral Deposits Section, Ontario Geological Survey, Toronto

ABSTRACT

Mineralogical associations are discussed as field indicators of microscopic or submicroscopic gold. Pyrite and arsenopyrite are the principal associates; both minerals may assay > 30 ounces per ton invisible gold. Links between arsenian pyrite and gold are discussed as field tools.

Gold in sericite schists is documented from Quebec; gold and the principal sulphide, pyrite, are microscopic, and vary sympathetically with graphite.

Commercial adsorption of gold by activated carbon is discussed as relevant to geological associations of gold and carbon. Evidence of activated carbon in the Archean may suggest there is potential for large deposits, grading 0.25 ounces Au per ton, marked by graphite leaders, but concealed by the minute grain size of both gold and sulphides.

INTRODUCTION

Archean lode gold deposits generally bear grains of visible gold. The site of the gold is commonly shown by veins of glassy, white quartz and carbonate, or by haloes of discolouration in the host "greenstone". These field markers were successful as practical tools for the prospector. The great number of finds which date from the early years of the search (Hodgson, this volume) shows this quite clearly.

The search is more difficult when gold cannot be seen and particularly so when it is found in unfamiliar host rocks.

This is the case for the hydrothermal gold ores of Carlin-type found in Nevada. Here no distinction can be made in hand specimen between barren rock and ore. The principal ore mineral, pyrite, occurs as microscopic grains, less than 5 μm[1] across, and gold is rarely seen, even at 15,000 X magnifications, although assays show grades of up to 200 ounces Au per ton from sulphide concentrates (Wells and Mullens 1973; Hausen 1981).

Examples like the Nevada deposits are important because they suggest field markers which can point to unexpected settings for gold. Two indicators which may have application to prospecting in Ontario are discussed in greater detail below: they are (1) the association of gold with different mineral species, and (2) the association of gold with carbonaceous material.

---

[1] $1\ \mu m = 1\ \text{micron} = 10^{-6}\ m = 0.001\ mm$.

GOLD ASSOCIATED WITH SULPHIDE MINERALS

In primary gold ores, gold is almost invariably intergrown with either gangue or sulphide minerals; the native metal is physically within or adjacent to various sulphide species.

Schwartz (1944) reviewed the host minerals of gold from 115 camps worldwide and recorded the frequencies (Figure 1). The seven leading hosts are base metal sulphides and of these pyrite and arsenopyrite are by far the most common. The next most frequent associations in-

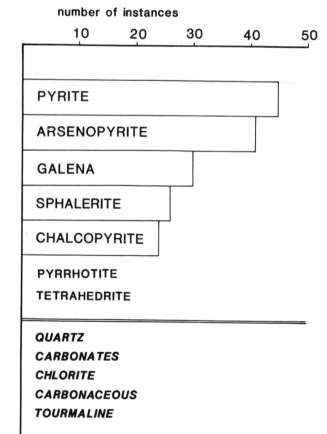

Figure 1. *Minerals intergrown with gold ores. Frequency recorded from 115 gold camps world wide (Schwartz 1944). Frequencies for pyrrhotite and tetrahedrite and gangue minerals (below line) are not plotted.*

Figure 2. *Auriferous pyrites from Carlin Mine, Nevada. (The spheroidal aggregates of pyrite assay best for gold, euhedral crystals give lowest, and the rims intermediate values (Wells and Mullens 1973; Hausen 1981).*

GRAIN SIZE OF GOLD PARTICLES

This grain size of gold particles in gold ores is important to their processing and economic success. In 1937 Haycock studied the sizes of gold particles from 50 Canadian ores; the source deposits were all producers or potential producers at that time.

Figure 4 plots Haycock's results on a graph of grain size in microns (μm) against percentage of grain size. The macroscopic and microscopic fields are marked to speed size comparisons.

Haycock observed that 75 percent of his total sample of visible grains fall into the microscopic range (between 0.1 and 100 μm); the most common size range of particles was 40-50 μm. He reasoned from the shape of the curves that submicroscopic gold (< 0.1 μm) either in the collodial or solid solution size range was of comparatively slight importance.

Since then new instrumentation has lowered the visible limits. Joralemon (1951), working at the Getchell mine in Nevada, showed a smooth decrease in grain size from the macroscopic down to the lowest microscopic limits. Joralemon's data have been replotted and are also shown on Figure 4. The original diagrams showed that over 43 percent of the total grains lay at the lower limits of the microscopic field. Joralemon concluded, from differences calculated between the visible gold and the assay values, that significant submicroscopic gold must be present.

clude quartz, carbonates, carbonaceous materials and the silicate minerals, chlorite and tourmaline.

The examples quoted by Schwartz show textures of intergrowth between gold and the sulphides at scales down to the microscopic. Russian literature on the Darasun goldfield (Sakharova 1969) shows that arsenopyrite, pyrite, pyrrhotite and chalcopyrite are the chief sulphide hosts, with the highest gold values found in arsenopyrite and pyrite. Other examples can be quoted: at the Carlin mine in Nevada, pyrite with minor sphalerite and chalcopyrite host gold; at the Cortez mine the hosts are pyrite and arsenopyrite (Wells and Mullens 1973).

Commonly, these ores show several generations of sulphide minerals; the Darasun ores have multiple phases of pyrrhotite, chalcopyrite and pyrite. This phenomenon is frequently recorded for pyrite and arsenopyrite; it can be seen in pyrite from the Carlin ores (Figure 2) and is shown in Figure 3 by the pyritic ores of the Agnico-Eagle Mine in northwestern Quebec.

Each of these examples shows three generations of pyrite, with characteristically differing form and gold values. At Agnico-Eagle, the highest values occur where gold attaches to fine-grained pyrite grains < 50 μm across; a coarser poikilitic type, in grains 200-300 μm across, is barren; 1 mm crystals of euhedral pyrite carry gold; but the large pyrite nodules, which occur with graphite in the cap rock to the ore body, are seemingly without gold values (Barnett *et al.*, in press).

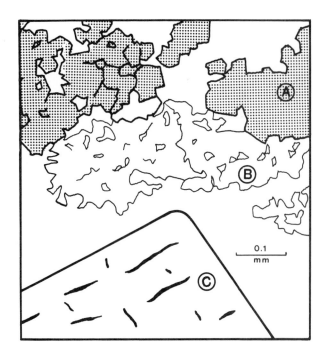

Figure 3. *Pyrite associated with gold, Agnico-Eagle Mine, Joutel, Quebec. Highest gold values are associated with phase A, C carries lesser gold values; B contains no visible gold (Barnett et al. in press).*

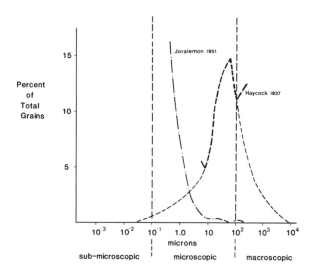

Figure 4. *Size ranges of gold particles, Canadian ores (Haycock 1937), Getchell ores (Joralemon 1951).*

Since then, as techniques improved, gold has been searched for at finer and finer scales within sulphide minerals. Hausen (1981) estimated that the resolution of the SEM-Autoscan U-1, using carbon-coated samples, is 200 angstroms (0.02 μm). He examined pyrite assaying up to 1 ounce Au per ton but failed to see particulate gold. Under the electron microscope, Russian workers (Gureyev *et al.* 1969) found submicroscopic inclusions of gold in pyrite.

SUBMICROSCOPIC GOLD CONTENT OF SULPHIDES

The content of submicroscopic gold has been plotted for examples of the two most common host minerals pyrite and arsenopyrite. The graph (Figure 5) shows a log scale in ppm gold against a listing of localities with a median line of 1 ounce per ton (30.61 ppm).

Values range from 2500 ppm gold in arsenopyrite and 1500-700 ppm in different generations of pyrite in concentrates from oxidized ores at the Carlin mine (Wells and Mullens 1973); through 765 ppm and > 1010 ppm, in pyrite and arsenopyrite respectively, found in the Fijian deposits (Stillwell and Edwards 1946); 0.6-0.9 ppm in pyrite from Queensland (McPheat *et al.* 1969); 23.9-2515 ppm in pyrite from the Transbaikal (Gureyev *et al.* 1969); < 1.64 ppm in pyrite from the Mindyak ores (Sorokin and

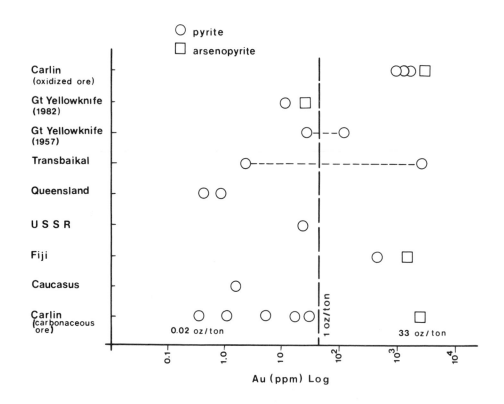

Figure 5. *Content of submicroscopic gold in pyrite, arsenopyrite from selected localities.*

Lomakin 1971); to a range of 31 to 107 ppm in pyrite ores from Giant Yellowknife (Coleman 1957). More recent data, from the carbonaceous ores at Carlin, show gold values in pyrite of 0.52-33.06 ppm (Hausen 1981).

The high values, of more than 30 ounces gold per ton, which can be contained in these two sulphides are important; recent development of dressing processes such as Carlin's "double oxidation" means that in some cases ores assaying as low as 0.05 ounces per ton can be treatable at an acceptable rate of return (Guay 1980).A mechanism by which gold can be invisibly in-cluded in sulphides, above the limits of solid solubility, is suggested by the work of Bancroft and Jean (1982). In experimental studies they observed native gold deposit-ing at room temperature on pyrite in thin layers.

GOLD DISSOLVED IN SULPHIDES

In synthetic systems gold is more soluble in arsenopyrite than in pyrite. Recent ion probe measurements on Giant Yellowknife ores (Falconbridge Metallurgical Laborator-ies, Thornhill, Ontario, personal communication, 1982)

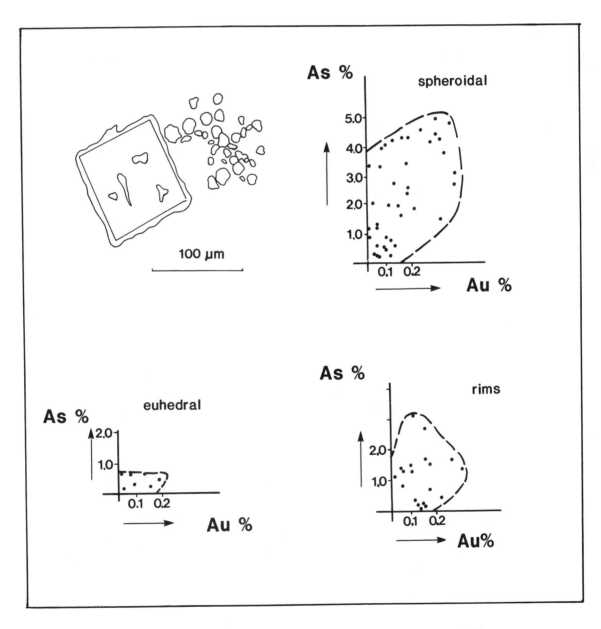

Figure 6. *Mutual variation of gold, arsenic in pyrite, Carlin, Nevada (Wells and Mullens 1973)*

show that pyrite may contain up to 10 ppm gold and arsenopyrite, 30 ppm gold in solid solution.

There are also observations from several sources which indicate that an increase in arsenic content of the pyrite lattice also increases the solubility for gold. This relationship is described from the Russian ores of Mindyak (Sorokin and Lomakin 1971), and from work at Carlin (Wells and Mullens 1973); it appears indirectly in references from the Witwatersrand (Saager and Mihalik 1967).

The arsenian pyrite of the Rand is softer, more porous and more easily oxidized than normal pyrite. Saager and Mihalik linked these features to strain in the pyrite lattice. Figure 6 is adapted from data by Wells and Mullens (1973) and Hausen (1981). From the small graphs it is evident that the gold content rises sympathetically with the arsenic content: differing values attach to generations of pyrite, distinct in form, size and texture.

The diagram shows that small framboidal pyrites, up to 10 μm across, have greater values of both gold and arsenic than coarser, euhedral pyrite (10-100 μm across) or late rims around the euhedral pyrite. Hausen reports that different grain sizes, pore diameters and surface areas influence the mineral dressing characteristics of the pyrites making them of different value economically.

These visible changes in pyrite, produced by lattice characteristics, may be useful tools for the field geologist. It is possible that pyrites which tarnish easily, are friable, or of particular form or colour may be preferentially gold-bearing. Data for Ontario are being collected for study by the Ontario Geological Survey.

GOLD IN SILICATE MINERALS

The phenomenon of substitution by gold in mineral lattices, so important in sulphides, is not significant in silicate minerals; substitution of less than 5 ppb may occur in iron-bearing species.

However, the association of gold intergrowths with silicate minerals is already apparent from Schwartz's data, plotted in Figure 1. Reports from deposits such as Silverstack (Guha *et al.* 1982) and Thomson Bousquet (Valliant and Hutchinson 1982; Valliant *et al.* 1982) in Quebec point directly to a different and significant mode of association between gold and layer lattice minerals.

These deposits show grains of free gold and pyrite only 10-20 μm in diameter intergrown along the cleavage planes or grain boundaries of sericite, muscovite, chlorite, carbonate and quartz. The fabric of silicate minerals enclosing the gold is coarser, thereby disguising the ore minerals.

Examples of this kind are important because they lie outside the normal expectations for gold. These deposits evoke the Carlin type in that the gold is largely invisible, the sulphide phases are microscopic or very small, and, moreover, the host rock offers few clues that it should be assayed.

EXAMPLES OF SILICATE MINERALS INTERGROWN WITH MICROSCOPIC GOLD ORES

Mine Doyon (Silverstack), Thompson Bousquet and the Agnico-Eagle Mine, all in Quebec, illustrate gold associated largely with silicate minerals as intergrowths.

1. At Silverstack (Guha *et al.* 1982) one type of orebody seen in the No. 1 zone, shows grains of free gold and pyrite, 10-20 μm across, intergrown along cleavage planes or grain boundaries of a coarser sericite-muscovite-quartz fabric. The quartz grains contain minute fluid inclusions less than 2 μm across. The authors called this "matrix" gold.

In this setting, gold values vary with pyrite content of the host; the orebody shows a halo in which pyrite content is 10-25 percent within a stratabound sericite-rich layer. In detail, fine pyrite grains are aggregated to form streaks up to 2 cm long, lying in the foliation planes. The pyrite content averages 2-5 percent but may rise to 30 percent. The presence of free gold suggests that if a causal relationship exists between the two minerals, it is different from the mineralogical control seen in the Carlin ores: at Carlin, pyrite encloses most of the gold, therefore as pyrite varies, so do the gold values. Another setting for gold at Mine Doyon, named "veinlet" type by the authors, is seen in the No. 2 zone orebody. Pyrite is again the principal sulphide, and chalcopyrite and several tellurides occur with free gold, both in the matrix of silicate minerals and in tiny discordant veinlets, whose gangue minerals are quartz, carbonate, and chlorite. Pyrite and gold are coarser grained in this ore type; gold grains range from 40-200 μm across; but the majority are still microscopic with a population maximum at 125 μm. Fluid inclusions 5-10 μm across are seen in the vein quartz.

The authors interpreted these ore types as different in age: the matrix gold reflects an initial concentration of gold, and the veinlet type, enrichment and re-concentration. The final grades average 0.19 ounces per ton.

2. Similar relationships were described by Valliant *et al.* (1982) and Valliant and Hutchinson (1982) for the gold deposits at Bousquet which lies immediately to the east of Mine Doyon; the authors compared Mines Doyon No. 1 zone with the Bousquet No. 3 lens.

Their description highlights other geological patterns: the orebodies are stacked clusters of stratabound lenses; assay boundaries define an average 400-500 m length within the foliation plane and a width of 4-30 m; the dip dimension in the foliation plane is not specified. Quartz, pyrite, sericite and graphite increase upwards to the main ore zone; in particular graphite and pyrite increase into the ore zone both laterally and vertically; the orebody of 50-70 percent massive pyrite is capped by 10 cm of graphitic shale, bearing 15-20 percent pyrite as nodules 0.3-1.5 cm in diameter. The base of the ore zone is marked by a layer with 1-12 percent manganiferous garnet.

Mineralogical variations are similar to those at Mine Doyon; in addition to the pyrite nodules in the graphite caprock, several grain sizes of gold and pyrite are present. Minor gold is visible in discordant veins of coarser quartz in the ore zone, but the principal ores are microscopic; gold is seen as native metal, in grains up to 5 μm across, within or adjacent to quartz and pyrite, 50-100 μm, or 200-1000 μm across. The enclosing fabric of silicate minerals (20-30 μm across) contains quartz, albite, sericite, carbonate and epidote.

Gold content increases as the pyrite content rises. Averages grades in No. 3 lens are 0.115 to 0.241 ounces per ton; the No. 5 zone grades 0.06 ounces per ton.

Tellurides, minor chalcopyrite, tetrahedrite, sphalerite and argentiferous galena are recorded. Valliant *et al.* (1982) did not distinguish the "matrix" and "veinlet" types of gold, which at Mine Doyon show distinctive associated gangue minerals.

3. Agnico-Eagle Mine at Joutel is a third example of pyritic gold ores. Its average grade is 0.23 ounces of gold per ton. It is described by Barnett *et al.*(in press).

The deposit consists of a stratabound pair of lenses, pinched near the centre; the east end is chloritic. Fine-grained siliceous rocks, darkened by carbonaceous material, are interbanded with layered pyritic horizons. The deposit is capped by carbonaceous schist containing bands and nodules of pyrite.

Once again several grain sizes of pyrite and gold are apparent. Figure 3 shows two generations of pyrite: a fine euhedral variety, in grains up to 100 μm across, is the principal ore sulphide. The gold grains associated with this form of pyrite average 4-5 μm across; almost exclusively, they abut or are enclosed by pyrite grains. In the ore zone, this type of pyrite varies from 30 to 70 percent by volume of the rock; it is layered and separate from other types; gold values rise with the content of euhedral pyrite. A second type of pyrite, seen in Figure 3, forms poikilitic aggregates which bear no visible gold. However, gold in another form, as minute veinlets discordant to pyrite, pyrrhotite or at silicate mineral boundaries, may reach 7-8 μm in grain size.

There are, in addition, coarse euhedral pyrites (> 1 cm across), which are gold bearing, found in the chloritic zone of the deposit. In the graphitic cap rock, nodular spheroids of pyrite 2-5 cm across are developed; these are apparently barren.

GRAIN SIZE IN PYRITIC ORES

Data on grain sizes from these three deposits are summarized in Figure 7; the meridian at 100 μm marks the lower macroscopic limit. Related sizes of gold and pyrite are looped together on the diagram.

The descriptions above show that the principal ore phases are usually the finest grained; the figure shows that these grain sizes are at or below the macroscopic limit.

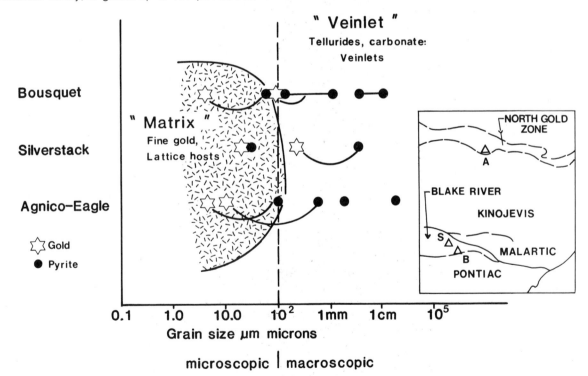

Figure 7. *Grain size of gold, pyrite in Quebec pyritic ores. Geological sketch compiled from Goldie (1982), Latulippe (1982), and Valliant and Hutchinson (1982).*

General characteristics of this fine (matrix) type are that gold varies with pyrite; that pyrite and gold show strikingly patterned variations with graphite, of these a thick graphite caprock with nodular pyrite is notable; that the host minerals are layer-lattice, often silicate, minerals; and that the geological patterns are conformable and stratabound. A different, sometimes later, generation of coarse-grained gold with pyrite is seen as discordant veinlets whose mineralogy includes tellurides, quartz and carbonate, and may include base metal sulphides.

GEOLOGICAL SETTING OF "MATRIX" PYRITIC ORES

Many lines of reasoning suggest that this association of fine matrix gold with pyrite in graphitic quartz-sericite schists is a still recognizable sedimentary assemblage which has undergone diagenesis and low-rank metamorphic alteration. The stratabound position of the orebodies and patterns of lithological variations around them are consistent with the idea.

New petrological work for Agnico-Eagle (Springer, unpublished data) shows detrital grains of rutile and zircon, and an overall fabric of sedimentary appearance. There are mineralogical textures which closely compare with those seen in pyritic base metal deposits of undoubted sedimentary origin. Such features include complex resorption patterns in the fine-grained euhedral pyrite (so called by Barnett *et al.* in press), diffuse margins of ilmenite seen around rutile cores, and syngenetic growth of hematite with pyrite.

Good comparisons of these textures can be made with the Russian "Kies" ores (Schadlun 1972), or with material illustrated for the Katangan ores by Bartholomé *et al.* (1972), or with the well-known Kupferschiefer (Jung and Knitzschke 1975).

If the reasoning is correct, these are large sedimentary accumulations of gold, grading up to 0.25 ounces per ton which differ distinctly from Archean lode gold deposits. Their size and amenability to open pitting obviously make them important. Equally, it becomes important to envisage a mechanism which can transport, concentrate, and fix such a volume of gold in an environment now marked by graphite and pyrite.

GOLD ASSOCIATED WITH CARBONACEOUS MATERIALS

Carbon has a known capacity to scavenge metals from aqueous environments. In commercial ore recovery, carbon is commonly used to extract gold selectively from cyanide solutions (MacDougall and Hancock 1981).

This process makes particular use of a general ability of carbon to adsorb: the method is widely used for removing or partitioning materials from gases or aqueous solution. But, as gold salts are readily reduced to the native metal by carbon, and the salts of silver and base metals are more soluble, it is possible to separate gold from other metals quite easily.

ACTIVATED CARBON AND GRAPHITE

The process of carbon adsorption builds upon a natural phenomenon: cellular organic material commonly displays an inherent adsorptive capacity which is seen equally in dead or living tissue (Tsezos and Volesky 1981, Chiu 1972)). In practice, organic matter is used as a starting substance because it is cheap and easily obtainable. But organic origin is not necessary for success; even fabricated materials like polystyrene possess the adsorptive capacity if they are rendered active by proper treatment. Gold-plated polystyrene beads are illustrated by McDougall and Hancock (1980).

In geological terms it is important to stress that activated carbons adsorb whether or not they are organic; life on earth is not a prerequisite for this mechanism. In commercial practice the adsorptive capacity of carbon is enhanced by controlled charring to increase pore size and internal surface area. In this state, the carbon lattice is semi-ordered with a layer spacing wider than true graphite; it shows a roughly planar structure of thin graphite-like platelets, only a few carbon atoms thick, arranged to form the walls of open cavities. The hexagonal carbon rings which characterize true graphite are split apart and randomly oriented, giving many broken edges at which reaction is possible.

As the temperature of charring is increased the adsorptive character of the carbon changes and finally, when the ordered lattice of a true graphite is produced by the temperature rise, the capacity to adsorb disappears. The same transition can reasonably be expected in geological systems.

GENERAL ASSOCIATIONS OF GOLD AND CARBON

In post-Cambrian rocks of many ages assays up to 2.5 ppm gold are recorded (Leutwein 1952) and modern black oozes from the Norway coast contain gold in the range 0.7 to 2.5 ppm (Leutwein 1951). In these examples and for many other black shales, the gold is specifically associated with organic carbon, and is bound to it by surface adsorption. In other geological settings the presence of the two elements together implies neither a relationship nor that carbon has fixed or concentrated gold.

The Carlin ores occur in metasediments which average 0.1 percent organic carbon. It has been suggested (Radtke and Scheiner 1970) that the sedimentary carbon was a source which permitted secondary epithermal concentration, or that the carbonaceous horizons fixed gold from circulating solutions. Wells and Mullens (1973) showed no correlation of gold with carbonaceous material. Later workers, amongst them Radtke *et al.* (1980) and Dickson *et al.* (1979), concluded from isotope studies that the patterns suggest leaching of introduced components, amongst them gold and organic materials from Paleozoic sediments below the gold deposits. The hydrothermal fluids rose up steeply-dipping faults and deposited their dissolved constituents in permeable carbonates as pressure and temperature fell.

In the Witwatersrand three associations of gold and carbon occur, of which only one is applicable to pyritic gold deposits in Quebec. The gold ores of the Rand are largely sheet-like placer concentrates formed by water-sorting of the heavy minerals on broad outwash plains. Firstly local accumulations of grain gold are seen where particles were trapped by the roughened surfaces of mat-like algae which grew on the sand flats. The decayed mats are now carbonized; thus gold is associated with carbonaceous layers (Figure 8b). Secondly, the pulverized remains of the algae collected in depressions and ripple hollows in the sandy surface. Heavy minerals, amongst them gold, also settled in these quiet conditions. Hence high concentrations of Au-U are accompanied by concentration of carbon, although the reverse is not necessarily true (Minter 1981).

The third association is seen in distal parts of this environment of sedimentation. Towards the margins, finer carbon debris deposits are mixed with clay materials. In this type of environment Simpson and Bowles (1981) and Schidlowski (1981) have suggested that the gold was deposited from solution by the action of organic matter (Figure 8). They have used textural evidence, supported by

microprobe studies, to show that, in addition to detrital gold and uranium, these elements were precipitated from solution by finely-broken organic debris. Subsequent metamorphism has recrystallized the gold, but it can be distinguished from the detrital population because the grains do not match in hydraulic equivalence with the characteristics of the other heavy minerals.

A further detailed study (Zumberge *et al.* 1978) showed gold grains with shapes that do not suggest a detrital origin. The authors showed new growth of gold at boundaries between clay particles and organic matter. They suggested it has resulted from recrystallization of colloidal or organically bound gold, stabilized on the surfaces of clay minerals or carbonaceous debris and transported by water at low temperatures.

A similar conclusion was reached by Reimer (in press), who has calculated a mass balance for gold in the Rand. He observed that the grain gold available from typical "greenstone" belts would supply only about 15 percent of that seen in the Witwatersrand deposits. He proposes that far greater amounts are transported as colloidal suspensions or in solution. The gold has then recrystallized diagenetically, but its final outward form com-

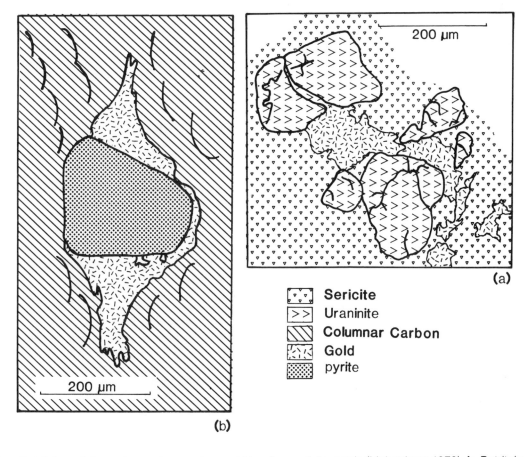

Legend:
- Sericite
- Uraninite
- Columnar Carbon
- Gold
- pyrite

Figure 8. a. *Detrital uraninite grains and secondary gold in a fine sericite matrix (Liebenberg 1970).* **b.** *Detrital pyrite with secondary gold overgrowths enclosed in the carbonized remnants of algal matter (Schidlowski 1981).*

monly appears detrital because of subsequent transport and flood winnowing.

MODERN EXAMPLES

In modern systems there are signs that a process of concentration by adsorption onto carbon and clay minerals can proceed, and on a large scale. Bensusan (1942) reported a huge concentration of colloidal gold in 120 square miles of mangrove swamp, averaging 25 feet deep and grading 0.03 ounces Au per ton. The gold was invisible then and impossible to recover. It is still only the grade of mine tailings, but nonetheless the concentration is significant.

A more rigorous examination of the role of organic carbon has been made for the Black Sea sediments (Hirst 1974; Volkov and Fomina 1974). There are few data for gold itself but the principles of the findings may be carefully extrapolated.

Several authors have shown how carbon and sulphur, principally as pyrite, direct the concentration and partitioning of metals. The physical conditions of deposition show complex but understandable patterns of influence on both the mineral species formed and their content of trace elements. Russian work concluded that how an element was transported — either as a colloid or in solution — determined its behaviour and subsequent availability in diagenesis. Suspensions settle rapidly into the silt fraction, whereas dissolved elements are swept farther away and thus a physical separation occurs. In the case of gold, the behaviour documented by Boyle (1979) suggests that the suspended colloidal form is more common and might therefore be expected in the silt fraction.

GOLD CONCENTRATION BY GRAPHITE IN THE PRECAMBRIAN

If a similar mechanism of gold concentration by carbonaceous matter and clay minerals as a function of their surface properties is to be invoked for the Precambrian, the basic requirements for the reaction must be met. Namely, there must be evidence for materials with the proper surface characteristics.

In the Quebec pyritic gold deposits it is reasonable to suggest that the muscovite-sericite chlorite assemblages now seen in part represent the clay mineral fraction.

From Agnico-Eagle (Barnett *et al.* 1983) diffraction patterns show that a disordered carbon is present. The observation is confirmed (Springer, unpublished data) by recent petrographic examination. The majority of "graphite" at Agnico-Eagle is a carbonaceous substance, although graphite is uncommonly present, separate from the carbon. Data from the Hoyle Pond gold occurrence (Downes and Hodges 1982, and personal communication) also show that the fine-grained carbon present here is not graphite; on the basis of chromatographic patterns, the compounds present resemble organic polymers. By recalculation it can be shown that 22 percent of the carbon may be organic in origin.

Elsewhere in the Superior Province there are signs that much of what is termed graphite is still unordered active carbon. This can be inferred from the behaviour of carbon in the mineral dressing of Archean gold ores: Agnico Eagle, where unordered carbon has been documented, uses diesel fuel to blank off the adsorptive capacity of the carbon (McQuiston and Shoemaker 1980); in this setting, adsorption is undesirable. The Kerr-Addison Mine (McQuiston and Shoemaker 1975) and Renabie Mine (G. Bennett, Resident Geologist, Ministry of Natural Resources, Sault Ste. Marie, personal communication) use kerosene to counter the problem; the ores from the former Hollinger Mine (W.A. Jones, Hollinger Mines Limited, personal communication, 1973) required remedial care for active carbon.

The former McIntyre Mine and the Coniaurum property, both strike extensions of the Hollinger, include "graphite" horizons (Furse 1948, and mine plans McIntyre, Coniaurum). The gold ores at Owl Creek (M. Cherry, Ontario Geological Survey, personal communication, 1982) are closely adjacent to banded "graphite" horizons.

Such associations of gold with active carbon have not been properly documented, but it seems probable that it is a common and widespread feature. "Graphitic" rocks merit careful consideration as collectors of gold. Results from Hoyle Pond (Downes and Hodges, personal communication, 1983) suggest that concentrations of gold (up to 200 ppb) may be found in graphitic argillite, and that, in discordant secondary alteration zones, values rise to 15 ppm with a corresponding rise of carbon content to a range of 0.01 to 0.3 percent.

CONCLUSIONS

Interesting empirical conclusions arise from this discussion:

1. Fine-grained mica schists can host up to 0.25 ounces Au per ton in microscopic form.
2. Both the gold and the sulphides may be invisible in the field.
3. Such ores are commonly closely associated with carbonaceous or graphite schist which can therefore be used as a marker.
4. Pyrite is the commonest natural associate of gold; it may appear in several generations, each of which must be carefully examined for gold.
5. Invisible gold in pyrite or arsenopyrite may give assays > 30 ounces Au per ton from the concentrate.
6. Some Precambrian "graphite" is active carbon; it may have influenced concentration and fixing of gold during ore formation.

These observations suggest that the many conductive horizons which were drilled in search of volcanogenic base metal deposits may have unsuspected potential: Graphite-bearing ores should be carefully examined for fine gold or finely dispersed auriferous sulphides.

REFERENCES

Bancroft, G.M. and Jean, G.
1982: Gold Deposition at Low Temperature on Sulphide Minerals; Nature, Vol. 298, August 1982.

Barnett, E.S., Hutchinson, R.W., Adamcik, A., and Barnett, R.
in press: Geology of the Agnico Eagle Gold Mine, Quebec; in Precambrian Sulphide Deposits, H.S. Robinson Memorial Volume, edited by R.W. Hutchinson, C.D. Spence, and J.M. Franklin. Geological Association of Canada, Special Paper 25.

Bartholomé, P., Evrard, P., Katekesha, F., Lopez-Ruiz, J. and Ngongo, M.
1972: Diagenetic ore-forming processes at Kamoto, Katanga, Republic of the Congo; p. 21-41 in Ores in Sediments, edited by G.C. Amstutz and A.J. Bernard, International Union of Geological Sciences, Series A, Number 3. Springer Verlag, Berlin, 350 p.

Bensusan, A.J.
1942: Two Unusual Gold Occurrences; Chemical Engineering Mining Review, Volume 34, No. 402, p.178.

Boyle, R.W.
1979: The Geochemistry of Gold and Its Deposits; Geological Survey of Canada, Bulletin 280, 584p.

Chiu, Y.S.
1972: Recovery of Heavy Metals by Microbes; Unpublished Ph.D. Thesis, University of Western Ontario, London, Ontario.

Coleman, L.E.
1957: Mineralogy of the Giant Yellowknife Gold Mine, Northwest Territories; Economic Geology, Vol. 52, p.400-425.

Dickson, F.W., Rye, R.O. and Radtke, A.S.
1979: The Carlin Gold Deposit as a Product of Rock Water Interactions; p.101-108 in International Association on the Genesis of Ore Deposits, Fifth Quadrennial Symposium Proceedings, Volume 2, 212p, edited by J.D. Ridge, Nevada Bureau of Mines and Geology, Report 33, Reno, Nevada.

Downes, M.J. and Hodges, D.J.
1982: A Free Carbon and Carbonate-bearing Alteration Zone Associated with the Hoyle Pond Gold Occurence, Ontario, Canada (Abstract); p. 27 in Gold '82, Geological Society of Zimbabwe, May 1982.

Furse, G.D.
1948: McIntyre Mine; p. 482-496 in Structural Geology of Canadian Ore Deposits, Canadian Institute of Mining and Metallurgy, Geology Division, Jubilee Volume, p.482-496.

Goldie, R.
1982: Lithostratigraphy and the Distribution of Gold in the South-central Abitibi Belt of Quebec; in Geology of Canadian Gold Deposits, edited by W. Petruk, and R.W. Hodder, Canadian Institute of Mining and Metallurgy, Special Volume 24.

Guay, W.J.
1980: How Carlin Treats Gold Ores by Double Oxidation; World Mining, March 1980, p.47-49.

Guha, J., Gauthier, A., Vallee, M., Descarreaux, J., and Lange-Brard, F.
1982: Gold Mineralization Patterns at the Doyon Mine (Silverstack), Bousquet, Quebec; p.15-26 in Geology of Canadian Gold Deposits, edited by W. Petruk, and R.W. Hodder, Canadian Institute of Mining and Metallurgy, Special Volume 24.

Gureyev, V.F., Konstantinov, M.M., and Alysheva, E.I.
1969: Ratio of Syngenetic (Finely Divided) and Imposed Gold in Pyrite; Dokl. Akad. Nauk. SSSR, Vol. 181, p.164-166.

Hausen, D.M.
1981: Process Mineralogy of the Auriferous Pyrite Ores at Carlin, Nevada; p. 271-289 in Process Mineralogy, Extractive Metallurgy, Mineral Exploration, Energy Resources: edited by D. M. Hausen and W. C. Park, Conference Proceedings, The Metallurgical Society of American Institute of Mining, Metallurgical and Petroleum Engineers.

Haycock, M.H.
1937: The Role of the Microscope in the Study of Gold Ores; Transactions, Canadian Institute of Mining and Metallurgy, Vol. 40, p.405-414.

Hirst, D.M.
1974: Geochemistry of Sediments from Eleven Black Sea Cores; p.430-456, in Association of American Petroleum Geologists, Memoir 20, edited by Degens, E.T. and Ross, D.A., (see also Branyko, O. and Hunt, J.M., p.575-592.)

Jung, W. and Knitzschke, G.
1975: Kupferschiefer in the German Democratic Republic (GDR) with Special Reference to the Kupferschiefer Deposit in the Southeastern Harz Foreland; p.253-406 in Handbook of Strata-bound and Stratiform Ore Deposits, Vol.6, edited by K.H. Wolf. Elsevir Amsterdam.

Joralemon, P.
1951: The Occurrence of Gold at the Getchell Mine, Nevada; Economic Geology, Vol. 46, p.267-310.

Khetagurov. G.V.
1969: Distribution of Silver and Gold in Ores, Minerals, and Enrichment Products of the Lead-Zinc Deposits of the Greater Caucasus; Geochemistry International, Vol. 6, p.1070-1077.

Latulippe, M.
1982: An Overview of the Geology of Gold Occurrences and Developments in Northwestern Quebec p. 9-14, in Geology of Canadian Gold Deposits, edited by W. Petruk, and R.W. Hodder, Canadian Institute of Mining and Metallurgy, Special Volume 24.

Leutwein, F.
1951: On the Occurrence of Gold in Thuringian Alum and Siliceous Shales; Hallesches Jahrb. Fuer Mitteldeutsche Erdgeschichte, Volume 1, No. 2, p.82-85. (Abstract in Selected Annotated Bibliography of Minor Element Content for Marine Black Shales and Related Sedimentary Rocks 1930-65; p. 49 edited by E.B. Tourtelot, United States Geological Survey Bulletin 1293, published 1970.)
1952: The Occurrence of Trace Metals in Organic Sediments; Acta. Geol. Volume 1, No. 1-4. (p.143-157 in Selected Annotated Bibliography of Minor Element Content for Marine Black Shales and Related Sedimentary Rocks 1930-65; edited by E.B. Tourtelot, United States Geological Survey Bulletin 1293, published 1970.)

Liebenberg, W.R.
1970: Mineralogy and the Metallurgist; Minerals Science and Engineering, Volume 2, No. 46, p.3-23.

McPheat, I.W., Gooden, J.E.A., and Townend, R.
1969: Submicroscopic Gold in a Pyrite Concentrate; Proceedings Australasian Institute of Mining and Metallurgy, Vol. 231, p.19-25.

McDougall, G.J. and Hancock, R.D.
1980: Activated Carbons and Gold - A Literature Survey; Minerals Science and Engineering, Volume 12, No. 2, April 1980, p.85-99.
1981: Gold Complexes and Activated Carbon; Gold Bulletin, Volume No. 4, p.138-153.

McQuiston, F.W. Jr and Shoemaker, R.S.
1975: Kerr Addison Mines Ltd; p. 103-107 in Gold and Silver Cyanidation Plant Practice, American Institute of Mining, Metallurgical and Petroleum Engineers, Monograph, Volume 1.
1980: Agnico Eagle Mines Limited, Joutel, Quebec, Canada; p. 139-144 in Gold and Silver Cyanidation Plant Practice, Volume 2, American Institute of Mining, Metallurgical and Petroleum Engineers p.139-144.

Minter, W.E.L.
1981: The Distribution and Sedimentary Arrangement of Carbon in South African Proterozoic Placer Deposits; p. P1-P4 in Genesis of Uranium and Gold-Bearing Precambrian Quartz-Pebble Conglomerates, edited by F.C. Armstrong, Proceedings of a Workshop, October 13-15 1975, Golden, Colorado, United States Geological Survey, Professional Paper 1161-A-BB.

Radtke, A.S., Rye, R.O. and Dickson, F.W.
1980: Geology and Stable Isotope Studies of the Carlin Gold Deposits, Nevada; Economic Geology, Volume 75, p.641-672.

Radtke, A.S. and Scheiner, B.J.
1970: Studies of Hydrothermal Gold Deposition (I) Carlin Gold Deposits, Nevada, The Role of Carbonaceous Materials in Gold Deposition; Economic Geology, Volume 65, p.87-102.

Reimer, T.O.
in press: Implications of Geochemical Mass Balance Calculations for the Origin of Gold in the Witwatersrand Conglomerates: A Non-Monetarian View of the Archean Gold Budget.

Saager, R., and Mihalik, P.
1967: Two Varieties of Pyrites from the Basal Reef of the Witwatersrand System; Economic Geology, Volume 62, No. 5, p.719-731.

Sakharova, M.S.
1969: Mineralogy of Darasun Goldfield in Eastern Zabaykal'ye; International Geological Review, Volume No. 11, p.45-59.

Schadlun, T.N.
1972: On the Origin of "Kies" Ore and the Pb-Zn Deposits in Sediments; p. 267-273 in Ores In Sediments, edited by G.C. Amstutz, and A.J. Bernard, International Union of Geological Sciences, Series A, Number 3. Springer Verlag, Berlin, 350p.

Schwartz, G.M.
1944: The Host Minerals of Native Gold; Economic Geology, Vol. 39, p.371411.

Schidlowski, M.
1981: Uraniferous Constituents of the Witwatersrand Conglomerates: Ore, Microscopic Observations and Implications for the Witwatersrand Metallogeny; p. P1-P4 in Genesis of Uranium- and Gold-bearing Precambrian Quartz-Pebble Conglomerates, edited by Armstrong, Proceedings of a Workshop October 13-15 1975, Golden, Colorado, United States Geological Survey, Professional Paper 1161-A-BB.

Simpson, P.R. and Bowles, J.F.W.
1981: Uranium Mineralization of the Witwatersrand and Dominion Reef Systems p. R1-R26 in Genesis of Uranium- and Gold-bearing Precambrian QuartzPebble Conglomerates, edited by F.C. Armstrong, Proceedings of a Workshop October, 13-15 1975, Golden, Colorado, United States Geological Survey Professional Paper 1161-A-BB.

Sorokin, V.N., and Lomakin, G.V.
1971: Auriferous Mineral Associations of the Mindyak Ore Field; International Geology Review, Vol. 13, p.752-759.

Stillwell, F.L., and Edwards, A.B.
1946: An Occurrence of Sub-microscopic Gold in the Dolphin East Lode, Fiji; Proceedings Australasian Institute of Mining and Metallurgy, Vol. 141, p.31-46.

Tsezos, M., and Volesky, B.
1981: Biosorption of Uranium and Thorium; Biotechnical and Bioengineering, Volume 23, p.583-604.

Valliant, R.I., and Hutchinson, R.W.
1982: Stratigraphic Distribution and Genesis of Gold Deposits, Bousquet Region, Northwestern Quebec p.27-40 in Geology of Canadian Gold Deposits, edited by W. Petruk and R.W. Hodder, Canadian Institute of Mining and Metallurgy, Special Volume 24, 286p.

Valliant, R.I., and Mongeau, C., and Doucet, R.
1982: The Bousquet Pyritic Gold Deposits, Bousquet Region, Quebec: Descriptive Geology and Preliminary Interpretations on Genesis p.41-49 in Geology of Canadian Gold Deposits, edited by W. Petruk and R.W. Hodder, Canadian Institute of Mining and Metallurgy, Special Volume 24, 286p.

Volkov, I.I. and Fomina, L.S.
1974: Influence of Organic Material and Processes of Sulphide Formation on Distribution of Some Trace Elements; p. 456-477 in Deep-water Sediments of Black Sea in The Black Sea - Geology, Chemistry and Biology, edited by E.T. Degens and D.A. Ross, Association of American Petroleum Geologists, Memoir 20, 633p.

Wells, J.D. and Mullens, T.E.
1973: Gold-bearing Arsenian Pyrite Determined by Microprobe Analysis, Cortez and Carlin Gold Mines, Nevada; Economic Geology, Vol. 68, p.187-201.

Zumberge, J.E., Sigelo, A.C. and Nagy, B.
1978: Molecular and Elemental Analyses of the Carbonaceous Matter in the Gold and Uranium Bearing Vaal Reef Carbon Seams, Witwatersrand Sequence; Minerals Science and Engineering, Volume 10, No. 4, p.223-246.

Geochemical Prospecting for Gold in Ontario

John A.C. Fortescue

Geophysics/Geochemistry Section, Ontario Geological Survey, Toronto

ABSTRACT

Geochemical techniques are becoming of increasing importance in prospecting for gold deposits in Ontario. The purpose of this review of the state of the art is to provide readers with a general introduction to the subject so that the content of specific papers on the subject may be brought into scientific focus. To begin with, three major constraints to geochemical prospecting for gold in Ontario are described: (1) geochemistry of gold and gold deposits; (2) Quaternary cover of bedrock gold occurrences; and (3) the problem of sampling gold in surficial materials upon which geochemical surveys are based. Then follows discussion of the history and evolution of geochemical techniques which are used for gold exploration in Ontario and the Canadian Shield today. At the end of the paper, general guidelines are given for the future development of techniques of geochemistry applied to exploration for gold deposits and general conclusions are drawn regarding the present state of the activity.

INTRODUCTION

Geochemical methods have been applied in the search for gold in Ontario for over 30 years but so far no proven scheme has been evolved to solve the problems encountered in the various terrains. Accounts of geochemical prospecting for gold are scattered throughout the literature of mineral exploration with the occasional review article pertinent to the general problem. Hodgson (1982), in a discussion of the discovery of gold deposits in Ontario, noted that 75 percent were found by traditional prospecting methods, 14 percent by drilling or trenching geological targets, 9 percent by drilling geophysical targets and only 2 percent by geochemistry. When one considers the relatively small progress made in geochemical techniques during the past 30 years this suggests that there are more deposits to be found by geochemical methods once the effectiveness of such surveys approaches that of the other, more established, disciplines. As we shall see, geochemistry has a unique contribution to make in the discovery of gold deposits in the glacial terrain of the Canadian Shield.

An example of a gold deposit discovered by reverse circulation drilling is that at Nighthawk Lake 20 miles east of Timmins, Ontario. According to Brown (1982), the deposit was discovered by probing bedrock and sampling basal till material methodically over the area where the glacial overburden thickness is about 250 feet thick. This is clearly a discovery of an gold deposit by geochemical methods of the type described here.

BACKGROUND TO GOLD PROSPECTING IN ONTARIO

Any review of the role of geochemistry in prospecting for gold in Ontario must include three aspects of the problem which may be overlooked in some of the other exploration techniques. These are the geochemistry of gold itself, the relationship between glacial overburden and geochemical prospecting for gold, and the problem of sampling rocks, soils and related materials for their gold content.

GENERAL GEOCHEMISTRY OF GOLD

Boyle (1979) succinctly outlined information on the geochemistry of gold as follows.

Gold is a member of Group 1B of the periodic table, which includes copper, silver and gold. In its chemical reactions gold resembles silver in some respects, but its chemical character is markedly more noble. The principal oxidation states of gold are Au(I)(aurous) and Au(III) (auric). These states are unknown as aquo-ions in solution, the element being present mainly in complexes of the type $[Au(CN)_2]$-, $[AuCl_2]$-, $[Au(OH)_4]$-, and $[AuCl_4]$-. There is only one naturally occuring isotope of gold: ^{197}Au.

In nature gold occurs predominantly in the native state or as a major constituent of various alloys containing mainly silver, copper or platinoid metals. Several gold and gold-silver tellurides are known of which the most common are sylvanite, calaverite, petzite, krennerite and nagyagite. The antimonide, aurostibnite, $AuSb_2$, occurs as a hypogene mineral in some auriferous deposits, and there is also a selenide, fischesserite, Ag_3AuSe_2, and a bismuthide, maldonite, Au_2Bi, which is fairly well differentiated. The principal ore minerals of gold are the native metal, aurostibnite and the various tellurides.

The abundance of gold in the upper lithosphere is about 0.005 ppm, and the Au/Ag ratio is about 0.1. The average gold content of igneous-type rocks in parts per million is — ultrabasic (0.004), gabbro-basalt (0.007), diorite-andesite (0.005) and granite-rhyolite (0.003). The average gold content of sedimentary rocks in parts per million is — sandstone and conglomerate (0.03), normal shale (0.004) and limestone (0.003). Certain graphitic shales, sulphide schists, phosphorites and some types of sandstones and conglomerates may contain up to 2.1 ppm Au or more.

The average gold content of soils is 0.005 ppm, and the average for natural fresh waters is 0.00003 ppm. Sea and ocean waters contain an average of 0.000012 ppm Au. Gold is a trace consituent of many plants and animals. Some coals are slightly enriched in gold with 0.05 to 0.1 ppm Au in the ash.

Gold is won both from deposits mined essentially for the element and as a by-product of the mining and treatment of nickel, copper, zinc, lead and silver ores. The following types of primary deposits, exploited mainly for gold, can be distinguished:

1. Auriferous porphyry dykes, sills and stocks; coarse-grained granitic bodies, aplites and pegmatites.

2. Auriferous skarn-type deposits.
3. Gold-silver and silver-gold veins, stockworks, lodes, mineralized pipes and irregular silicified bodies in fractures, faults, shear zones, sheeted zones and breccia zones essentially in volcanic terranes.
4. Auriferous veins, lodes, sheeted zones and saddle reefs in faults, fractures, bedding plane discontinuities and shears, drag folds, crushed zones and openings on anticlines essentially in sedimentary terranes; also replacement tabular and irregular bodies developed near faults and fractures in chemically favourable beds.
5. Gold-silver and silver-gold veins, lodes, stockworks, silicified zones, etc. in a complex geological environment, comprising sediments, volcanics and igneous or granitized rocks.
6. Disseminated and stockwork gold-silver deposits in igneous, volcanic and sedimentary rocks.
    (a) Disseminated and stockwork gold-silver deposits in igneous bodies.
    (b) Disseminated gold-silver occurrences in volcanic flows and associated volcaniclastic rocks.
    (c) Disseminated gold-silver deposits in volcaniclastic and sedimentary beds: deposits in tuffaceous rocks and iron formations and deposits in chemically favourable sedimentary beds.
7. Gold deposits in quartz-pebble conglomerates and quartzites.

From the viewpoint of exploration geochemistry, gold, unlike many elements, is rare[1] in most rocks although it may occur in significant concentrations in many types of mineral deposits. In general it occurs in three ways: (1) in ores in which it is visible by hand lens or the eye; (2) in ores in which indicator minerals known to contain significant gold may be observed — such as gold tellurides; and (3) in ores where neither the metal, nor indicator minerals may be seen and an assay is required to establish the tenor of the ore. Geochemical prospecting techniques must be effective in all three of these situations. These disadvantages are offset by the importance of indicator elements which occur with certain types of gold deposits. Because the indicator elements may often be more easily detected than the gold, they are of considerable importance in geochemical prospecting. Those most important are As, Ag, Sb, Cu, Pb, Zn, Mo, W and Te.

Hodgson (1982) summarized the mineralogy of 809 mineral deposits and showings in Ontario. He concluded:

The dominant mineralogy of the mineralization is as might be expected: virtually all zones contain quartz, carbonate, and pyrite. There are, however, some minor minerals which show much more limited distribution, and some interesting relationships to the types of rocks which occur in the deposits.

Galena occurs in 14 percent of the deposits and, in 55 percent of these cases, one of the suites of felsic alkalic intrusive rocks is also present, whereas only 40 percent of the entire deposit population contains this rock suite. Molybdenite (9 percent of deposits) and tellurides (2.4 percent) show an even stronger association with the alkalic felsic intrusions; these rocks occur in 64 percent of molybdenite-bearing and 73 percent of telluride-bearing deposits. There is also a strong association of molyb-

denite with quartz porphyritic intrusions; 26 percent of molybdenite-bearing deposits contain these lithologies, whereas only 14 percent of the total deposit population contains them. Tellurides and galena are not, however, preferentially associated with quartz-porphyry intrusions. Tourmaline (5.3 percent of deposits) is strongly associated with quartz porphyry intrusions; 36 percent of deposits with tourmaline also contain these rocks. However, tourmaline is negatively related to the alkalic felsic intrusive suite, which only occurs in 21 percent of the tourmaline-bearing deposits, whereas 40 percent of the deposits in the population contain them. Scheelite, which is reported in only 1.5 percent of the deposit population, also is strongly associated with quartz porphyry intrusions. Arsenopyrite, another supposed common associate of gold, is reported in only 6.3 percent of the deposits. It is negatively correlated with the felsic intrusive suite, and positively correlated with ultramafic volcanic and/or intrusive rocks. Sphalerite, which occurs in 11 percent of deposits shows no obvious positive or negative associations with any of the lithologies.

It is evident that geochemical prospecting for gold deposits in certain areas of Ontario is complicated by the fact that different mineral associations occur within differing environments and thus specific techniques may be required in the search for particular types of deposits. Consequently, very close cooperation between the economic geologist and the exploration geochemist is required at all stages of a prospecting program.

NATURE OF THE GLACIAL COVER

Hodgson (1982) noted that 75 percent of the gold mineralization in Ontario was found by traditional methods of prospecting. Such methods are effective only in areas where the glacial overburden is non-existent, thin, or in patches. In areas where the overburden is thick such methods are not effective. Clearly, to equal the record of direct prospecting methods, the indirect methods, including geochemistry, will have to become more effective and be applied in areas of the Canadian Shield as yet not prospected.

Some idea of complexity of the glacial overburden commonly found in Ontario may be gained from the conceptual models included in Figure 1. The ideal situation for the old-time prospector is depicted in Figure 1a. Benny Hollinger found the Hollinger Mine in this way by seeing gold in outcrop (Townsley 1935). Other prospectors found mines by tracing float back to the source. For example, R. Clark found gold in float at the surface some 250 feet in the down-ice direction from what became the main vein of the Lamaque Mine at Val d'Or, Quebec (Freeman and Ferguson 1973).The relationship of surface mineralized float to the outcrop is also evident on Figure 1a. On Figure 1b a slightly more complicated situation is depicted where the outcrop of the mineralized zone is covered with a single till which, during ice movement has brought boulders to the surface in the down-ice direction from the deposit. In this situation a "boulder fan" would form, of the type described by Dreimanis (1958) from Canada and by Grip (1953) from Scandinavia. Under favourable conditions gold anomalies in subsoil, soil, humus or plant material might be expected in terrain of this type in addition to the location of mineralized bould-

---

[1]The low values for gold in rocks posed the most difficult analytical problems for chemists until about ten years ago when detection limits under 20 ppb became common. (See paper by Riddle in this volume).

ers. A more complicated situation is shown in Figure 1c. In this case the bedrock surface over which the till moved has modified the distribution of float from the mineral deposit at the left of the diagram. The material from the mineral deposit does not occur at the surface and subsoil, soil, humus and biogeochemical prospecting methods might be required to locate the "geochemical anomaly" in the till. If a reverse circulation drill were available several holes would be required to locate the deposit, particularly if mineralization was first detected as a layer relatively high up in the till section. Note that the mineral deposit at the right of the diagram does not produce an anomaly in the till because it is on the down-ice side of the outcrop and is not subjected to scouring by the glacier, but rather, is itself buried by drift. As a consequence, it could be missed by most of the geochemical techniques just described with the possible exception of humus sampling.

The second series of conceptual models (Figure 1d,e,f) involves till and glaciofluvial deposits. In Figure 1d there is the simple situation of glaciofluvial deposits lying on glacially polished bedrock. Under these conditions humus sampling for gold might be effective, although it is doubtful unless the deposit has pre-glacial weathering associated with it. In Figure 1e a layer of till containing boulders with mineralization underlies the layer of glaciofluvial sands. In this case also, a weak anomaly may be expected under favourable conditions in soil and humus or plants. The third example is similar to that in Figure 1e, except that the till layer is thicker and more complicated leading to a weaker geochemical signal in the overlying material.

The third series of conceptual models involves glaciolacustrian (and/or glaciomarine) sediments, glaciofluvial deposits and tills. Figure 1g is typical of the Hudson Bay Lowlands where Holocene peat deposits frequently develop on glaciolacustrian deposits which in turn may overlie glaciofluvial deposits. Under these conditions, locating gold mineralization using orthodox geochemical prospecting techniques is almost impossible and drilling of geological/geophysical anomalies is likely to be more productive. In the second model of the series (Figure 1h)

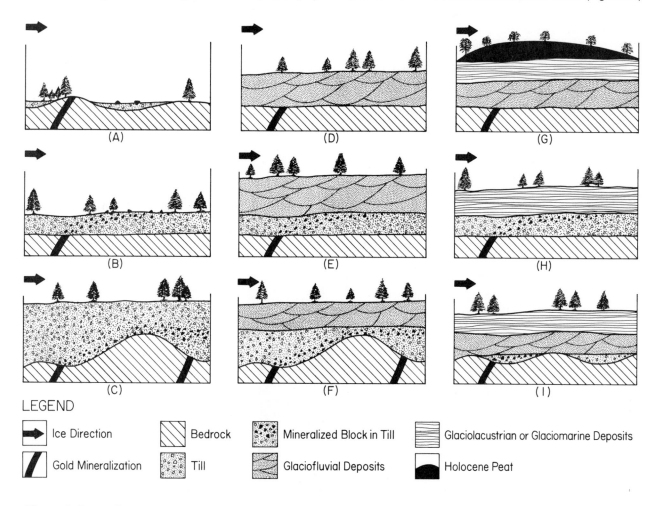

LEGEND

→ Ice Direction   ⊘ Bedrock   ▦ Mineralized Block in Till   ▤ Glaciolacustrian or Glaciomarine Deposits

▞ Gold Mineralization   ⊙ Till   ▨ Glaciofluvial Deposits   ◼ Holocene Peat

Figure 1. *Generalized conceptual model landscape sections drawn to illustrate common features of glacial terrain of the Canadian Shield of Ontario.*

the situation is that found in large areas of the "clay belt" in Ontario where glaciolacustrian clays overlie till on the bedrock. In this case surface geochemical techniques are likely to give negative results although reverse circulation drilling to obtain samples of the basal till material may be very effective as an aid to the location of gold mineralization. It should be stressed here that idealized hypothetical conceptual models are being described. At a particular field site, glacial overburden conditions can be much more complicated than in the situations described here. Finally, in Figure 1i patches of till underlie glaciofluvial sands which in turn are overlain by glaciolacustrian deposits. Here again, surface methods are likely to be negative and, because of the nature of the till, reverse circulation drilling is also likely to give poor results.

Together, these simplified conceptual models provide an introduction to common landscape complexities which occur in the Canadian Shield. The models should be considered as merging into each other within the glaciated landscape. The problem then becomes one of interpreting data from geochemical surveys in relation to Quaternary geology *in three dimensions.* Particularly in areas of glaciolacustrian deposits, Quaternary maps are not sufficient for the interpretation of geochemical survey patterns. The Quaternary maps must be accompanied by data from seismic surveys and stratigraphic drilling if this is practical.

Some idea of the effectiveness of the geochemical prospecting techiques, which have been employed in the search for gold in Ontario, may be obtained from Figure 2.

OCCURRENCE OF GOLD IN SURFICIAL MATERIALS

The third basic constraint to geochemical prospecting for gold in the Canadian Shield concerns the way in which gold occurs in samples of rock, till, sand, soil humus and related materials which are used as a basis for geochemical prospecting techniques. Figure 3 is a useful diagram prepared by Tourtelot (1968) showing the grain size of gold versus the number of particles of gold in different sample weights of a sample. It is evident from this diagram that a 10 g sample containing 1 particle of gold 0.1 mm in diameter would contain 1 ppm (i.e. 1000 ppb) gold, whereas more than 1000 particles of 0.0068 mm diameter would be present to give 1 ppm gold. Unfortunately, as we shall see, gold particles are not always of a small diameter in samples of surficial material (Lakin *et al.* 1974). Lakin *et al.* (1974) also provided information on data obtained for gold in eighteen 10 g subsamples of a single soil sample (Table 1).

Table 1. *Determination of gold in 18 subsamples of a soil (each 10 g) sample collected from the Copper Basin district of Arizona (from Lakin et al.1974).*

Number of Subsamples	Gold (ppm)
14	less than 0.04
1	0.06
1	0.12
1	0.25
1	1.00

These writers concluded that in this case a representative 10 g subsample of the soil could not be taken.

Few studies of this type have been reported from Canada although recently Harris (1982, p.58) discussed the problem of gold occurrence in stream silts from British Columbia as follows.

Some 3,000 standard silt samples collected for a programme of regional reconnaissance in southern British Columbia were analyzed for Cu, Pb, Zn, Ag, Mo, W, As and Au. The gold data consisted of atomic absorption analyses on single 5 g portions of prepared (–80 mesh) sample material. Selected groups of sam-

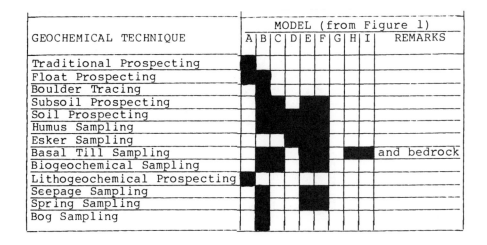

Figure 2. *A general overview of the relative effectiveness of geochemical prospecting techniques employed in gold exploration in Ontario.*

ples showing a significant frequency of anomalous Au values were later rerun, in duplicate, for check purposes (by the same laboratory, using the same method). Table . . . [*see Table 2, this paper*] summarizes the results. Of the 12 samples which were anomalous (20 ppb) on the original run, only 6 gave confirmatory anomalous values in 13 other samples, all of which had shown background values on the original run.

Based on the "best values" (i.e., the averages of the three determinations), a total of 19 samples proved anomalous, including 10 of the original 12 anomalous samples and 9 unrecog-

nized by the initial work. Maps produced by plotting these triplicate averages are very different from those based on the original single analyses and undoubtedly constitute a superior assessment of the region for follow-up purposes. Fig. . . . [*see Figure 4, this paper*] shows the comparison for one anomalous area.

In view of the sampling problems in gold geochemistry, it is probably unwise to discount any anomaly, even when check values are erratic. The spatial abundance or clustering of anomalous values, regardless of magnitude, should constitute the guide to follow-up work.

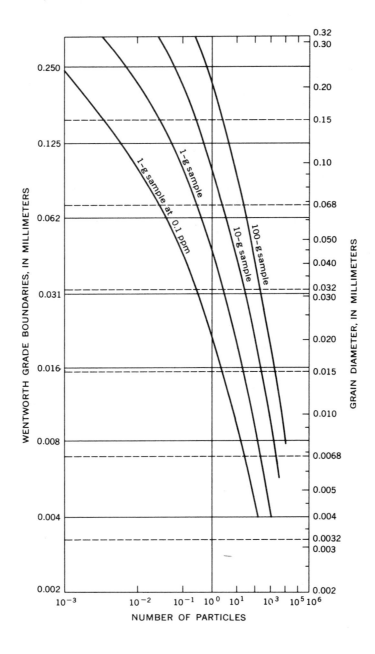

Figure 3. *Number of particles of gold at 1 ppm in samples having different sample weights, and for a 1 g sample at 0.1 ppm (from Tourtelot 1968).*

Table 2. Results of analytical reruns on southern British Columbia reconnaissance silt samples (from Harris 1982).

Sample No.	Au Analyses (ppb) Orig.	Rpt 1.	Rpt 2.	Mean (>20 ppb)	Sample No.	Au Analyses (ppb) Orig.	Rpt 1.	Rpt 2.	Mean (>20 ppb)	Sample No.	Au Analyses (ppb) Orig.	Rpt 1.	Rpt 2.	Mean (>20 ppb)
L65	<10	<10	<10		L98	<10	*340*	*320*	*220(c)*	T402	20	<10	<10	
66	<10	<10	<50		99	<10	<10	<10		403	20	<10	<10	
67	<10	<10	<50		100	<10	<10	<10		404	<10	<10	<10	
68	<10	<10	<10		101	<10	<10	<10		405	<10	*240*	<10	*80(c)*
70	<10	<10	<10		102	<10	<20			406	20	<10	<10	
71	<10	<10	<10		103	<10	<10	<10		407	<10	<10	40	
72	<10	<10	<10		T376	<10	16	*26*		408	20	*1460*	<10	*495(c)*
73	<10	<10	<10		377	<10	*22*	*40*	*22(c)*	409	16	<10	<10	
74	<10	<10	<10		378	<10	<10	<10		410	*24*	<10	<10	*(b)*
75	<10	<10	<10		379	<10	<10	<10		411	*168*	<10	<10	*56(a)*
76	<10	<10	<10		380	<10	<10	<10		K611	*520*	*7300*	*6400*	*4740(a)*
77	<10	<10	<10		381	<10	<10	<10		612	<10	<10	<10	
78	<10	<10	<10		382	<10	<10	<10		613	*660*	*220*	*166*	*350(a)*
79	*40*	<10	*34*	*26(a)*	383	<10	<10	<10		614	*120*	<10	*300*	*140(a)*
80	<10	<50			384	<10	<10	<10		615	*30*	14	<10	*(b)*
81	<10	<10	*76*	*29(c)*	385	<10	*380*	*360*	*250(c)*	616	<10	<10	<10	
82	<10	<10	*2230*	*745(c)*	386	<10	18	<10		617	<10	<10	<10	
83	<10	<10	<10		387	*44*	*32*	*24*	*33(a)*	618	<10	<10	<10	
84	<10	<10	<10		388	*80*	<10	<50	*30(a)*	619	<10	<10	<10	
85	<10	<10	<10		389	*80*	*22*	*60*	*55(a)*	620	<10	<10	<10	
86	<10	*22*	*370*	*133(c)*	390	<10	<10	<10		621	20	<10	*32*	
87	10	*60*	<10	*25(c)*	391	20	<10	<10		622	<10	<10	<10	
88	<10	12	<10		392	<10	<10	<10		623	<10	<10	<10	
89	<10	<20			393	<10	<10	<10		624	<10	*24*	<10	
90	<10	<10	20		394	<10	<10	<10		625	<10	<10	<10	
91	<10	<10	<10		395	<10	<10	<10		626	<10	<10	<10	
92	<10	<10	<10		396	<10	<10	<10		627	<10	<10	<10	
93	<10	<10	<20		397	<10	<10	<10		628	<10	<10	<10	
94	<10	<10	<10		398	<10	<10	<10		629	<10	<10	<10	
95	20	<10	<10		399	<10	<10	<10		630	<10	<10	<10	
96	*490*	<10	<10	*165(a)*	400	<10	<10	<10		631	<10	<10	<10	
97	*700*	<10	<10	*235(a)*	401	<10	<10	<10						

Values in italics are anomalous. "Rpt" means "repeat analysis".

(a) Anomalous in the original run and also on the three-run average.

(b) Anomalous in the original run, but below threshold on the three-run average.

(c) Background in the original run, but anomalous on the three-run average.

Harris (1982) also made suggestions for the improvement of the reliability of gold data obtained from geochemical surveys which are summarized in Table 3. The reader is referred to Harris (1982) for detailed information on variability introduced by field sampling, subsampling and analysis, the effect of pulverising samples and comparisons between gold data obtained from whole and the heavy mineral fraction of silt samples.

In summary, geochemical prospecting for gold in Ontario is complicated by three important constraints which vary in importance from geochemical technique to geochemical technique and from deposit to deposit. The nature of gold geochemistry and its occurrence in mineralized zones may either complicate, or simplify, gold prospecting; similarly, the nature of the glacial overburden may either complicate or simplify gold prospecting. In either case the difficulty of sampling materials for the

chemical analysis of gold is an important factor except in the case of waters and organic materials. These have other difficulties which are described below.

TECHNIQUES FOR GEOCHEMICAL PROSPECTING FOR GOLD IN THE CANADIAN SHIELD

Exploration in Ontario is usually conducted at one or more of three levels of intensity by geological, geophysical and geochemical methods. At the regional level, at a scale of 1:250 000 (or greater), the maps used generally stem from the activity of government surveys. At the follow-up, (or local) level, most work is done by exploration companies and related organizations with some mapping and methods development carried out by government

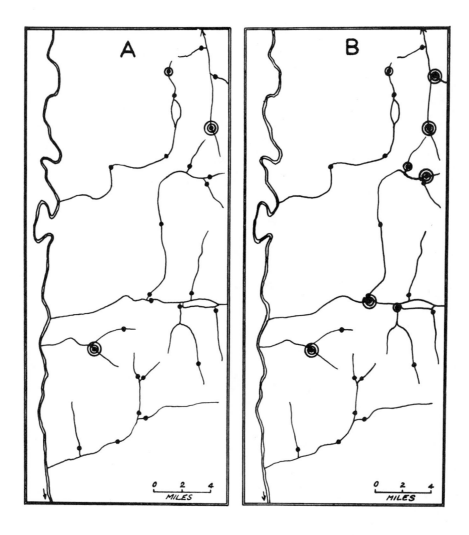

Figure 4. *Comparison of gold anomaly distribution in the same area obtained by (A) single 5 g analyses, and (B) three 5 g analyses. Dots are sample points: single circles > 20 < 100 ppb gold levels and double circles > 100 ppb gold levels in stream sediments (from Harris 1982).*

GEOCHEMICAL PROSPECTING FOR GOLD

Table 3. *Suggestions for increasing the reliability of data in gold geochemistry (from Harris 1982).*

Area of Improvement	Suggestions
1. Field sampling stage	– Collect larger samples – Collect duplicated samples – Pre-sieve samples – Strive for consistency in sample site selection
2. Laboratory preparation	– Maximize yield of prepared sample – Pulverize or make heavy mineral concentrates if orientation results show significant benefit
3. Analytical stage	– Replicate analyses; use averages – Analyze larger sub-samples

agencies. Detailed studies designed to examine the tenor of mineralization and the tenor of ores are normally conducted by the mineral industry.

Exploration methods at the regional or follow-up level usually evolve in three stages which may be called feasibility, developmental and established. In geology and geophysics, methods of regional mapping (e.g. magnetics, gravity, etc.) are relatively well-established in Ontario. Similarly, at the follow-up level, geological and much geophysical work are also done by established methods although these methods are often accompanied by some experimentation. In geochemistry at the regional level, surveys are mainly in the feasibility or early developmental stage and the number of examples described for a particular technique is generally small. At the follow-up level there has been standardization of techniques for soil sampling for some years, but otherwise the techniques are either in the feasibility or developmental stage at the present time. This statement is aimed at geochemical methods in general and applies particularly to techniques developed for searching specifically for gold.

LITHOGEOCHEMISTRY

So far, little attempt has been made to include gold in regional geochemical surveys in Ontario although the indicator elements, Ag and As, were included in some of the regional geochemical surveys based on lake sediments which were included in the National Geochemical Reconnaissance Program completed during the late 1970s. The potential of lithogeochemical surveying for gold prospecting at the regional level was realized over 30 years ago when Gross (1950, 1952) attempted to distinguish mineralized and unmineralized plutons in the Canadian Shield on the basis of silica/zircon mineral studies combined with radioactivity measurements for uranium/thorium made on hand specimens. More recently Wolfe (1975), using a fire assay/atomic absorption technique with a detection limit of 5 ppb for gold, reported the content of the

element in 345 rock specimens from Early Precambrian felsic plutons in Ontario. He concluded that:

The data indicate that (1) ore-stage hydrothermal metsomatism has produced widespread Au enrichment in Precambrain intrusions that host epigenetic vein-type gold deposits, and (2) geochemical Au analysis of samples collected from 30 to 50 randomly distributed sites can be used to estimate the gold exploration potential of stock-sized bodies and to outline internal patterns of Au variation which may be useful in directing exploration to particular contacts or portions of a stock. The results do not conclusively indicate unusually high Au content in primary unaltered igneous rocks.

Quite apart from these practical studies there are many theoretical schemes for relating gold to indicator minerals or elements in the search for the metal. For example, Boyle (1979) concluded that the mobility of indicator elements with respect to gold and silver in primary haloes follows the general sequence:

Gangue elements:
$Si>B>K>Na>Ca = Mn>Mg>Co>Fe = Ni>Al$

Gaseous compounds:
$CO_2 = S = Se>As>Sb>Te$

Base metals:
$Hg>Zn>Cd>Cu>Pb>Mo = Bi = Sn = W$

Precious metals:
$Ag>Au>Pt$

Boyle (1979, p.453) also reported on an interesting study by Seeland (1973a,b) which attempts to set the scene for regional prospecting for gold in Ontario and elsewhere.

Seeland . . . carried out a broad scale reconnaissance for gold in the sedimentary and metamorphic rocks of the United States south of the Great Lakes region, the aim being to discover fossil placers in clastic rocks on the southward dipping paleoslope draining the auriferous areas in the Canadian Shield north of the Great Lakes. In 799 samples gold was detected in only 36. Four samples yielded 0.1 to 0.4 ppm Au. Seeland . . . concluded from the data that the frequency with which gold was detected in the

258

Table 4. *Composite geochemical signatures of gold from South Pass Atlantic City area and Dickie Springs area, Wyoming (from Antweiler and Campbel l 1982).*

	South Pass– Atlantic City lodes	Dickie Springs– Oregon Gulch placers
Total number of analyses		
Ag content, %	69	45
Au content, %	9.8	8.0
Cu content, %	90.0	91.9
	0.092	0.082
Ratios:		
Au/Ag	9.2	11.5
Au/Cu	1000	1100
Ag/Cu	100	100
Percentage of analyses with:		
Pb	100	91.1
Bi	97.1	57.8
As	92.8	8.8
Sb	89.9	31.1
V	66.7	31.1
Sn	55.1	2.2
B	55.1	42.2
Nb	47.8	6.7
W	23.2	6.7
Mo	21.7	26.7
Zn	32.0	0
Cr	24.6	4.4
Ni	13.0	4.4
Co	11.6	0
Te	4.3	0
Cd	0	44.4
Be	0	28.9
Pd	0	2.2

rocks of the region suggested the possibility that certain undetermined syngenetic chemical processes have concentrated anomalous amounts of gold in rocks of chemical origin (Grenville marble, glauconitic sandstone, gypsum, etc.). He thought that these chemical processes may be more effective concentrators of gold than the expected placer-forming physical processes, even in a region relatively close to a source of clastic gold. In addition he speculated that the general lack of gold and the small grain size that was found (less than 5 percent of the hydraulic equivalent size in the nonglauconitic sandstone-quartzite category) are results of postdepositional leaching.

Finally, he postulated that the apparent abundance of chemically or biochemically precipitated gold and the relative lack of clastic gold in a region close to a major gold source could also be explained by the presence of an east-west late Precambrian-early Paleozoic continental divide just north of the Great Lakes separating a known south- and southeast-trending paleocurrent system from a probably north-trending system. Thus, he concluded that most Canadian Shield gold deposits would lie north of this divide, and the logical place to look for fossil placers would then be in the basal Paleozoic clastic rocks near James Bay.

From the geochemical viewpoint, gold itself may be used as an entity which can be used to determine its source in placer deposits and glacial material. An interesting account of this approach is found in Antweiler and Campbell (1982, p.41) who described the general geochemical signatures for gold obtained from the Wind River Range in west-central Wyoming. They distinguished between two gold sources: one in place (in the South Pass – Atlantic City Precambrian lodes) and the other in fossil placers (Dickie Springs – Oregon Gulch area). The criteria used were not the Au/Ag, Au/Cu or Ag/Cu ratios as might be expected but the signatures for other trace elements within the gold. They discussed their findings (Table 4) as follows.

Gold from some of the lodes contained Zn, Co, and Te, but not Cd, Be, or Pd. Gold from some of the placers contained Cd, Be, and Pd, but not Zn, Co, and Te. Moreover, the lodes were much more abundant in Sb, Nb, and W, whereas the placers were more abundant in Mo. Removal of the trace elements in lode gold is probable during oxidation, weathering, and transport, but addition of Cd, Be, Pd, and Mo is quite unlikely.

It is evident from the above that regional level lithogeochemical surveys aimed at gold exploration are in their infancy in Ontario although the fundamental ideas for such surveys are well known. In a general discussion of exploration criteria for exploration for gold based on Ontario conditions, Hodgson *et al.* (1982) considered the role of lithogeochemical surveys in mineral exploration in Ontario (Figure 5). They concluded that at present lithogeochemical surveys are most effective at the mining camp (follow-up) level of effort and stressed the importance of As, Sb, W, Hg and Ag as indicator elements.

The potential for lithogeochemical surveys is further discussed in geological contributions to this volume and will not be repeated here. Other current literature sources for lithogeochemistry of gold-bearing rocks of Ontario are Davis et. al. (1982), Kerrich and Fyfe (1981) and Kerrich and Hodder (1982).

BASAL TILL GEOCHEMICAL SURVEYS

Some idea of the importance of basal till geochemical prospecting for gold in the Canadian Shield may be obtained from the idealized conceptual models discussed previously (see Figure 1). Basal till is used in two ways in geochemical prospecting. When it is at the surface the till itself may be used as a basis for geochemical surveys including descriptive geochemistry of one or more size fractions of the material. Descriptive mineralogy of surface till samples may also be used as a guide to ores. The study of till, at, or close to, the surface may also include subsoil or soil sampling, humus sampling or biogeochemistry.

In this section we are concerned largely with the second approach to the use of basal till in geochemical prospecting, especially tills which are overlain by glaciofluvial, glaciolacustrian and/or glaciomarine deposits (Figure 1d-i). It is important to note that sampling of till material

under these conditions is always an indirect operation and the first problem is to establish the presence, or absence, of till material under the glacial material observed at the surface. It should be stressed that a Quaternary geology map is an aid to locating drill holes for the collection of basal till samples, but without stratigraphic drilling being included in the Quaternary study, simple use of the Quaternary geology map patterns may not be much help. Quaternary geology is important in basal till geochemical prospecting in the identification of the stratigraphy of the glacial material as a whole so that changes in the conditions of the glacial overburden section (as evidenced by the idealized conceptual models in Figure 1) may be considered when the data are interpreted.

EVOLUTION OF BASAL TILL SAMPLING IN ONTARIO

In areas where extensive till sheets occur at the surface (see Figure 1a,b,c) a number of Quaternary geological/geochemical techniques may be used to locate boulder fans and other indications of mineralization. Details of techniques of this type are given in the review paper by Nichol and Bjorkland (1973) and will not be repeated here. Information of this type was also reviewed by Grip (1953) with reference to Scandinavian experience. Briefly, in these methods till is seen to be composed of boulders in a finer-grained matrix. The preferred orientation of pebbles, stone counting, and related techniques are used to establish the direction of movement of a till (or tills) within an area. The lithology of boulders and stones, the mineralogy (including the study of the heavy mineral fraction) of the till material, the texture of the till and the geochemistry of the till fractions are systematically studied in order to establish the location of a mineralized zone. In many areas of Ontario, the conditions of glacial cover are too complicated for the effective application of these methods. A pioneer study of this type at the regional level by Wolfe *et al.* (1975) in the Moose River Basin of the Hudson Bay Lowlands was aimed at the discovery of kimberlite and diamond indicators. A total of 20 till, 38 esker and 85 alluvium samples were collected. Heavy minerals were separated from them and examined under the microscope. Although no diamonds (or gold) were discovered, 20 grains of pyrope garnet and one grain of magnesian ilmenite were found during this interesting study.

So far, areas where tills are exposed at the surface (see Figure 1a,b,c) have been considered. Let us now consider experience in areas where the basal till is covered by other glacial deposits or peat (see Figure 1c,d,e,f,g,h,i). Using samples of basal till material collected during civil engineering studies in the vicinity of the Kidd Creek orebody at Timmins, Fortescue and Hughes (1965) were able to indicate the potential importance of basal till as a sample medium for geochemical prospecting in areas overlain by glaciolacustrian sediments (see Figure 1h). They also noted the absence of an anomaly in areas where the clays lie directly on the bedrock. Later work reported by Fortescue and Hornbrook

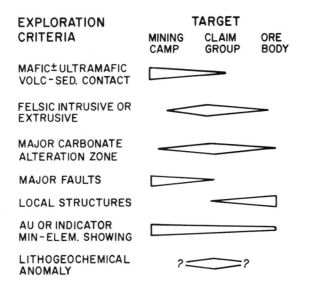

Figure 5. *Exploration criteria for gold deposits in the Superior Province of Ontario (from Hodgson et al.1982)*

(1969) from the same site, focused attention on the importance of the relief of the bedrock surface in the interpretation of data from basal till sampling. Since then, many workers have studied the use of basal till in prospecting in the Canadian Shield of Ontario and elsewhere (Nichol and Bjorkland 1973; Smee and Sinhan 1979). An interesting and informative example of successful exploration in an area of surface glaciolacustrian clays overlying basal till (at depth) was described by Thompson (1979). He described how the Currie Bowman deposit was discovered on the basis of the chemical analysis of the heavy mineral fraction of till material collected from beneath 80 feet of glaciolacustrian sediments. The elements involved in this study were Cu, Zn, Pb, Ag and Au. An example of a gold deposit discovered by reverse circulation drilling is that at Nighthawk Lake 20 miles east of Timmins, Ontario. According to Brown (1982) the deposit was discovered by sampling bedrock and basal till material methodically over the area where the glacial overburden thickness is some 250 feet thick. This is clearly a discovery of an orebody by geochemical methods of the type described here.

AN EXAMPLE OF A DESCRIPTIVE GEOCHEMISTRY AND DESCRIPTIVE MINERALOGY STUDY ON BASAL TILL

So far we have been concerned largely with exploration activity. In 1979, the Ontario Geological Survey initiated a multidisciplinary, multi-year program (the Kirkland Lake Initiatives Program: KLIP) in the Kirkland Lake area to stimulate the economy of the area by providing geophysical survey data for exploration companies and to explore the potential of basal till as a prospecting medium for gold and diamonds in the area (Averill and Thomson 1981; Routledge et al. 1981; Lourim 1982a,b; Fortescue and Lourim 1982). In total, 326 samples of basal till material were collected; 95 by reverse circulation drilling and 231 by backhoe sampling. All samples were subjected to a sub-sampling scheme which separated out different size fractions and heavy mineral fractions from the till material. The sub-samples were then examined for minerals and rock fragments using a binocular microscope. The elements were Au, Ag, As, Mo, Cu, Pb, Zn, and U. A hot acid leach procedure was used for all elements except Au and U, which were determined by neutron activation. This study is considered here because it facilitates a comparison between the effectiveness of descriptive mineralogy and descriptive geochemistry in gold exploration in the Kirkland Lake area, thus providing a starting point for further research in a much neglected field.

Because the detailed description of the findings of the KLIP project is too complex to be described here, a hypothetical idealized conceptual model situation has been drawn to illustrate some of the important points of the interpretation of the data (Figure 6). Using the model from Figure 1h, a series of 10 drill hole sites from which a basal till sample was collected were added to the diagram (Figure 6). Four parameters measured in the sub-samples of the ten samples are graphed in Figure 6.

These are (1) abundance of gold, (2) abundance of silver (an example of an indicator element), (3) the occurrence of pyrite and, (4) the occurrence of tourmaline (pyrite and tourmaline are examples of indicator minerals for gold, see Hodgson et al. 1982). Further details of the subsampling techniques required to obtain the different size and weight fractions are fully described by Averill and Thomson (1981). Figure 6 is interpreted as follows.

Gold. Flakes of gold may be observed on the shaking table during sample preparation. Usually flakes relate directly to the mineralized zone although on occasion they may be found away from known mineralized zones. Minor gold is found in till close to the mineralized zone. In the coarse heavy fraction the gold has moved a small distance in contrast to the fine heavy fraction where the maximum is further down-ice from the source.

Silver. In the coarse heavy fraction, the fine heavy fraction, and the whole till samples, high values for this element occur in the vicinity of the source, with a decreasing gradient down-ice. The small peak for silver in the coarse heavy fraction is inserted to remind us that even in the best of patterns, erratic values may also occur.

Pyrite. The percentage of pyrite estimated under the microscope has a pattern similar to silver, except that the high values persist down-ice in the heavy fraction. Because pyrite is a relatively heavy mineral, it tends to be concentrated in the heavy mineral fraction, though minor amounts are found in the medium density fraction.

Tourmaline. Tourmaline is also a gold indicator mineral but tends to be concentrated in the medium, rather than the heavy, fraction.

Figure 6 illustrates the point that by fractionating the till material, one enhances the contrast of high to low values for indicator elements and minerals associated with gold deposits. Note that different fractions enhance different parameters. It must be stressed that these are *idealized* patterns which are simplified deliberately to minimize erratic data points due to sampling and analytical problems as described earlier in this paper.

A good example of a basal till study closely integrated with geophysical techniques was described by Middleton et al. (1982). Briefly, three areas of gold mineralization were discovered in Hoyle Township, near Timmins, using a combination of geochemical and geophysical techniques. They reported (1982, p.4):

After a regional program of magnetometer and electromagnetic surveys to define the regional stratigraphy, the western part of the survey area was tested by the first of three stages of overburden drill holes using reverse circulation equipment on 800-1200 ft centres along east-west lines. Anomalous gold values in the till section (usually 15-40 ft of till) were encountered which prompted an induced polarization and resistivity survey to outline the carbonatization zones indicated by bedrock chips.

It was concluded that (p.5):

. . . gold in the till gives the best definition of bedrock sources where pathfinder elements have erratic patterns and values. The presence of till is of course absolutely necessary for the technique to work and other material such as the esker on the west side of the area mark the limit of the glacial till. Therefore one has to rely on geophysics in these problem areas.

This interesting and important study stresses the importance of the intimate relationship between geochemical and geophysical techniques during the gold exploration process in glacial terrain. Although this paper is focused on geochemical techniques exclusively, it must be remembered that in active exploration, particularly at the local level, geophysics is also most important as clearly described by Middleton *et al.* (1982).

GLACIOFLUVIAL DEPOSITS IN GEOCHEMICAL PROSPECTING

The idealized conceptual models included in Figure 1 indicate that in addition to glacial tills, glaciofluvial materials may occur at the surface in areas where mineral deposits occur in bedrock. In areas where significant amounts of indicator minerals or geochemical signals occur in the material, they can be used for the location of gold deposits. The most prominent glaciofluvial deposits in the Canadian Shield are eskers, which have been sampled systematically for mineralogical and geochemical prospecting largely as a result of the activity of a Quaternary geologist H.A. Lee. Lee (1971) reviewed progress in till and esker prospecting in Canada based largely on descriptive mineralogy. He described a classic study of this type as follows (p.36).

An orientation study for the Kirkland Lake region illustrates the esker clast to bedrock relationship. Auriferous pyrite in the esker massive gravel unit is in greatest concentration just less than 1 mile down esker from its bedrock source at the Upper Canada Mine. A kimberlite dyke was found within the bedrock of the Kirkland Lake region after a diagnostic mineral pyrope was found in an esker. A position of peak concentration was determined. Moving up-esker, the already established displacement for the auriferous pyrite, a source of pyrope was found in the bedrock.

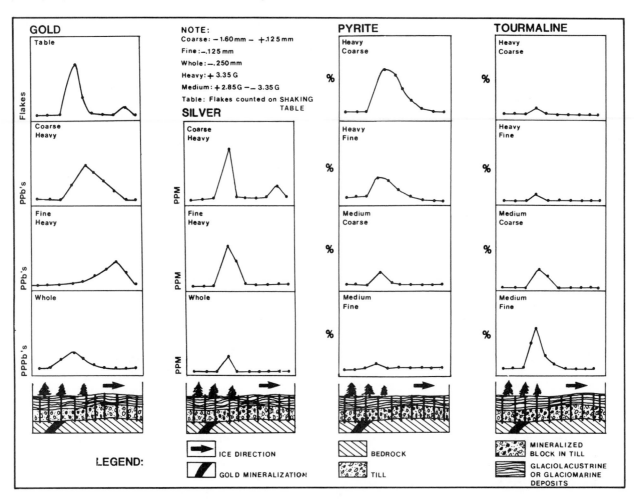

Figure 6. *Generalized conceptual model of a glaciated landscape from which 10 basal till samples have been obtained by reverse-circulation drilling. Graphs are generalized models for four indicators (gold on the shaking table, silver, pyrite and tourmaline) derived from the sub-sampling, descriptive geochemistry and descriptive mineralogy of the different fractions of the till samples.*

This study clearly established the feasibility of using esker material for geochemical prospecting in the Canadian Shield, and indicating that further research on this promising approach is warranted.

WATERS, STREAM SEDIMENTS AND LAKE SEDIMENTS IN GEOCHEMICAL PROSPECTING

The use of rocks, basal tills or esker material for geochemical prospecting, utilizes what may be termed a primary approach to gold exploration. These techniques measure directly minerals and related material derived from the mineralized zone. In this section we are concerned with geochemical anomalies due to gold deposits, anomalies which result from chemicals from the deposit being transported and accumulated elsewhere in the landscape by groundwater, surface water, or plants.

Boyle *et al.* (1971) summarized the pioneer work in this field in the Canadian Shield. They noted that pre-Pleistocene weathering of gold deposits in place had been observed at Timmins, Matachewan and at Kirkland Lake and postulated that groundwater might be a convenient sampling medium for prospecting for such deposits. In support of this contention, he noted that at Yellowknife, waters at seepages, springs and faults are enriched in As, Sb, Cu and Zn in the vicinity of gold deposits. Later work showed that the dispersion of these elements in natural waters is often severely restricted, due to strong absorption by humic matter in the bottoms of nearly all streams studied. Boyle *et al.* (1971) noted that trains near gold deposits longer than 1,000 feet were rare, owing to the organic matter in beaver ponds, muskegs and organic silts. Consequently, hydrogeochemical surveys were not recommended at the regional level, although at the local level they would be expected to be valuable under favourable conditions. Outside the Canadian Shield modern methods of hydrogeochemical surveying for gold deposits have, on occasion, been shown to be most effective. For example, Turner and Ikramuddin (1982) working in the Republic Graben area of northeastern Washington State were able to detect 15 of 17 gold/silver deposits on the basis of the content of Au, Ag, Si and As in water samples.

With respect to the use of stream sediments for regional level geochemical surveys in the Canadian Shield, a pioneer study by Wolfe (1976) in the Pukaskwa area to the north of Lake Superior is of interest. Like other writers on this general subject, he stressed the importance of Quaternary geology as an aid to the interpretation of geochemical surveys in the Canadian Shield. He summarized the Pukaskwa study as follows.

Reconnaissance stream sediment geochemistry in parts of the Pukaskwa and University River Basins has contributed to a rapid preliminary evaluation of the base metal potential of the two major Archean metavolcanic-metasedimentary belts and has further clarified the role of certain independent variables (i.e., distributions of bedrock types and Pleistocene surficial deposits, sparsely mineralized rocks, surface Eh-pH environments and metal absorbing manganese-iron hydroxides) in controlling regional geochemical dispersion patterns in areas of continental glaciation.

Fast flowing streams and rivers, within 5 to 10 miles (8 to 16 km) of the Lake Superior shore, drain a region of moderate relief covered by a thin till sheet and have steep gradients suitable for significant mechanical transport. Reconnaissance stream sediment geochemistry can be applied in this area with results similar to those observed in glaciated regions of the northern Appalachians. However, a temporary halt in the withdrawal of the Wisconsin ice sheet, approximately 18 miles (30 km) north of Lake Superior, is marked by an irregular east-west band of outwash sand and gravel that modifies significantly the regional geochemical response to underlying metavolcanics and metasediments. Regional patterns of Cu, Zn, and Ni distribution in bedrock and in stream sediments illustrate the assocation of low metal background in drainage sediments with areas of thick outwash cover.

Regional level geochemical surveys based on stream sediments in New Brunswick in the 1950s, led to experimentation with lake sediments as a medium for regional geochemical surveys in the 1960s by the Geological Survey of Canada (Allan *et al.* 1973). The feasibility of such surveys had been indicated by the classic work of Schmidt (1956). By the mid 1970s, experience with regional lake sediment surveys in the Canadian Shield led the Geological Survey of Canada to design the "National Geochemical Uranium Program". This was a joint activity involving the Geological Survey of Canada and Provincial agencies, including the Ontario Geological Survey. Although this activity was directed towards uranium prospecting, some gold indicator elements were included in the 1:250 000 scale geochemical surveys. For example, the geochemical map sheet to the north and east of Lake Superior (OGS-GSC Open File 5267) includes maps for uranium, silver, copper, lead, nickel, manganese, iron, pH, zinc, arsenic, molybdenum, cobalt and loss on ignition of lake sediments and uranium and fluorine in lake waters. The interpretation of patterns on these maps is facilitated by the inclusion of general bedrock geological information on the basemaps. Unfortunately, no information on the Quaternary geology of the area is available at the same map scale, and the detection limit for silver is not low enough for most practical geochemical prospecting purposes.

This brief review of the use of waters, stream sediments and lake sediments for geochemical surveying at the regional level in Ontario, focuses attention on the small volume of work done and the need for cross checking the effectiveness of the three techniques, under a given set of glacial conditions in the vicinity of known gold mineralization. At the local level, the role of stream sediments in the Canadian Shield is little known, although the work of Boyle *et al.* (1971) and Schmidt (1956) suggests that springs and small streams and lakes may be used as a basis for streamwater and lake sediments surveys at this level of detail.

SOIL GEOCHEMICAL SURVEYS

Traditionally, soil is used for follow-up level geochemical surveys. A classic survey of this type in Ontario was comleted by Chisholm (1950), who used the then new "heavy metal test" (including copper, lead and zinc) at a gold showing near Kenora, Ontario, where chalcopyrite, galena and sphalerite were known to be associated with gold mineralization. This study established the feasibility of using soil for tracing mineralization under overburden up to 5 feet thick, when conditions are favourable. Progress in using soil for geochemical prospecting in the Canadian Shield was summarized by Ermagen (1957). He noted that soil geochemical surveys could trace mineralization under bouldery tills up to 40 feet thick at Chibougamau, Quebec. He also suggested that soil samples should be collected at regular intervals along lines 200 feet apart, and that in level areas the spacing should be 50 feet between stations. He considered that, in areas of relief, 100 foot spacing was adequate. He recommended the B horizon of the soil as the most reliable material upon which to base such surveys.

Bradshaw (1975) collected case histories of geochemical prospecting based on soil in the Canadian Shield, and used the data to synthesize a series of soil profile and landscape conceptual models for geochemical prospecting in glacial terrain. Of the 18 case histories included in the study, 7 were from Ontario and 3 included references to gold. This study was a step forward in the display of geochemical prospecting information, because the generalized conceptual models related directly to practical experience.

Since 1975, many soil geochemical surveys have been completed in the Canadian Shield. For example, in the Assessment Files at the Ontario Geological Survey, over 40 references to geochemical exploration for gold are listed. The majority of these include reference to soil surveys.

Wolfe (1977) provided a succinct summary of a geochemical soil survey study completed in Ben Nevis Township northeast of Kirkland Lake as follows.

In an area measuring 2.5 km (1.6 miles) east-west by 1.5 km (0.9 miles) north-south and extending southward from the Canagau Mines Limited shafts, soils and glacial till were sampled at 50 locations to outline patterns of metal dispersion in glacial deposits situated 'down-ice' from the known base metal sulphide mineralization. At each site samples were collected from the upper 'B' soil horizon and from the parent glacial till scraped from the walls of 75-100 cm deep pits located along traverse lines oriented normal to the local ice-flow direction (S20E). Till samples weighing approximately 3.5 kg (7.7 pounds) were oven-dried at 80°C and passed through 80- and 250-mesh screens. The minus 80-mesh fraction of 'B' horizon soils and the minus 250-mesh fraction of glacial tills were leached with hot HNO_3-HCl and analyzed for copper, zinc, lead, nickel, cobalt and manganese by atomic absorption spectroscopy methods. Heavy minerals were separated in tetrabromethane (specific gravity 2.96) from till sample material in the minus 80-mesh, plus 250-mesh particle-size range. The heavy mineral concentrates were examined microscopically and were analyzed for hot HNO_3-HCl leachable copper, zinc, lead, nickel, cobalt, and manganese.

He drew the following conclusions.

Geochemical analyses of 'B' horizon soil and components of glacial till down-ice from a known mineralized bedrock source indicate:

(1) That pre-glacial topography immediately up-ice and for some distance down-ice from a mineralized sub-cropping source, has an important influence on the nature and extent of erosion and transport by the ice.

(2) That secondary post-glacial weathering has been extremely important in the redistribution of mobile trace elements in the upper 1 to 2 m (3 to 6 feet) of permeable, well-drained, silty to sandy boulder till. Sulphide minerals are completely leached from the heavy mineral fraction of gray, apparently unoxidized samples of near-surface till.

Closs and Sado (1978) carried out an orientation drift-prospecting investigation near areas of known vein-type gold mineralization in the Beardmore-Geraldton area of northwestern Ontario. They compared data obtained from parallel sampling of soils and glacial tills and concluded:

Gold provides the most consistent indicator of its deposits. It is frequently difficult to obtain sufficient sample material for gold determinations in the heavy mineral separate of tills. Optimum sample fraction selection is aided by a knowledge of the mineralogical nature of gold occurrences within a particular area. The trace element pathfinder suites which can aid in raising anomaly selection confidence vary with the content of vein and gangue minerals associated with specific deposits. A sound appreciation of both the regional and local Quaternary geology is essential to the successful planning, field sampling and interpretation of a drift prospecting program.

Further information on the use of soils for geochemical prospecting in the Canadian Shield may be obtained from Levinson (1974); Rose *et al.* (1979); Nichol and Bjorkland (1973); and Smee and Sinhan (1979).

BIOGEOCHEMICAL SURVEYS

The use of plant material as a basis for geochemical prospecting became popular in Canada largely as a result of the research activities of H.V. Warren, R.E. Delavault, and their students at the University of British Columbia in the 1940s and 1950s. Their activity in eastern Canada was limited, but did result in two papers (Warren and Delavault 1955a,b). Other pioneer biogeochemical prospecting in Quebec (and elsewhere) was carried out by J.E. Riddell at McGill University. Between 1962 and 1967, a unit for plant prospecting methods research was established by the Geological Survey of Canada, which completed a number of studies at drilled, undisturbed mineral deposits, including the Texas Gulf Sulphur base metal deposit near Timmins (Fortescue and Hornbrook 1967, 1969). Other activity of the group included a small scale stream sediment study in the Moose River area and a small scale systematic study of vertical and horizontal distribution of chemical elements in the Mer Bleu peat bog near Ottawa (Fortescue and Usik 1969). Early progress in traditional biogeochemical prospecting was reviewed by Cannon (1960), Fortescue (1970), and Wolfe (1971).

Today, geochemical prospecting based on the chemical analysis of organic material is divided into three kinds of activity. One is based on the collection of living plant material, usually tree organs; another is based on the chemical analysis of humus and a third on the chemical analysis of peat material.

At present, there is no detailed study of the vertical and horizontal distribution of gold in Ontario peat bogs located in the vicinity of mineralized zones. Consequently, a multi-element study of the Mer Bleu bog peat carried out some years ago (Fortescue and Usik 1969) is still of interest. These workers provided a section for the daylight and mineral matter surfaces of the bog traverse across the Mer Bleu on the core sample recovery and the general nature of the peat (Figure 7a). Plant cover types on the bog at the time of sampling were included in the section and areas where woody material occurred in the peat were also noted (Figure 7a). The vertical distribution of nine elements in each of the 10 peat cores are listed on Figure 7b. It should be noted that although the Mer Bleu peat bog is situated far from any mineral deposit, the content of nickel, copper, lead, chromium and zinc tended to increase at the bottom of the peat cores. Evidently, in geochemical prospecting based on peat cores, very careful attention should be paid to the interpretation of data for trace elements close to the mineral surface so that false geochemical anomalies of this type are not mistaken for real ones. Most important, in the search for gold, one must distinguish in the field between humus (which is a part of soil) and peat (which is a bog constituent) and behaves quite differently with respect to the generation of geochemical anomalies. Geochemical anomalies in peat result largely from groundwater movement in the bog and may be quite remote from mineralized zones, if they relate to such zones at all. Detailed and careful work on geochemical techniques in the peat bogs of Ontario is long overdue, although the pioneer studies by Gleeson (1960), and Gleeson and Coope (1967) showed the way long ago.

Brooks (1982) provided a general review of biogeochemical prospecting for gold using plant material. Briefly, the use of horsetails (*Equisetum* sp.) as direct indicators of gold or silver mineralization is now discredited although Brooks *et al.* (1981) showed that plants of this genera are accumulators of arsenic and may be used as indirect indicators of gold mineralization. Otherwise, Brooks (1982) listed 134 plant species which have been reported as gold accumulators world wide with 10 (including *Equisetum*) from Canada. No data on case histories for gold exploration in the Canadian Shield were included in the review article. Wolfe (1971) noted that plant biogeochemistry may be effective in sampling deep transported overburden if the upper horizons of podzol soils do not not adequately reflect anomalous conditions at depth. He also stated that biogeochemical surveys may show moderate to high anomaly contrasts for Mo, U, Pb, Co (and probably Fe and Mn) in deep-rooted plant species in the Canadian Shield, whereas Cu, Zn, Ag and Ni are expected to show low contrast. It would have been valuable to include arsenic and gold in this research activity because Warren *et al.* (1964) found up to 2000 ppm As accumulated in Douglas Fir foliage in the vicinity of gold mineralization in British Columbia.

The use of humus for prospecting in the Canadian Shield has become popular during the past few years largely as a result of the publication of an article by Gleeson and Boyle (1979) and a paper by Curtin *et al.* (1968) describing the use of mull humus in prospecting for gold in the Empire District, Colorado. Later work in the same area reported by Lakin *et al.* (1974) included an account of difficult research, which established that the mecha-

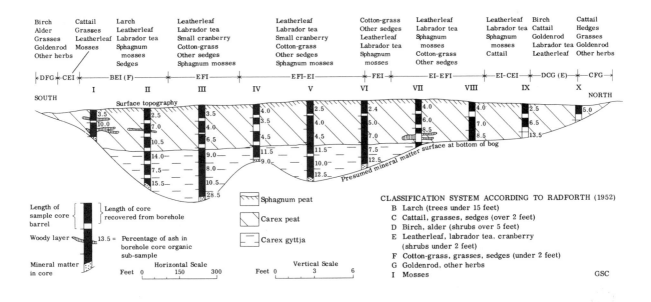

Figure 7a. *Geochemical study of the Mer Bleu peat bog near Ottawa. Ecological section of the Mer Bleu peat bog showing vegetation cover types and stratification of peat material (from Fortescue and Usik 1969).*

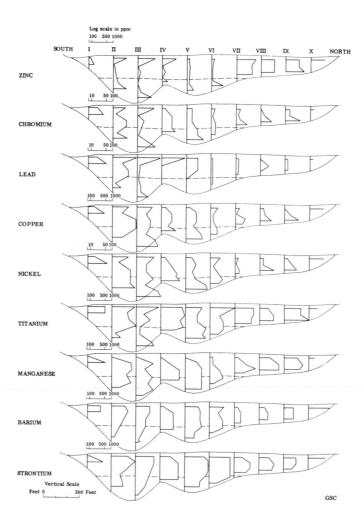

Figure 7b. *Vertical distribution of minor elements in ash of peat collected from boreholes located along a traverse across the South Arm of the Mer Bleu peat bog.*

nism for gold transfer in the trees was likely to be as the cyanide and showed that the gold was almost certainly very finely divided in the mull humic material (Figure 8). With the advent of sensitive and reliable methods for the determination of gold and arsenic in humic materials, several workers in Ontario have used humus as an aid to gold prospecting in the Province. Much of this work is in company files and remains unpublished. A selection of data culled from Ontario Geological Survey assessment files for the content of gold and/or arsenic in humus is included in Table 5. The important point apparent from this table is that the number of humus samples analysed for gold is over 200 in each example and that for gold, the background is below 20 ppb except in Bateman Township. In general, there appears to be a clear increase in values from "background" to "anomalous" (Table 5). The values for arsenic (except in Bateman Township) also

appear reasonable because the level of As in the Earth's crust is 2 ppm. In Bateman Township, arsenic values are significantly higher than in the other areas. A map showing a part of the Sannes (1980) study (Figure 9) indicates that the high gold values are clustered within the area of the arsenic highs, particularly when a 50 ppb contour is used for the gold values and a 150 ppm contour is used for the arsenic values. These data suggest but do not prove, that contamination from some type of smelter operation is responsible for these high values (which may also receive a contribution from underlying gold- and arsenic-rich glacial material). The data are included here to underline the importance of very careful interpretation of gold and arsenic values obtained from humus material, particularly in areas where airborne contamination cannot be ruled out.

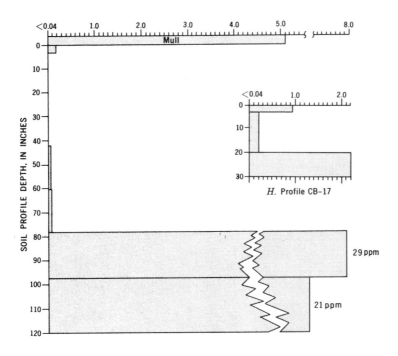

Figure 8. *Histogram for gold content of mull humus and subsoil in a soil from Empire deposit, Clear Creek County, Colorado (from Lakin et al. 1974).*

DISCUSSION

This brief review of the role geochemistry currently plays in mineral exploration for gold in Ontario focuses attention on the difficulty of the problem and the large number of techniques which have been tried in order to find effective solutions during the past 30 years (see Figure 2). It seems clear that at the present time we are approaching the end of the beginning. In the 1980s, geochemical prospectors for gold in Ontario have many new approaches which require detailed evaluation in relation to the types of glacial terrain illustrated on Figure 1. But in spite of this progress, there is still the problem of the occurrence of gold in mineralization and the sampling of tills, soils, stream sediments and related materials to obtain reliable information for interpretative purposes.

In summary, the following points appear of particular interest and importance.

1. Recent advances in instrumental chemical analysis have made the detection of gold at levels down to 1 ppb practical for the numbers of samples required for geochemical surveys.

2. Recent advances in instrumental chemical analysis have made the detection of numerous indicator elements for gold (see Table 4) a relatively simple matter, thus facilitating the search for the metal in rocks, tills and related materials.

3. Recent advances in till sampling techniques (e.g. reverse circulation drilling) have been demonstrated to lead to successful prospecting for gold in basal tills lying below other types of glacial deposits.

4. Recent studies in the sampling techniques required for the estimation of gold and indicator elements in waters, soils and related materials suggest that the reliability of such activities may be substantially increased in the near future, leading to more effective geochemical surveys for gold.

5. The work of Lakin *et al.* (1974) suggests that sufficient amounts of gold may participate in the biogeochemical cycle for geochemical anomalies to be detected in humus in glaciated areas. Although this work is still in its infancy, it shows some promise of being a useful tool for gold prospecting under favourable conditions in Ontario. More research is needed to facilitate the firm interpretation of humus/gold survey data.

6. Basal till and related studies (when aimed at gold deposits) should include descriptive mineralogy of the till and heavy minerals in the till as a part of the geochemical survey.

With respect to the exploration industry, the following points are of importance.

1. The industry needs clear demonstrations of the relative effectiveness of geochemical techniques for prospecting for gold at the regional and followup levels of activity. This will enable the techniques most effective in searching for gold under specific terrain conditions to be selected for the exploration of new areas.

Table 5. Data for gold and arsenic in humus collected from Ontario (from Assessment Files Research Office, Ontario Geological Survey, Toronto).

ACCESSION NUMBER	AREA	DATE	WRITER	TOTAL # OF SAMPLES	GOLD (PPB)				ARSENIC (PPM)			
					BACKGROUND		ANOMALOUS		BACKGROUND		ANOMALOUS	
					N	RANGE	N	RANGE	N	RANGE	N	RANGE
2.1943	McGarry Township	July 1975	S.A. Scott	337	333	10	4	20-40	240	0-4	9	11-20
63.3705	Baden Township	Oct. 1979	M. Ogden	526	449	0-3	33	5-48	-	-	-	-
63.3660	Balmer Township	Jan. 1980	D.L. Sannes	428	306	0-40	49	110-420	233	40-150	45	250-610
2.4450	Deloro Township	Dec. 1981	D.R. Pyke	270	141	5-20	47	31-76	75	10-20	16	20-49
2.4455	Horwood Township	Dec. 1981	P. Dadson	408	393	2-3	5	8-29	-	-	-	-

2. Industry requires reliable geochemical methods for gold prospecting at a reasonable cost in time and funds. Hence, those engaged in methods research should provide case histories and conceptual models showing clearly the scope of each technique together with very specific instructions for how surveys should be conducted.

3. Industry should be persuaded to report both positive and negative experiences with geochemical techniques aimed at gold prospecting in Ontario, so that all can learn from the experiences of the few.

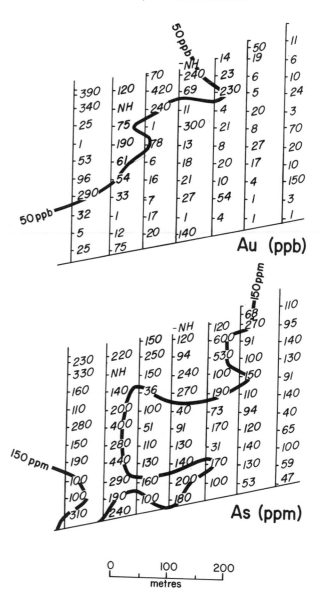

Figure 9. Sketch map of a part of a humus geochemical survey in Bateman Township near Red Lake, Ontario, showing high gold and arsenic values believed to be due to fallout from the atmosphere (from Sannes 1980).

With respect to government agencies, the following points appear important in relation to gold exploration based on geochemical techniques.

1. An effective approach to regional geochemical surveying for gold as a part of the "Geochemical Map of Ontario" must be devised, tested and proven reliable in areas of known gold mineralization. This can later be applied in areas favourable for gold mineralization where no ore bodies are known.

2. At the follow-up level, extensive testing of geochemical techniques is required in the vicinity of a small number of drilled, undisturbed gold deposits, so that the relative effectiveness of different approaches to geochemical (and combined geochemical-geophysical) exploration can be determined.

With respect to universities and other organizations which carry out research into methods of gold exploration in geochemistry, the following appears important.

1. New ideas and approaches to gold exploration are always welcome, but field research should be restricted to a few areas in Ontario so that the relative effectiveness of new, versus old methods, can be demonstrated clearly.

2. The appplication of existing techniques to new types of gold deposits, or new kinds of terrain conditions is important.

3. More technical research is required into the feasibility of better sampling and sample preparation methods for tills and related materials.

4. There is also a need for the application of modern techniques of Quaternary geology to mineral exploration, particularly gold exploration.

CONCLUSIONS

1. Although gold exploration by geochemical methods has been used for over 30 years in Ontario, relatively little progress has been made until recently, owing to a number of complicating factors which have tended to confound each other.

2. At the present, the future for the development of techniques for gold prospecting in Ontario looks bright due to: recent developments in the study of lithogeochemistry in gold mineralization; advances in our understanding of Quaternary geology as it affects the interpretation of the data of exploration geochemistry; and developments in sampling, sample processing and chemical analysis for gold and its associated elements.

3. This review has focused attention on the different types of gold deposits, the different kinds of glacial conditions in which they occur, and on the different geochemical techniques which are used for gold prospecting. Because resources are relatively small for geochemical exploration and research and because the problems are many and varied, it seems reasonable that government agencies should establish a small series of test ranges for the development of gold

prospecting methods at the regional and follow-up levels of activity. The data from geology, geophysics, geochemistry, Quaternary geology and related disciplines obtained from such ranges would be available to all and promote the increase in scientific rigour of gold prospecting in Ontario.

ACKNOWLEDGEMENT

The writer is indebted to Dr. Chris Gleeson who read an early draft of this paper and offered several suggestions which were incorporated in the final paper.

REFERENCES

Allan, R.J., Cameron, E.M., and Durham, C.C.
1973: Lake Geochemistry — a Low Sample Density Technique for Reconnaissance Geochemical Exploration of the Canadian Shield; p.131-160 in International Geochemical Exploration Symposium Proceedings, London, no.4.

Antweiler, J.C., and Campbell, W.L.
1982: Gold in Exploration Geochemistry; p.33-44 in Precious Metals in the Northern Cordillera, Proceedings of a Symposium Held April 13-15, 1981 in Vancouver, British Columbia, Canada, 214p.

Averill, S.A., and Thompson, I.
1981: Reverse Circulation Rotary Drilling and Deep Overburden Geochemical Sampling in Marter, Catherine, McElroy, Skead, Gauthier, and Hearst Townships, District of Timiskaming; Ontario Geological Survey, Open File Report 5335, 276p.

Boyle, R.W.
1979: The Geochemistry of Gold and its Deposits (Together with a Chapter on Geochemical Prospecting for the Element); Geological Survey of Canada, Bulletin 280, 296p.

Boyle, R.W., Hornbrook, E.H.W., Allan, R.J., Dyck, and Smith, A.Y.
1971: Hydrogeochemical Methods — Application in the Canadian Shield; Canadian Institute of Mining and Metallurgy Bulletin. Vol.64, p.60-71.

Bradshaw, P.M.D. (editor)
1975: Conceptual Models in Exploration Geochemistry; the Canadian Cordillera and Canadian Shield; Journal of Geochemical Exploration. Vol.4, (Special Issue) 213p.

Brooks, R.R.
1982: Biological Methods of Prospecting for Gold; Journal of Geochemical Exploration, Vol.17, p.109-122.

Brooks, R.R., Holzbecher, J., and Ryan, D.E.
1981: Horsetails (EQUISETUM) as Indirect Indicators of Gold Mineralization; Journal Geochemical Exploration, Vol.16, p.21-26.

Brown, M.R.
1982: Asarco's Nighthawk Lake Gold Project Reaches a Most Interesting Stage; The Northern Miner, Vol. 68(23), August 12, 1982.

Cannon, H.L.
1960: Botanical Prospecting for Ore Deposits; Science, Vol.132, no.3427, p.591.

Chisholm, E.O.
1950: A Simple Geochemical Method of Tracing Mineralization Through Light Non-Residual Overburden; Canadian Institute of Mining and Metallurgy Bulletin, Vol.43, p.64-68.

Closs, L.G., and Sado, E.V.
1978: Geochemical Drift Prospecting Studies Near Gold Mineralization, Beardmore-Geraldton Area; Northwest Ontario, Canada; p.459-477 in Proceeding of the Seventh International Geochemical Exploration Symposium, Golden, Colorado.

Curtin, J.F., Lakin, H.W., Neuerburg, G.J., and Hubert, A.E.
1968: Utilization of Humus-Rich Forest Soil (Mull) in Geochemical Exploration for Gold; United States Geological Survey, Circular 562. I19, 4/2, 11p.

Davis, J.F., Whitehead, R.E.S., Cameron, R.A., and Duff, D.
1982: Regional and Local Patterns of CO_2-K-Rb-As Alteration: A Guide to Gold in the Timmins Area, Ontario; Ontario Geological Survey, Open File Report 5376, 77p.

Dreimanis, A.
1958: Tracing Ore Boulders as a Prospecting Method in Canada; Canadian Institute of Mining and Metallurgy Bulletin, Vol.51, p.73-80.

Ermagen, S.V.
1957: Geochemical Prospecting in Chibougamau, Quebec; Canadian Mining Journal, Vol. 78(4), p.99-104.

Fortescue, J.A.C.
1970: A Research Approach to the Use of Vegetation for the Location of Mineral Deposits in Canada; Taxon, Vol. 19(5), p.695-704.

Fortescue, J.A.C., and Hornbrook, E.H.W.
1967: A Brief Survey of Progress Made in Biogeochemical Prospecting Research at the Geological Survey of Canada; p.111-113 in Proceedings, Symposium on Geochemical Prospecting, Ottawa, April 1966.
1969: Section F Two Quick Projects, One at a Massive Sulphide Orebody Near Timmins, Ontario and the Other at a Copper Deposit in Gaspe Park, Quebec; p.39-63 in Progress Report on Biogeochemical Research at the Geological Survey of Canada, 1963-1966; Geological Survey of Canada, Paper 67-23, part II.

Fortescue, J.A.C., and Hughes, O.L.
1965: Copper, Zinc, Nickel and Lead in Lower Till Material Collected Near a Massive Sulphide Orebody in the Clay Belt of Northern Ontario; Geological Survey of Canada, Paper 65-2, part II, p.23-27.

Fortescue, J.A.C., and Lourim, J.
1982: Descriptive Geochemistry and Descriptive Mineralogy of the Basal Till in the Kirkland Lake Area, Districts of Timiskaming and Cochrane; p.168-170 in Summary of Fieldwork, 1982, by the Ontario Geological Survey, edited by John Wood, Owen L. White, R.B. Barlow, and A.C. Colvine, Ontario Geological Survey, Miscellaneous Paper 106, 235p.

Fortescue, J.A.C., and Usik, Lily
1969: A Biogeochemical Investigation at Mer Bleu Bog; p.95-101 in Progress Report on Biogeochemical Research at the Geological Survey of Canada, 1963-1966, Geological Survey of Canada, Paper 67-23, part II.

Freeman, E.B., and Ferguson, S.A.
1973: Tracing Float and Mineral Fragments; p.43-61 in Mineral Exploration Topics, Ontario Department of Mines, Miscellaneous Paper 55, 173p.

Gleeson, C.F.
1960: Studies on the Distribution of Metals in Bogs and Glaciolacustrine Deposits; Unpublished Ph.D. Thesis, McGill University, Montreal, Quebec, Canada.

Gleeson, C.F., and Boyle, R.W.
1979: Consider Geochemistry When Seeking Gold; The Northern Miner, March 8, 1979, p.4.

Gleeson, C.F. and Coope, J.A.
1967: Some Observations on the Distribution of Metals in Swamps in Eastern Canada; p.145 in Proceedings, Symposium on Geochemical Prospecting, April 1966, Ottawa, Ontario, Canada.

Grip, E.
1953: Tracing Glacial Boulders as an Aid to Ore Prospecting in Sweden; Economic Geology, Vol.48, p.715-725.

Gross, W.H.
1950: A Study of the Spatial Relation of Gold Ore to Intrusive Bodies in Northwestern Ontario; in Geological Association of Canada Proceedings, Vol.3, p.123-129.
1952: Radioactivity as a Guide to Ore; Economic Geology, Vol.47, p.722-742.

Harris, J.F.
1982: Sampling and Analytical Requirements for Effective Use of Geochemistry in Exploration for Gold; p.53-67 in Precious Metals in the Northern Cordillera, Proceedings of a Symposium Held April 13-15, 1981, in Vancouver, British Columbia, Canada, 214p.

Hodgson, C.J.
1982: Gold Deposits of the Abitibi Belt, Ontario; p.192-197 in Summary of Field Work, 1982, by the Ontario Geological Survey, edited by John Wood, O.L. White, R.B. Barlow, and A.C. Colvine, Ontario Geological Survey, Miscellaneous Paper 106, 235p.

Hodgson, C.J., and MacGeehan, P.J.
1982: A Review of the Geological Characteristics of 'Gold-Only' Deposits in the Superior Province of the Canadian Shield; p.221-229 in Geology of Canadian Gold Deposits, Proceedings of the Canadian Institute of Mining and Metallurgy, held in September, 1980, (Special Volume 24).

Hodgson, C.J., Chapman, R.S.G., and MacGeehan, P.J.
1982: Application of Exploration Criteria for Gold Deposits in the Superior Province of the Canadian Shield to Gold Exploration in the Cordillera; p.173-206 in Precious Metals in the Northern Cordillera, Proceedings of a Symposium held on April 13-15, 1981 in Vancouver, British Columbia, Canada, 214p.

Kerrich, R., Robinson, D., Barnett, R.L., Hodder, R.W., and Hutchinson, R.W.
1982: Field Relations and Geochemistry of Au, Ni and Cr Deposits in Ultramafic-Mafic Volcanic Rocks; Ontario Geological Survey, Open File Report 5390, 91p. and Appendices A, B, and C.

Kerrich, R. and Fyfe, W.S.
1981: The Gold-Carbonate Association: Source of CO_2 and CO_2 Fixation Reactions in Archean Lode Deposits; Chemical Geology, Elsevier, Vol.33, p.265-294.

Kerrich, R., and Hodder, R.W.
1982: Archean Lode Gold and Base Metal Deposits: Evidence for Metal Separation into Independent Hydrothermal Systems; p.144-160 in Geology of Canadian Gold Deposits, Proceedings of the Canadian Institute of Mining and Metallurgy Gold Symposium held in September 1980, (Special Volume 24).

Lakin, H.W., Curtin, G.C., Hubert, A.E., Shacklette, H.T., and Doxtader, K.G.
1974: Geochemistry of Gold in the Weathering Cycle; United States Geological Survey Bulletin 1330, 80p.

Lee, H.A.
1971: Mineral Discovery in the Canadian Shield Using the Physical Aspects of Overburden; Canadian Institute of Mining and Metallurgy, Bulletin, Vol.64, p.32-36.

Levinson, A.A.
1974: Introduction to Exploration Geochemistry; Applied Publishing Ltd., Calgary, 612p.

Lourim, J.
1982a: Mid-Density (S.G. 2.81-3.32) Mineralogy of Glacial Over-burden as an Indicator of Gold Mineralization in Benoit, Maisonville, Grenfell, Eby, Otto, Boston and McElroy Townships, (Supplement to Open File Report 5356); Ontario Geological Survey, Open File Report 5394.
1982b: Mid-Density (S.G. 2.81-3.32) Mineralogy of Glacial overburden as as indicator of Gold Mineralization in Melba and Morrisette Townships and portions of Lebel, Eby, Bisley and Arnold Townships, (Supplement to Open File Report 5356; Ontario Geological Survey, Open File Report 5395.

Middleton, R.S., Durham, R.B., Harron, G., Philipp, A., and Markov, R.A.
1982: Geophysical and Geochemical Techniques for Gold Exploration in the Timmins Area; Preprint of a Paper Delivered at the Symposium on Precious Metals in the Northern Cordillera, April 13-15, 1981, Vancouver, British Columbia, 214p.

Nicol, I., and Bjorklund, A.
1973: Glacial Geology as a Key to Geochemical Exploration in Areas of Glacial Overburden with Particular Reference to Canada; Journal of Geochemical Exploration, Vol.2, p.133-170.

OGS-GSC
1979: Regional Lake Sediment and Water Geochemical Reconnaissance Data, Eastern Shore Lake Superior, Ontario; Ontario Geological Survey-Geological Survey of Canada, Ontario Geological Survey Open File Report 5267, 83p. with accompanying maps.

Plant, J., and Coleman, R.F.
1972: Application of Neutron Activation Analysis to the Evaluation of Placer Gold Concentrations; Geochemical Exploration 1972, p.373-381.

Rose, A.W., Hawkes, H.E., and Webb, J.S.
1979: Geochemistry in Mineral Exploration; 2nd edition, 657p.

Routledge, R.E., Thomson, I., Thompson, I.S., and Dixon,J.A.
1981: Deep Overburden Drilling and Geochemical Sampling in Benoit, Melba, Bisley, Maisonville, Morrisette, Arnold, Grenfell, Lebel,Eby, Otto, Boston and McElroy Townships, Districts of Timiskaming and Cochrane; Ontario Geological Survey, Open File Report 5356, 423p. Accompanied by maps.

Sannes, D.L.
1980: *Unpublished report,* on file in Assessment Files Research Office, Geoscience Data Centre, Ontario Geological Survey, Toronto, Technical File No. 63.3660, Redcon Gold Mines Ltd., 1980.

Schmidt, R.C.
1956: Adsorption of Copper, Lead and Zinc on Some Common Rock-Forming Minerals and its Effect on Lake Sediments; Unpublished Ph.D. Thesis, McGill University, Montreal.

Seeland, D.A.
1973a: Geochemical Reconnaissance for Gold in the Sedimentary Rocks of the Great Lakes Region, Minnesota to New York; United States Geological Survey Bulletin 1305, 16p.

1973b: Geochemical Reconnaissance for Gold in Sedimentary and Metamorphic Rocks of the Great Lakes Region, Tabulated Dates on 799 Samples; National Technical Information Service, Reprint 222892/2; Chemical Abstract Vol.80, 50676, 1973, 60p.

Smee, B.W., and Sinhan, A.K.
1979: Geological, Geophysical and Geochemical Consideration for Exploration in Clay-Covered Areas: A Review; Canadian Institute of Mining and Metallurgy Bulletin, Vol.72, p.67-82.

Thompson, I.S.
1979: Till Prospecting for Sulphide Ores in the Abitibi Clay Belt of Ontario; Canadian Institute of Mining and Metallurgy Bulletin, Vol.72, p.6572.

Tourtelot, H.A.
1968: Hydraulic Equivalence of Grains of Quartz and Heavier Minerals, and Implications for the Study of Placers; United States Geological Survey, Paper 594-F, 13p.

Townsley, B.F.
1935: Mine-Finders — the History and Romance of Canadian Mineral Discoveries; Saturday Night Press, Toronto, 246p.

Turner, L.D., and Ikramuddin, M.
1982: Electrothermal Atomic Absorption Determination of Gold, Silver and Arsenic in Stream Water and their Relationship to Gold-Silver Occurrences in the Republic Graben, N.E. Washington; p.79-88 in Precious Metals in the Northern Cordillera, Proceedings of a Symposium held April 13-15, 1981, in Vancouver, British Columbia, Canada, 214p.

Warren, H.V., and Delavault, R.E.
1955a: Some Biogeochemical Investigation in Eastern Canada; Canadian Mining Journal, Vol.76, p.49-54.
1955b: Some Biogeochemical Investigation in Eastern Canada; Canadian Mining Journal, Vol.76, p.58-63.

Warren, H.V., Delavault, R.E., and Barakso, J.
1964: The Role of Arsenic as a Pathfinder in Biogeochemical Prospecting; Economic Geology, Vol.59, p.1381-1389.
1968: The Arsenic Content of Douglas Fir as a Guide to Some Gold, Silver and Base Metal Deposits; Canadian Institute of Mining and Metallurgy Bulletin, Vol.61, p.860-868.

Wolfe, W.J.
1971: Terrain of the Canadian Precambrian Shield; Canadian Institute of Mining and Metallurgy Bulletin, Vol.64, p.72-80.
1975: Gold in Early Precambrian Plutonic Rocks, The Relation Between Geochemical Abundance and Concentration to Exploitable Leach; Society of Mining Engineers, American Institute of Mining Engineering, precr. 75-L-5, 17p.
1976: Regional Geochemical Reconnaissance of Archean MetavolcanicMetasedimentary Belts in the Pukaskwa Region; Ontario Geological Survey, Geological Report 158, 54p.
1977: Geochemical Exploration of Early Precambrian Sulphide Mineralization in Ben Nevis Township, District of Cochrane; Ontario Geological Survey, Study 19, 39p.

Wolfe, W.J., Lee, H.A., and Hicks, W.D.
1975: Heavy Minerals Indicators in Alluvial and Esker Gravels of the Moose River Basin, James Bay Lowlands, District of Cochrane; Ontario Geological Survey, Geological Report 126, 60p. Accompanied by Map 2334, scale 1 inch to 4 miles.

Analytical Methods for Gold

C. Riddle

Chief Analyst, Geoscience Laboratories, Ontario Geological Survey, Toronto

ABSTRACT

There are several sensitive methods for the accurate determination of gold in geological materials. As gold is often unevenly dispersed in its host rocks, proper sampling procedures are essential and there is a need for geologists and analytical chemists to discuss sample collection and analytical methods before the field program begins. They should also confer on the interpretation of analytical data.

INTRODUCTION

This article provides a review of the available methods for the determination of gold in geological materials. It is also intended to provide some guidance for the geologist faced with designing an analytical program for gold that will best meet the requirements of a particular project.

Difficulties arise from dealing with two disciplines, analytical chemistry and geology, when the practitioners in each discipline are largely unfamiliar with the demands of the other. The analytical chemist rarely questions how a sample brought to him for analysis was collected or checks on the interpretation given to the result that he produces. Similarly the prospector or geologist will often fail to consult with the laboratory to discover what significance may be given to a result.

Sidney Abbey, former head of the Analytical Chemistry Section, Geological Survey of Canada, once remarked that "the reliability of a result depends more on *who* produced it than on *how* it was done. There is no such thing as a *bad* method — only bad analysts who fail to allow for its limitations" (Abbey 1981). His comment is worth attention, first because there is a widespread belief that there are "bad" methods and second, because it is quite true that the quality of analysis is variable.

In addition the usefulness of a result depends more on how a sample was collected and how the analytical result was interpreted than on who performed the determination. "Bad collectors" fail to take representative samples and "bad interpreters" fail to appreciate the significance of a result.

The way out of the situation where each discipline blames the other for errors is for the analyst to become familiar with geological practice: to take responsibility for discovering the origin of the samples he handles and for the end use of his results. Likewise the geologist must become familiar with laboratory procedures, and become aware of what constitutes an acceptable sample and what significance can be placed on the results he gets.

Practitioners of each discipline must acquire some degree of understanding of both disciplines. This understanding should go beyond mere cooperation although in many cases we have yet to achieve that goal.

SAMPLING: SPECIAL FEATURES OF GOLD ORES

The theory behind sampling is beyond the scope of this article. It is a subject of great importance and simple principles, and is often overlooked. A multitude of variables may baffle the sample collector if the basic principles are not clearly understood. This subject is covered in part by John Fortescue in the preceding article, but I shall make a few observations relating to gold in particular.

In sampling, a small amount of material is taken to be representative of some larger amount. If an outcrop is to be sampled, it is just as important that the field sample be representative of the outcrop as it is for the laboratory subsample to be representative of the field sample. Recommended sample sizes have been proposed for rocks of various grain sizes; for example, if the maximum grain size is 1 mm then 2.5 kg is considered suitable in most cases. Sampling for gold poses a special problem due to the heterogeneous nature of its occurrence and the difficulty of grinding free gold; there is no single sample size suitable for all occurrences. The prospector or geologist needs an appreciation of the reliability required from data. He can then decide what constitutes an acceptable sample.

In general, larger samples in greater numbers should be collected in a gold survey than in other routine geological work.

To obtain the most value from a gold determination it is important to know what the sample is representative of and what the precision and accuracy of the result are. It is useful to take several samples from any one geological feature (outcrop) so that a mean value and the extent of variation from the mean can be determined.

Once the field sample is submitted to the laboratory, crushed and ground, it is composed of particles of differing sizes. The nature of a gold occurrence is critical in determining which size fraction will contain the gold and hence the number of gold particles that will be present in a given sample for a particular concentration of gold. Screen analysis of silicate rocks ground to pass either 100 or 200 mesh has shown that the number of grains per gram can vary widely — from ca. 2 million to ca. 15 billion. The grain-size distribution will vary depending on the sample mineralogy and the type and manner of grinding. For example, a rapid grind, that produces material whic h will completely pass 100 mesh, may have 50 percent of the material as +150 mesh, 20 percent as –150 +400 and 30 percent as –400. More prolonged grinding, to material that is all –150 mesh may produce a more even particle size distribution and a greatly increased number of fine particles (Table 1).

Consider native gold occurring at the 1 ppm level. In a 10 g sample, using the average particle size (from Table 1), we would expect ca. 15,000 gold grains to be present. If the gold was all in the –100 +170 fraction then a single gold grain would be expected. If only light grinding had been used then these figures could be off by a factor of 10,000. Such a worst case is unfortunately quite possible as native gold does not grind well and tends to smear. Only when it is well disseminated and locked in silicate grains will fine grinding actually result in an increased distribution of the gold. This is the best case situation, represented in Table 2.

Table 2 shows that a 1 g sample could be used for gold at the 5 ppb (background) level quite satisfactorily, however, it should be remembered that this is the most favourable case for a truly homogeneous sample.

Gold in alluvial material may occur as flakes that will typically be retained in a –150 +400 mesh sieve fraction. In this case, so long as the gold distribution is random, a 25 g sample will be adequate for gold occurring at the 1 ppm level (Harris 1982). At the 60 ppb level a 200 g sample would be required. These figures assume that the entire field sample is used to prepare the laboratory subsample and that no selective sieving takes place. In such a case a 20 g laboratory subsample of 60 ppb gold may contain only one gold particle on average. Using a 1 g subsample would mean that 19 out of 20 times a null value would be obtained; the 1 time in 20 that gold was recorded would give a value of 1200 ppb and this would likely be interpreted as anomalous (if duplicates were checked) or as being unduly significant. No sample of 1 g will produce the true value of 60 ppb. As Harris concluded, it is unwise to discount any anomaly, even when check values are erratic. The clustering of anomalous values should be an indication that follow-up work is needed.

TERMINOLOGY: UNITS OF MEASUREMENT

Confusion in terminology and units exists even between analytical chemists and is particularly prevalent when an additional discipline is involved.

Many prospectors still prefer to use ounces per ton as the unit of gold concentration in a sample and the following table may be of help in converting to ppb and ppm values as used by most geochemists. Fire assay results are still generally reported in ounces per ton; geochemical results in parts per billion.

10 ppb = 0.00033 oz/long ton = 0.00029 oz/short ton
1 ppm = 1000 ppb = 0.029 oz/short ton = 1 g/tonne = 1 microgram/g
100 ppm = 65.33 dwt/long ton = 58.33 dwt/short ton
100 ppm = 3.267 oz/long ton = 2.917 oz/short ton
20 dwt = 1 oz = 31.1 g
100 dwt/long ton = 153.07 ppm = 89.29 dwt/short ton
100 dwt/short ton = 171.44 ppm = 112.00 dwt/long ton
0.01 oz/short ton = 0.343 ppm = 343 ppb = 0.011 oz/-long ton
1 oz/long ton = 30.61 ppm = 0.893 oz/short ton
1 oz/short ton = 34.286 ppm = 1.120 oz/long ton
(Note: oz = troy ounce, dwt = pennyweight, long ton = 2240 pounds, short ton = 2000 pounds, tonne = 1000 kg)

ANALYTICAL PRACTICE

TERMINOLOGY

Abbey (1981) has proposed definitions for analytical work which cause one to consider the individual steps that contribute to an analysis. The practice is useful in resolving the misconceptions that arise due to confused terminology.

For example, it is often stated that atomic absorption (AA) analysis gives unreliable results for gold. The analyst, who knows this to be untrue, will perhaps assume that it hides some real problem as yet unstated. He then needs to know the entire sequence of operations that resulted in the 'unreliable' result. This must include details of sample collection, preparation, decomposition, separation, manipulation, instrument calibration, configura-

Table 1. *Typical grain size distribution for a silicate rock ground to pass 150 (Tyler) mesh.*

Radius	%	No. of particles per gram
0.050	10	85,000
0.040	10	166,000
0.030	10	393,000
0.020	10	1,327,000
0.010	10	10,616,000
0.005	20	169,852,000
0.002	20	2,653,928,000
0.001	10	10,615,711,000

Table 2. *"Optimum" distribution of gold particles in a finely ground silicate rock.*

Concentration	Number of grains 10 g sample
100 PPM	1,500,000
10 PPM	150,000
1 PPM	15,000
100 PPB	1,500
10 PPB	150
1 PPB	15

tion, etc. Each of these variables may contribute to the reliability of the overall result and any one may be more significant than the fact that AA was used for the final measurement. As we have seen already the sample size alone is critical.

Within the laboratory there are four basic operations. According to Abbey (1981), these are:
1. Sample attack, e.g. acid digestion
2. Separation, e.g. solvent extraction
3. Measurement, e.g. gravimetry (for fire assay gold), furnace atomic absorption (for geochemical gold)
4. Data Reduction, e.g. use of a calibration curve.

He proposes calling each operation a *TECHNIQUE* The word *METHOD* then may be used to refer to a combination of techniques, and a *PROCEDURE* will refer to the specific details of a unit operation or technique that make up a method.

In the following discussion of analytical methods I shall consider the range of techniques that are available and then discuss how they may be combined into reliable methods. In this way I hope to emphasize the individual importance of each step that results in the production of an analytical result.

It will be assumed that both the analyst and the person submitting the sample are aware of what the sample represents and that there is value in determining the level of gold in the submitted sample.

SAMPLE PREPARATION

Routine preparation techniques are generally applied to geological materials submitted for the determination of gold. The following proviso, special to gold, requires close attention.

As a result of the heterogeneous nature of gold ores, the normal rules for safely reducing sample weight, as successive steps of crushing, grinding and pulverizing are performed, do not apply (Gy 1979). For this reason the laboratory should work with the complete submitted sample as far as possible, given the constraints of cost and productivity, whenever ore grade material is being investigated. For stream sediments and soils it is common practice to sieve the sample and work only with the −80 mesh fraction. This procedure tends to concentrate the gold and whilst it may be useful as a survey technique to identify anomalous areas, the laboratory subsample is not representative of the field sample and may give values greatly in excess of actual field occurrences.

Contamination is a potential problem in the preparation of gold-bearing material. Grinding of ore grade samples can cause the gold to be smeared rather than ground and thus the grinding mechanism becomes contaminated with gold whilst the sample is slightly depleted in gold. In this laboratory we find that up to ten subsequent sample grindings may be required before contamination is removed from a jaw-crusher. The main concern here is not slight gold depletion in the original sample but contamination of subsequent samples. When gold is visible in a sample, it should be standard practice to clean the crusher with barren silica; when high values are subsequently obtained on other samples, a review of the sample crushing order can answer fears of contamination.

This may seem to be idealistic and impracticable for a large scale analysis project. But it indicates the care that is needed in planning an analytical program. A cheap analysis is not necessarily a good analysis.

SAMPLE ATTACK

1. Acid treatment. A wide variety of procedures has been reported in the literature. Most rely on the solubility of gold in aqua regia (a 3:1 mixture of hydrochloric:nitric acid) but vary in the extent of breakdown of the sample. Aqua regia will not dissolve silicate rock, for example, and a simple aqua regia leach will only allow the 'free' gold or gold in sulphides to be dissolved. Additional gold enclosed in the silicate minerals will remain untouched. This may be advantageous if a selective recovery process is being used; however, most geologists prefer a 'total' analysis for which complete sample dissolution is required. Some ores require roasting before acid digestion is attempted, for example, those containing copper sulphide or arsenopyrite (Johnson and Maxwell 1981).

Johnson and Maxwell's proposed acid treatment for geological samples is as follows:

A 25 g subsample is mixed with 10 g of ammonium nitrate and sintered in a muffle furnace. Hydrofluoric acid (HF) and perchloric acid ($HClO_4$) attack produces a residue that is treated with sodium chloride, hydrochloric acid (HCl) and nitric acid HNO$_3$. Evaporation produces wet salts that are dissolved in dilute HCl. (Full details are given in their text.)

Other acid decomposition schemes involve aqua regia and bromine (Brooks *et al.* 1981) or hydrobromic acid containing free bromine (see Fletcher 1981, p.64).

2. Fusion. Fusion schemes are common in whole rock analysis procedures but are rarely used as a means of getting the sample into solution for gold determination. The fire assay procedure for gold uses a reductive fusion and without doubt the classical lead assay has proved to be the most important procedure for the concentration and isolation of the noble metals (Van Loon 1981). The success of fire assaying depends on the expertise of the assayer, as variations in flux composition are required depending on the acidity or basicity of the slag. This is still an art rather than a science. The possibility of gold losses during fusion has been studied by several workers. It is difficult to establish conditions under which there will be no loss of gold for any type of geological sample but fire assay is still one of the most attractive analytical procedures.

SEPARATION

1. Solvent extraction. Gold in a solution sample may be concentrated by extraction into an organic solvent. For example, Johnson and Maxwell (1981) follow acid attack by extraction into dibutyl sulphide (DBS) in toluene. Many other solvent extraction media are used, e.g. methylisobutylketone (MIBK) and butyl acetate. The advantages of solvent extraction are that gold is separated from the other matrix elements of the sample, it is concentrated, and signal enhancement may be achieved if the AA technique is subsequently applied.

2. Doré bead preparation. In the conventional fire assay procedure lead oxide is included in the initial fusion pot. The oxide is reduced to lead metal in the fusion process and the lead quantitatively extracts and collects any gold or silver from the sample. The lead is separated from the fusion slag once it has cooled, hammered into a cube or 'button' and placed on a heated cupel of bone ash or magnesia. This in turn is placed in a cupellation furnace where oxidation occurs, turning the lead into litharge which is absorbed into the cupel and leaving a small gold-silver alloy bead — the Doré bead—which contains all the gold that will be determined.

3. Column separation. An aqua regia digestate of an ore sample may be evaporated, redissolved in the HCl and passed through an Amberlite column. The gold retained in the column is diluted with an acetone - HCl mixture.

MEASUREMENT

1. Gravimetric. In conventional fire assay the Doré bead is digested in hot nitric acid to remove silver and the remaining gold is weighed. The limitation of this procedure is the smallest amount of gold that can be weighed reliably; most laboratories report a detection limit of ca. 0.01 ounces per ton.

Other gravimetric procedures are of historic importance. For example, hydroquinone has been used to precipitate gold in a directly weighable form from a prepared solution.

2. Flame Atomic Absorption. This is probably the most widely used determinative technique for gold. Interferences are usually overcome by using organic extraction preseparation. An air-acetylene flame is preferred to the higher temperature nitrous oxide – acetylene flame to improve sensitivity, although interferences may be more pronounced. The most commonly reported interferences are due to Pt, Pd, Al, Fe, Ca, SO$_4^{2-}$ and CN$^-$.

3. Graphite Furnace Atomic Absorption (GFAA). The graphite tube furnace replaces the flame unit in a conventional (flame) AA instrument. The optical beam passes through the graphite furnace tube which is heated briefly but strongly by an electrical current. The liquid sample is dried, charred and atomised in three discrete steps. This results in a very sensitive technique which is now offered by an increasing number of commercial laboratories for geochemical gold, i.e. for samples with gold present at low part per billion levels. The technique is used in combination with several sample attack and separation techniques. For example the sample solution for GFAA may be derived from a Doré bead, an organic extract or a simple acid digestion.

4. Optical Emission. This form of spectroscopy may be applied to both solid and solution samples. It is used on Doré beads and can produce data in the low part per billion range; reliable calibration can be a problem however. Preconcentration and separation are essential so the direct use of rock powders is not practical. The new generation of optical emission spectrometers employing inductively-coupled argon plasma sources may also prove useful, especially when simultaneous determination of a range of precious metals is required.

5. Nuclear Techniques. Neutron activation analysis is widely used for sensitive gold determination. Concern over the small sample size commonly used has been overcome by some laboratories which irradiate the Doré bead; this is derived from 10 g or more of sample material.

6. X-Ray Fluorescence (XRF). There has been considerable interest recently in "portable gold analysers" based on XRF technology. Whilst the XRF technique is applicable to gold determination it is not commonly used in the laboratory due to poor sensitivity, matrix correction problems and calibration difficulties. When used in a portable system such problems will increase and, although of potential use as a survey tool, one cannot expect this instrumentation to be of great use for gold analysis.

DATA REDUCTION

Without going into considerable detail it is not possible to present the variety of data reduction manipulations that may be performed with each of the various methods that are used for gold determination. However it is important to realize that data reduction is a separate step in the analytical method and contributes to the validity of the final result just as much as any of the other analytical techniques. Proper calibration, interference correction, matrix correction and blank subtraction are all important.

PARTICULAR METHODS USED BY THE GEOSCIENCE LABORATORIES

Having reviewed the range of techniques it may be useful to consider briefly how these techniques may be combined to form analytical methods. For convenience I shall consider the methods in use at the Ontario Geological Survey.

ROUTINE FIRE ASSAY

(Flux fusion, extraction into lead, parting of Doré bead, gravimetric determination, factoring).

The standard crucible assay requires the following steps:

a. weigh out pulp (14.583 g, ½ assay ton)
b. add stock flux (listed below) approx. 100 g.
c. mix ore and reagents in crucible
d. place in furnace (preheated to 1025°C) and heat for 35 minutes
e. pour molten charge into cast iron mold
f. inspect crucible for lead loss
g. note slag colour for possible interference
h. note size and appearance of lead button
i. break slag and free lead button (20-25 g)
j. cube lead button with hammer
k. place lead cube in furnace on preheated cupel (950°C) and heat in vented atmosphere for approximately half an hour, until lead is absorbed in cupel
l. remove silver bead and note any peculiarities
m. brush and accurately weigh silver bead using fine balance
n. digest silver in hot nitric acid and wash residue with distilled water
o. anneal and accurately weigh (to 2 micrograms) gold using fine balance
p. record all results and observations
q. calculate silver weight and report gold and silver results

The stock flux contains the following:

litharge	80 g
sodium carbonate	40 g
silica	12 g
borax glass	12 g
flour	2.5 g

SPECIAL ASSAYS (ASSAYS OF COMPLEX OR UNUSUAL ORES)

Changes from the stock flux or standard assay method are often necessary with complex or unusual ores for analysis.

In the standard assay, although the ore is diluted (approximately 1 ore to 5 charge) chemical pecularities of the ore may not be made ineffective (e.g. excess silica may cause loss of precious metals by slagging or matte formation). Knowledge of the ore, fluxes, and reagents available will allow the adjustment of the assay process to give accurate and reproducible results.

The various reagents (fluxes, reducing, oxidizing and desulphurizing agents) and processes used by the Laboratories are:

Acid fluxes (used with basic ores) – silica (SiO_2), Borax glass ($Na_2B_4O_7$).

Basic fluxes (used with acid ores) – sodium carbonate (Na_2CO_3), litharge (PbO).

Oxidizing (used with reducing ores) – potassium nitrate (KNO_3), roasting (at 650°C).

Reducing (used with oxidizing ores) – materials containing carbon flour, Argol.

Desulphurizing agents – Na_2CO_3, PbO, KNO_3 act as desulphurizing agents.

GEOCHEMICAL GOLD DETERMINATION

(Doré bead preparation, acid digestion, graphite furnace atomic absorption, calibration calculation).

The logic behind the fire assay concentration is to (1) take a large enough sample to get enough of the precious metal present to give good precision, and (2) to transform the possibly complex matrix of the ore into a simple metal alloy.

The method used for concentrating precious metals for AA analysis is as follows:

a. weigh out 10 g of sample pulp
b. mix with approximately 75 g of standard flux
c. add 2 drops silver nitrate ($AgNO_3$) solution (this furnace charge makes a bead of approximately 15 mg)
d. follow "regular gold and silver assays" from step (c) to step (e)
e. pass on beads to AA laboratory for analysis.

Blanks and control standards are processed with every batch of samples.

Dissolution of the silver bead is accomplished with nitric acid in a 10 by 75 mm test tube placed in an aluminum rack and set on a hot-plate. The silver is precipitated as the chloride with hydrochloric acid, whereby the gold is dissolved in the aqua regia. The acid mixture is diluted with water, mixed and the AgCl allowed to settle on the bottom of the test tube. An aliquot of the supernatant liquid is atomized in a graphite furnace and the atomic absorption signal observed as a recorder trace.

The concentration of gold in the sample solution is read with the aid of a calibration graph. The net concentration is obtained by subtracting the average overall-blank value. The gold content in rock is calculated according to the formula:

$$Au = CV/W \times 1000$$

Where

Au = ppb of gold in rock,
C = net concentration of gold in micrograms/ml in solution,
V = volume in ml of the sample solution (usually 2 ml), and
W = weight of sample in grams (usually 10 g)

The optimum working range is 0.05-0.20 micrograms Au per millilitre in solution. The detection limit is 2 ppb in rock.

PRACTICAL NOTES FOR GEOCHEMICAL GOLD DETERMINATION

1. Standards must be prepared with the same acid concentrations contained in the samples, that is, nitric acid (1 + 15) and hydrochloric acid (1 + 15).
2. All dilutions must be made with an acid mixture containing these same concentrations.
3. Standards should be prepared every 2 weeks and stored in polyethylene containers.
4. Concentrations of 50 ppm of platinum, palladium and silver had no interfering effect on gold absorbance represented by 0.2 ppm.

OTHER METHODS

Some other methods are also worthy of mention. At the British Columbia Ministry of Mines a method is in use which involves aqua regia attack on a 10 g sample, filtration, addition of tin chloride and silver nitrate, dissolution of the co-precipitated gold and silver chlorides in aqua regia, dilution, air-acetylene AA, and calibration calculation. This method can determine gold to a limit of 10 ppb with a recovery in excess of 93 percent.

The most common method in geochemical exploration involves acid digestion, solvent extraction, flame atomic absorption and calibration calculation; this is performed on a 5 g sample.

A rapid method has been described for sulphide ores and rocks by Brooks *et al.* (1981) which involves aqua regia and bromine attack, organic extraction, graphite furnace AA detection and calibration calculation. A detection limit of 0.3 ppb is reported and up to 50 samples per day may be determined.

West (1973) reported a field method for 'geochemical assaying'. This involves an adaptation of the conventional cyanide method and will determine 'available' gold. To this author's knowledge West's method has not been applied to Ontario gold occurrences but it may be of interest in a limited number of situations.

Field tests for gold are often requested but the reliability of reported methods in all situations is questionable. The following reagents are listed in the literature (Feigl and Anger 1972): p-dimethylaminobenzylidenerhodanine, benzidine, and rhodamine B.

These chemicals are the reagents used in a chromatographic method of contact printing developed for gold particles in the Witwatersrand reefs described by Hallbauer and Joughin (1972) as follows.

Chromatographic contact prints have been used for many minerals, . . . however, a special technique had to be developed for gold. In this method photograhic paper is placed in fixing solution to remove the silver, washed for about 20 min. and dried. The paper is then soaked in aqua regia, diluted 1:1, for 1 min., and placed between filter paper until all visible drops of acid have been removed. The flat, nearly polished surface of the specimen is than pressed on to the damp paper for 1 min. After removing the paper from the specimen a small amount of alcoholic solution of p-dimethylaminobenzylidenerhodanine (0.05 g in 100 ml of ethanol) is poured over the paper and dispersed with a glass rod. The colour does not develop in the presence of a strong acid and, therefore, the paper is dipped into a buffer solution of sodium acetate and acetic acid and again treated with the rhodanine solution. The paper is then washed in running water and dried.

All areas on the paper that were in contact with the gold particles finally appear as red dots or dark red areas, depending on the particle size. Benzidine solution, with a few drops of acetic acid added, may be used instead of the rhodanine solution. In this case the contact areas on the paper appear as a violet colour, but they are less distinct.

Small particles can be emphasized by increasing the time during which the specimen is in contact with the paper, since the coloured image diffuses and gives a larger impression than the actual cross-sectional area of the gold particles. The actual contact area can still be recognized under a microscope as an intensely coloured spot. Particles as small as 0.02 mm leave a clearly visible impression after a 1 min exposure.

The area of the chromatographic contact prints is of the order of 100 cm².

The samples examined by Hallbauer and Joughin contained heavy mineral segregations of pyrite, gold and uraninite in pebbly sandstones. Striking displays of grain size and pebble distribution were obtained where a matrix of sulphide minerals supports quartz-rich clastic fragments; infrequent and isolated gold grains were also clearly visible, down to diameters of 0.02 mm.

This method has recently been tested on Archean rocks in this laboratory (W.D. Hicks, personal communication 1983). On slabbed rocks the wet chemical process enhances visible patterns of gold distribution by showing gold grains as red blots. It is limited in field application but may be particularly useful where the gangue is largely silicate minerals.

COMPARISON OF METHODS

It should be clear that there is no single 'best' method for gold determination and it may be as important to compare analysts as to compare methods. When choosing an analytical laboratory one should be prepared to ask a number of questions. In particular sample handling techniques are important, as is the size of the analytical subsample. At this point it is probably wise to be prepared to make a realistic compromise based on cost and the requirements for quality in the analysis. If at all possible any extensive analytical program should have quality control samples included by the client as well as those that the laboratory will use.

If a detection limit of 500 ppb is acceptable, conventional fire assay done by a reputable laboratory would be a favoured method. For lower limits of detection, a fire assay (Doré bead) concentration step is favoured because of the large sample size that this allows. Adequate homogenity may be exhibited by samples as small as 1 g even at low part per billion levels of occurrence; then direct neutron activation analysis would be quite acceptable. The client must check this before embarking on an extensive analytical project, or ensure preliminary discussion with the laboratory staff before analytical methodology is fixed.

REFERENCES

Abbey, S.
1981: Reliability in the Analysis of Rocks and Minerals; Analytical Chemistry, Volume 53, p.528-534A.

Brooks, R.R., Holzbecher, J., Ryan, D.E., Zhang, H.F., and Chatterjee, A.K.
1981: A Rapid Method for the Determination of Gold and Silver in Sulphide Ores and Rocks; Atomic Spectroscopy, Volume 2, Number 5, p.151-154.

Feigl, F. and Anger, V.
1972: Spot Tests in Inorganic Analysis; Sixth Edition, Elsevier, p.240-244.

Fletcher, W.K.
1981: Handbook of Exploration Geochemistry; Volume 1, Analytical Methods in Geochemical Prospecting, Elsevier. p.64

Gy, P.M.
1979: Sampling of Particulate Materials, Theory and Practice; Elsevier, Chapter 26, p.311-321.

Hallbauer D.K., and Joughin, N.C.
1972: Distribution and Size of Gold Particles in the Witwatersrand Reefs and Their Effects on Sampling Procedures; Transactions of the Institute of Mining and Metallurgy, Volume 81, Section A, p.A.133-142.

Harris, J.F.
1982: Precious Metals in the Northern Cordillera; Published by The Association of Exploration Geochemists, p.53-67.

Johnson, W.M. and Maxwell, J.A.
1981: Rock and Mineral Analysis; Second Edition, John Wiley and Sons, p.297-301.

Van Loon, J.C.
1981: Fire Assay Favoured Method in Noble Metal Analysis; (Excerpted from an Unpublished Paper Presented at the Precious Metals in the Northern Cordillera Symposium, Geological Association of Canada Meeting, Vancouver, April 1981), as reported in The Northern Miner, June 18, 1981.

West, W.F.
1973: Geochemical Field Assaying Made Easy; Chamber of Mines Journal, p.33-35.